OXFORD

Statistics GCSE for AQA

2nd edition

Jayne Kranat

Principal examiner at GCSE and A Level. Mathematics Consultant for West Sussex County Council and the STEM Education Advisor for the Royal Academy of Engineering.

Great Clarendon Street, Oxford OX2 6DP

Oxford University Press is a department of the University of Oxford.
It furthers the University's objective of excellence in research,
scholarship, and education by publishing worldwide in

Oxford New York

Auckland Cape Town Dar es Salaam Hong Kong Karachi
Kuala Lumpur Madrid Melbourne Mexico City Nairobi
New Delhi Shanghai Taipei Toronto

With offices in

Argentina Austria Brazil Chile Czech Republic France Greece
Guatemala Hungary Italy Japan Poland Portugal Singapore
South Korea Switzerland Thailand Turkey Ukraine Vietnam

First published 2001, this edition 2009

British Library Cataloguing in Publication Data

Data available

ISBN 978-0-19-913430-4

10 9 8 7 6 5 4 3 2 1

Printed in Great Britain by Bell and Bain Ltd., Glasgow

Paper used in the production of this book is a natural, recyclable product
made from wood grown in sustainable forests. The manufacturing process
conforms to the environmental regulations of the country of origin.

Acknowledgements

The author would like to thank David Hodgson for his invaluable contribution to the previous edition of this book.

The publishers would like to thank AQA for their kind permission to reproduce the past paper questions. AQA accept no responsibility for the answers to the questions which are the sole responsibility of the publishers.

Figurative artwork is by Angela Lumley

The publisher is grateful for permission to reproduce the following photographs;

Page 48; OUP/Chris King; page 59 istockphoto/Fertnig Photography; page 88 istockphoto/ArchMen; page 103 Dreamstime/Adisa; page 179 Photodisc; page Alamy/Keith Morris; page 231 Photodisc

Cover photograph reproduce courtesy of istockphoto/LcSdesign

About this book

This book has been written by experienced examiners specifically for the AQA GCSE Statistics Specification 4310.

The book is organised into eight units containing all the up to date content and methods you will need in your exam.

How to use this book

The first seven units give you the content of the specification and broadly follow the same order as the specification.

Each of the content sections starts with a list of learning objectives. This will help you plan your work effectively. The **Before you start** section gives questions to check the prior knowledge you need before you start the unit.

Shaded boxes in the text highlight important information you need to remember:

> Qualitative data describes a quality that cannot be counted.

Activity boxes give you a chance to try out what you have learned.

Each unit ends with a **Summary** page detailing what you should know after studying the unit. There are also **Links to the Real World** to help you put statistics in context.

At the end of the section there is a **Revision exercise** containing past paper questions from AQA and other Statistics papers. They will help you get ready for the style of question you will see in the actual exam.

At the end of the book there are **Practice exam papers** written by experienced examiners to help you prepare for the real thing.

Unit 8 is about **Controlled Assessment**. Work through this unit carefully before you do your controlled assessment and it will help you make the most of this important element.

There are **ICT** opportunities throughout the book.

Colour coding

Blue and grey are used to show whether the material is Foundation or Higher or both.

Foundation	Higher	Both

You will find the coding in:

- Section headings
- Key points
- Examples
- Activities
- Exercises
- Revision exercises

Remember that all the Foundation content is also examined in the Higher tier.

GCSE Statistics for AQA Contents

■ This symbol shows you the content of the GCSE Statistics specification that is not in the GCSE Mathematics specifications.
□ This symbol shows you where the content of the chapter is from both specifications.

1 Data all around

One picture is worth ten thousand words
Frederick R Barnard

This advertising is misleading because the 'extra free' part of the label represents more than 15%

This unit will show you how to

- Find information from tables
- Explain why diagrams can be misleading

Before you start

You should be able to answer these questions

1 Write these percentages as fractions.
(a) 30%, (b) 42%, (c) 50%, (d) 75%, (e) 89%

2 Draw 5 lines 6 cm long.
Scale the lines
(a) in 5s 1 cm apart
(b) in 10s 2 cm apart
(c) in 20s 1 cm apart
(d) in 100s 3 cm apart
(e) in 1s 2 cm apart.

3 Write as ratios
(a) 17 girls and 13 boys
(b) 21 orange and 14 lemon sweets
(c) 9 tabby and 4 Siamese cats
(d) 12 brown and 8 white eggs.

Write your answers in their simplest form.

Activity

Gather newspapers, magazines, leaflets or any printed material. Go through them and look for the mathematics; in headlines, in tables, in the text and in diagrams.

- Do the headlines give an accurate picture?
- Is the data in the tables easy to read?
- Are the diagrams a fair representation or do they mislead?

1.1 Misleading statements

It is often not what is written, but what has been left out that is important.

Example

Critically analyse the statement:

> 'Sales increased by £3 million over the last year.'

This appears to mean that the company had a very successful year but . . .

- If in the previous year sales were £10 000 it would represent a huge increase.
- If in the previous year sales were £300 million it would be a small increase.

The 'sales' only tell you how much is sold; you also need to know what happened to the profits.

Example

Critically analyse the statement:

> 'Eight out of ten owners who expressed a preference said their cats preferred Catto.'

This does not mean that every owner asked expressed a preference, and it does not say how many of those asked actually expressed a preference.

You also need to consider:

- Where the researcher found the cat owners to ask.
- Whether the owners were found randomly or buying Catto tins in a supermarket?
- Whether the researchers were brandishing discount vouchers to be given out if owners said their cat preferred Catto.

It could be that 1000 people were asked and only 100 expressed a preference of which 80 prefer Catto.

A statement concerning a simple set of statistics rarely proves anything.

Exercise 1A

1. A survey of members of a gardening club found that 78% of its members preferred home grown vegetables.
   Explain why this result is not necessarily representative of all people.

2. The following headline was seen in a newspaper.

   Explain why this news is not shocking.

3. Criticize the following statements.
   (a) 90% of people questioned approved of the site for the new maggot farm.
   (b) Air accident fatalities increased from 1927 to 1987, so it is more dangerous to fly in 1987 than it was in 1927.

1.2 Reading tables

Data is often summarized in tables. This makes comparisons easier. You need to be able to read information from these tables.

Example

The table shows data for antibiotic prescriptions per 1000 patients.

	Age	0–4	5–15	16–24	25–34	35–44	45–54	55–64	65–74	75–84	85+
	Year										
Males	1994	1691	714	550	386	404	407	536	737	913	1050
	1995	1805	823	636	437	444	451	576	784	940	1120
	1996	1727	702	597	404	412	428	582	767	927	1081
	1997	1656	713	571	404	418	431	571	764	937	1010
	1998	1403	606	539	359	372	391	519	709	850	1002
Females	1994	1529	834	853	812	770	735	799	852	879	1012
	1995	1631	948	964	898	830	782	866	905	910	1056
	1996	1541	829	897	841	780	753	843	892	933	1067
	1997	1495	831	898	841	791	754	852	901	952	1069
	1998	1259	724	811	757	703	687	775	849	910	1038

Adapted from Key Heath Statistics from General Practice 1998
Office for National Statistics

(a) Which age group had the least number of antibiotic prescriptions?
(b) Describe the trend in prescribing antibiotics.

(a) Males 25–34
(b) Increased from 1994 to 1995, but has decreased each year since then.

Exercise 1B

1. The composition of British coinage is

	Copper	Nickel	Zinc	Tin
1p, 2p	97%	–	2.5%	0.5%
5p, 10p, 50p	75%	25%	–	–
20p	84%	16%	–	–
£1	70%	5.5%	24.5%	–

(a) Which coin(s) contains the least amount of copper?
(b) Which coin(s) contains no zinc? What colour of coinage are they?

2. The table shows the distribution of blood groups amongst the population of some countries in the mid-1980s.

% Blood group / Country	A	B	AB	O
England	42	8	3	47
Ireland	32	11	3	54
Scotland	35	11	3	51

(a) What percentage of Scottish people have blood group A?
(b) Which country has the highest percentage of blood group O?
(c) People from Wales are thought to be closely related to the Scots and the Irish. What percentage of Welsh people would you expect to have blood group B?

3. The nutrition (per 100 g) of some breakfast cereals is summarized in the table.

/100 g	Energy (kcal)	Protein (g)	Carbohydrate (g)	Fat (g)	Fibre (g)	Sodium (g)
Rice Krispies	370	6	85	1	1.5	0.65
Cornflakes	370	8	82	0.9	3	1
Shreddies	343	9.8	71.7	1.9	11.2	0.5
Weetabix	340	11.2	67.6	2.7	10.5	0.3
Shredded Wheat	330	11.2	66.1	2.1	11.5	Trace

Which cereal should a dietician advise someone to choose if
(a) they must not have any salt (sodium) in their diet,
(b) they should not have any fibre in their diet,
(c) they need to have a high fibre, low fat diet?

4. Rachael and Reuben changed schools. They were told that they had to attend at least two exercise classes. The table outlines the amount of benefit they may enjoy from some of the exercises.

Exercise	Amount of benefit		
	Strength	Stamina	Suppleness
Badminton	**	**	***
Cricket	*	*	**
Football	***	***	***
Gymnastics	***	**	****
Rowing	****	****	**
Squash	**	***	***
Swimming (hard)	****	****	****
Tennis	**	**	***
Weightlifting	****	*	*
Yoga	*	*	****

Key:
* no real effect
** beneficial
*** very good
**** excellent effect

(a) Which exercises should Rachael choose if she wants to become more supple?
(b) Which exercises should Reuben choose if he wants to increase his stamina and become stronger?
(c) Which exercises would provide the same amount of benefit?
(d) Give a reason for someone to choose Football instead of Squash.

1.3 Pictorial misrepresentation

False zeros

The most common way to present correct, but misleading, data is to use a false origin.

Example

Critically comment on these bar charts which represent the number of kettles sold over two years at a local store.

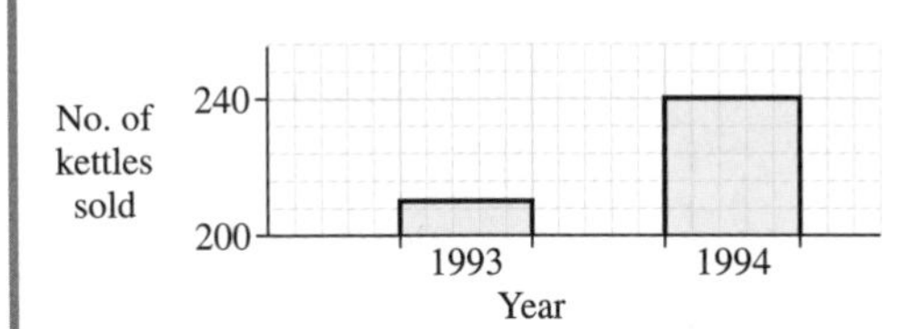

This chart gives the impression that sales were four times greater in 1994 compared with 1993. However, the sales do not start at zero.

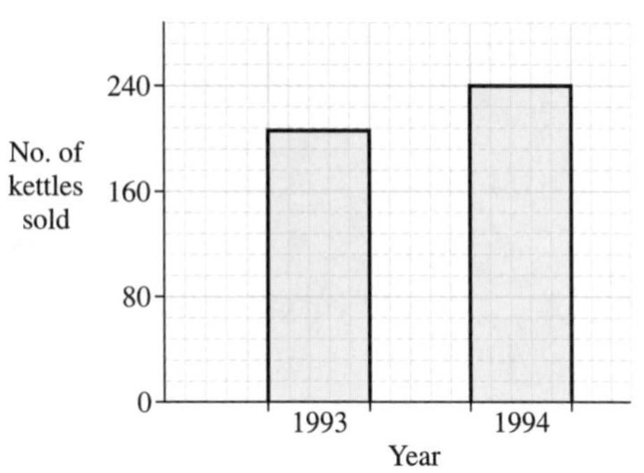

When the whole chart is drawn you can see that although sales have increased they have not even doubled.

Profits for the store, over three years, are shown on this line diagram.

The impression given is that there was a sharp rise in profits over the years.

However, the origin has been omitted.

It is impossible to comment on the graph unless you can work out the scale on the vertical axis.

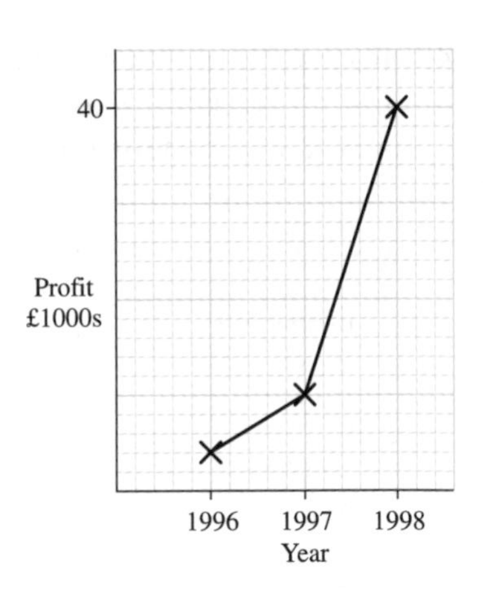

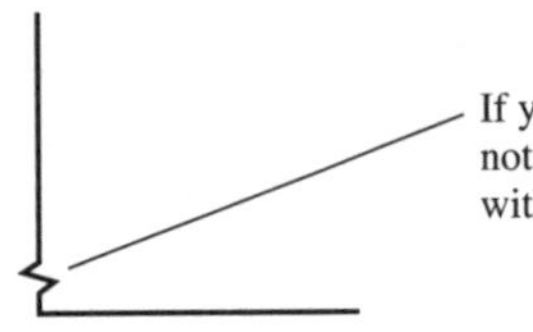

If you draw a graph with a scale that does not begin at zero then it should be identified with a squiggle on the axis as shown.

Scales and labelling

> You can change the impression given by a graph by varying the scale or omitting a scale.

For example, these graphs have been drawn with no vertical scale.

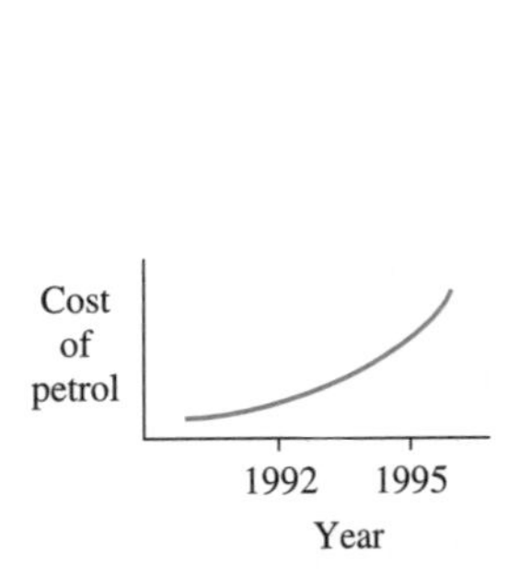

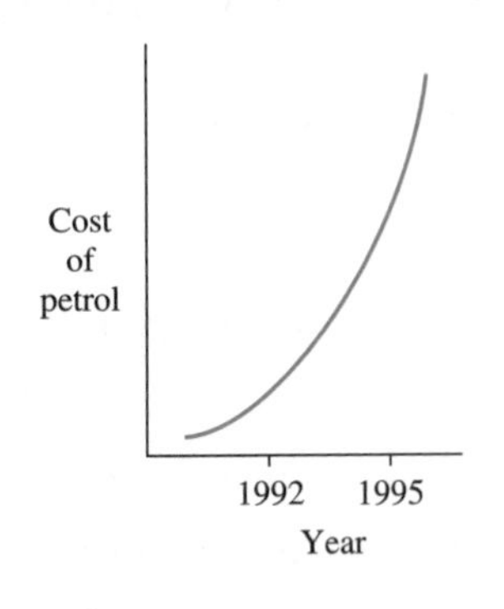

Both graphs may have been drawn to the same scale. You cannot decide if the cost of petrol has increased slowly, as in the first graph; or quickly, as in the second graph.

These two graphs represent exactly the same data.

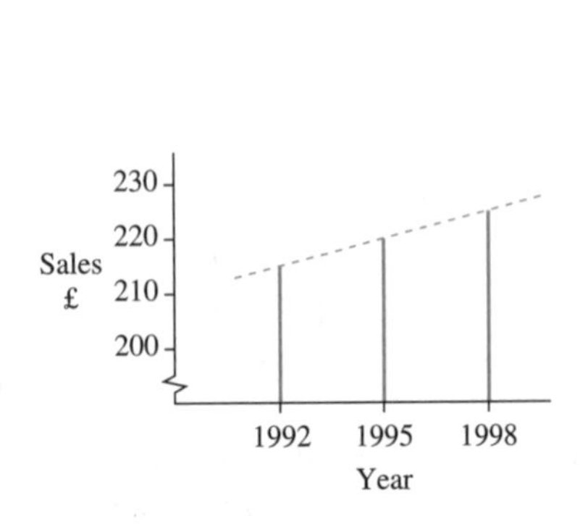

The growth rate of sales, shown by the dotted lines, give different impressions.

> Omission or misuse of a scale is misleading.

All diagrams should

- ✦ Have the scales clearly identified.
- ✦ Have the units given.
- ✦ Be clearly labelled and titled.

Presentation

> A false impression can be given using a graph by carefully selecting which figures to show.

For example, these graphs show the change in share price for a company.

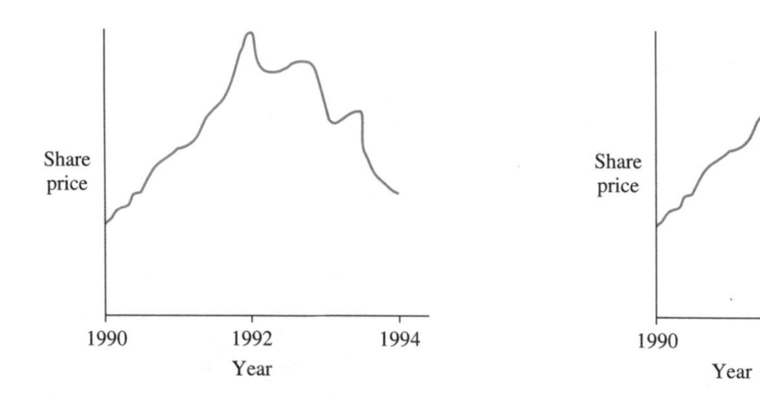

This graph stops before the share price started to fall. This makes the company look more attractive to investors.

You can also see that using shadows or thick lines to join points makes it difficult to read graphs.

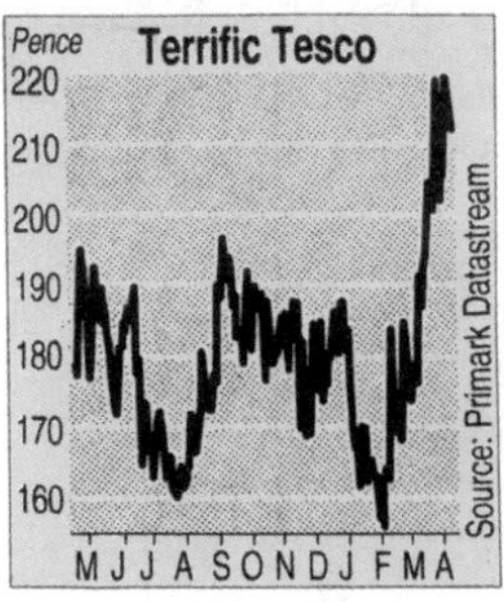

The Mail, April 15th, 2000

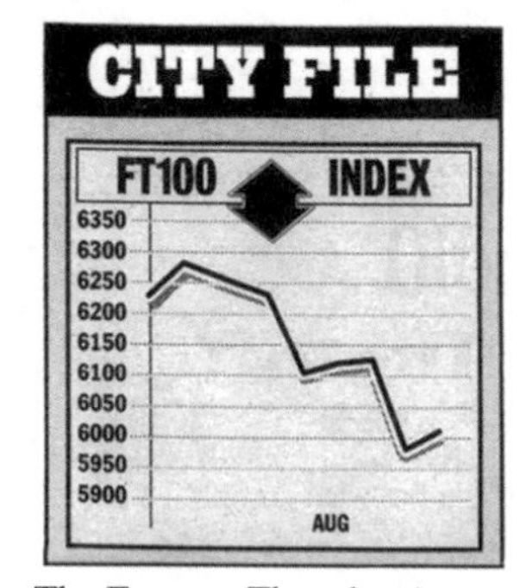

The Express, Thursday August 12th, 1999

Exercise 1C

1. The following graphs all appeared in national newspapers. Criticize their presentation.

(a)

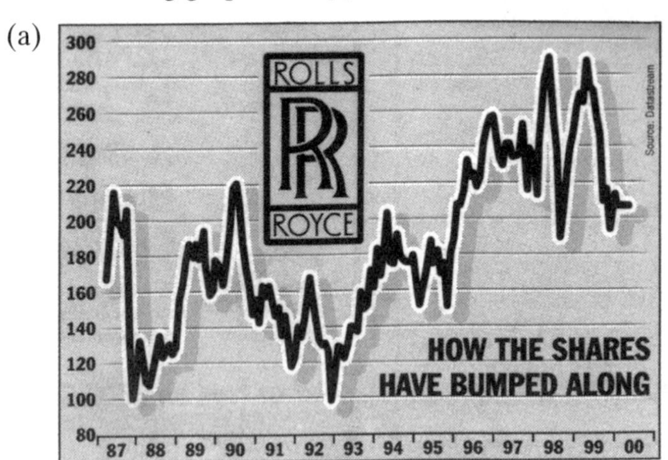

The Express, April 11th, 2000

(b)

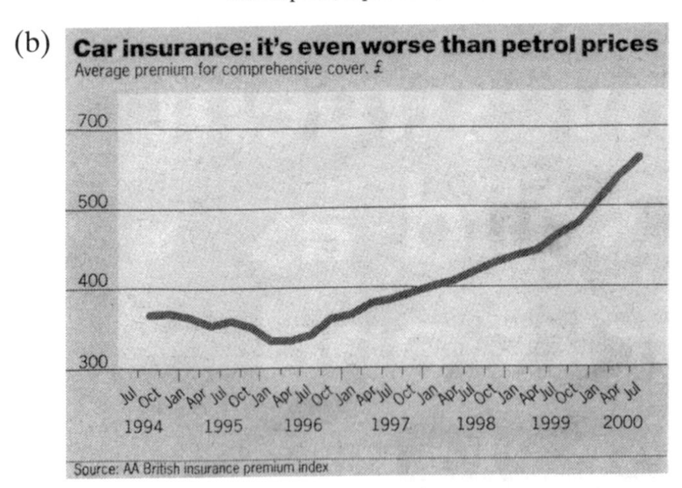

The Guardian, August 26th, 2000

(c)

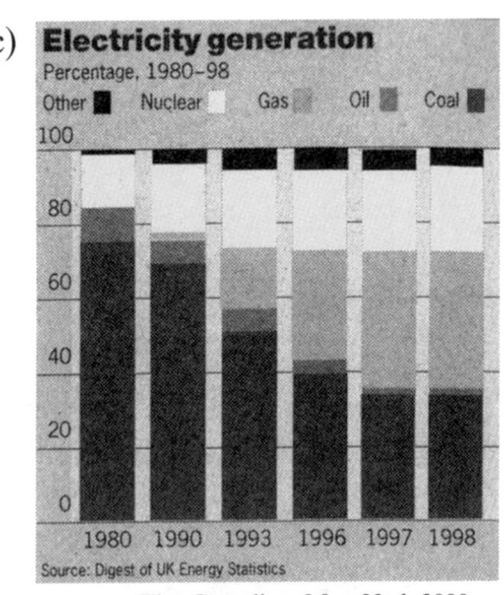

The Guardian, May 23rd, 2000

(d)

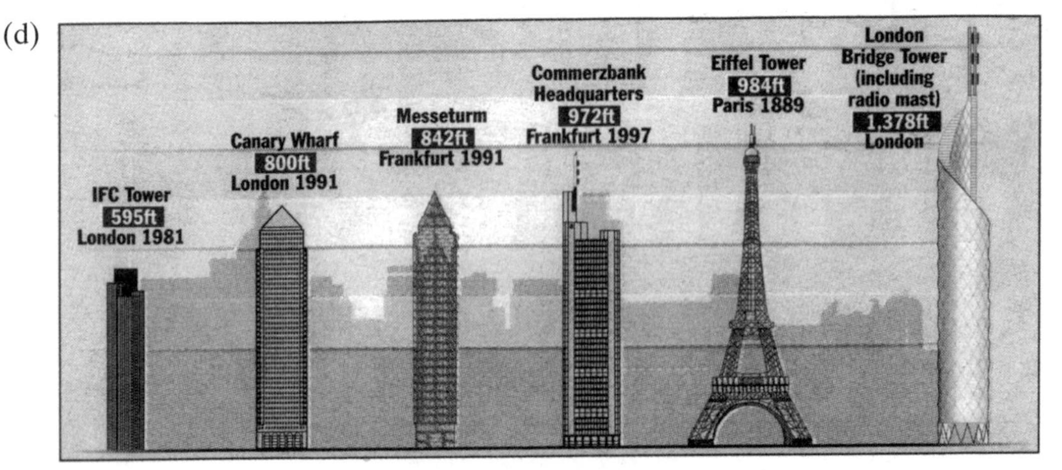

The Express, April 11th, 2000

2. This graph appears to show a big increase in sales of Brisk.

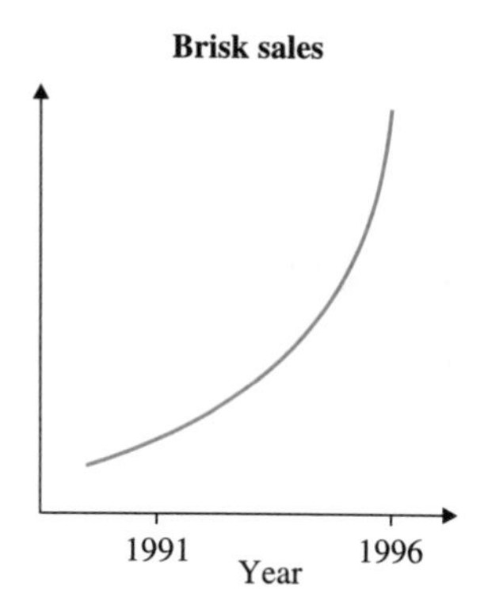

Are you convinced of the success of Brisk?
Give a reason for your answer.

3. This graph implies that price rises in the cost of CDs are slowing down.

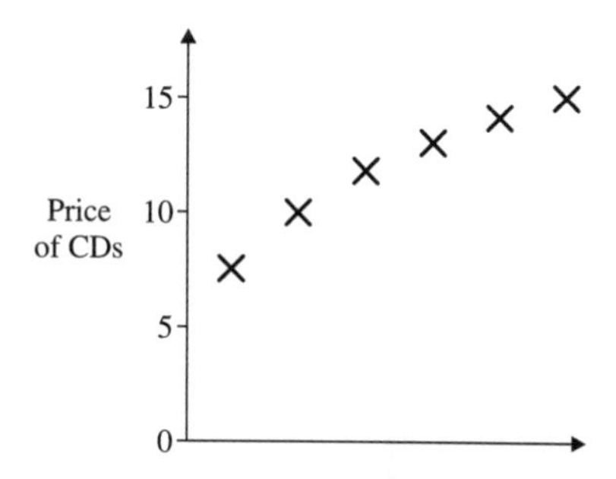

Why might this not be true?

4. Which of these two businesses is growing faster?
Explain how you found your answer.

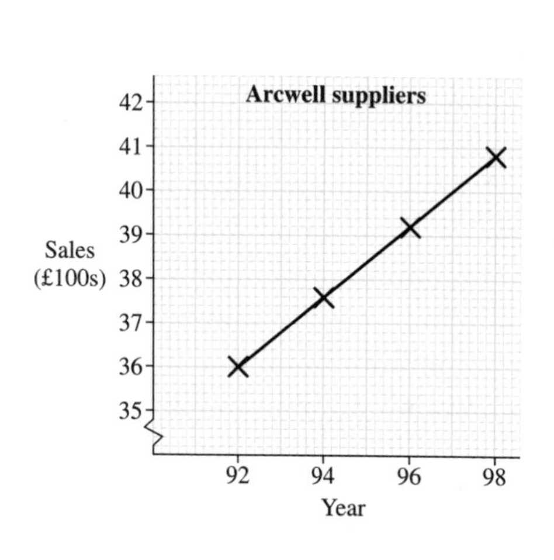

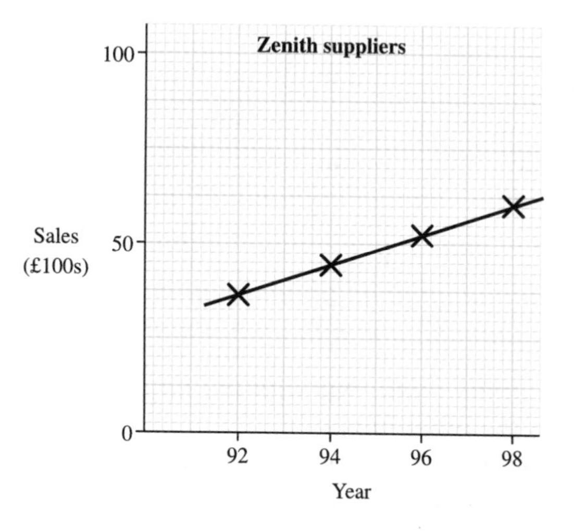

5. The following diagrams appeared in a financial report to represent sales and profits over two years.

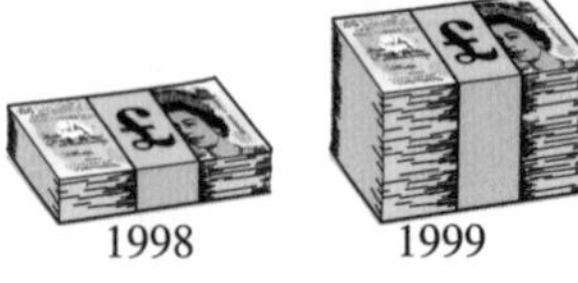

(a) Explain why the sales diagram is misleading.
(b) Explain why the profit diagram is misleading.
(c) What extra data is needed before you could redraw the sales diagram to make it fair?

6. Sales of calculators in a school shop are given in this table.

Term	Sales
Autumn	74
Spring	62
Summer	86

Draw two line graphs to represent this information with a vertical scale
(a) from 60 to 90 with 2 cm representing 10 calculators,
(b) from 0 to 90 with 2 cm representing 30 calculators.

Comment on the different impressions given by the two graphs.

1.4 Misleading diagrams

Diagrams can be misleading if they are not drawn in the correct proportions.

Example

What is wrong with this bar chart showing the distribution of fat in a tin of salmon?

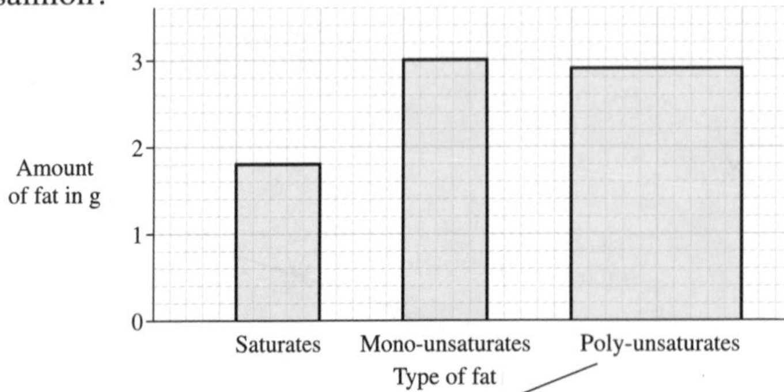

Your eye is drawn to the bar with the largest width, as its area is greater than the other bars.
This gives the impression that there is more of this type of fat than the others; or at least that it is more important than the others.

This diagram was used during the 1983 election campaign.

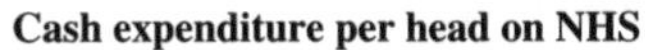

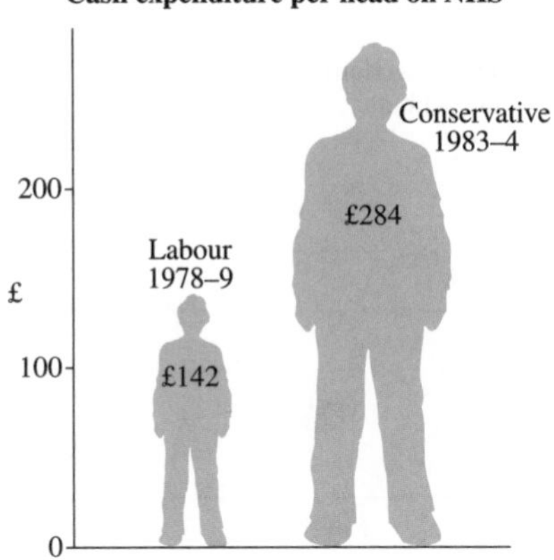

Your eye is drawn to the larger diagram. Most people would tend to ignore the figures, which show that expenditure had doubled, and concentrate on the visual impact of one diagram compared with the other, which is four times larger.

The heights of the diagrams are in proportion to the amounts spent, but the areas of the diagrams are not in proportion.

> When you draw diagrams for pictorial comparisons you should take care not to misuse length, area and volume.

Exercise 1D

1. The diagram represents sales of cakes in a bakery.

(a) What is the ratio of
  (i) their heights,
  (ii) their areas?

(b) Does the diagram give a fair representation of the cake sales? Give a reason for your answer.

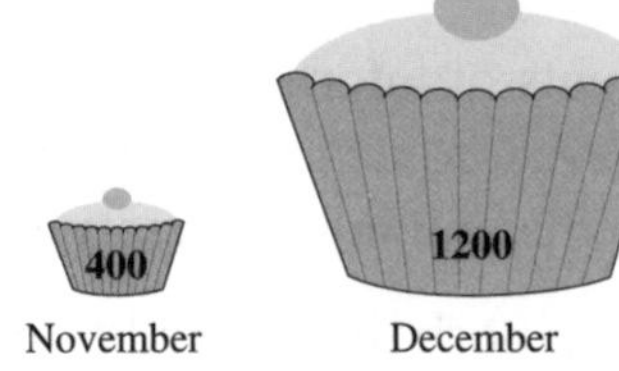

2. The diagram shows information about the sales of razor blades in 1989.

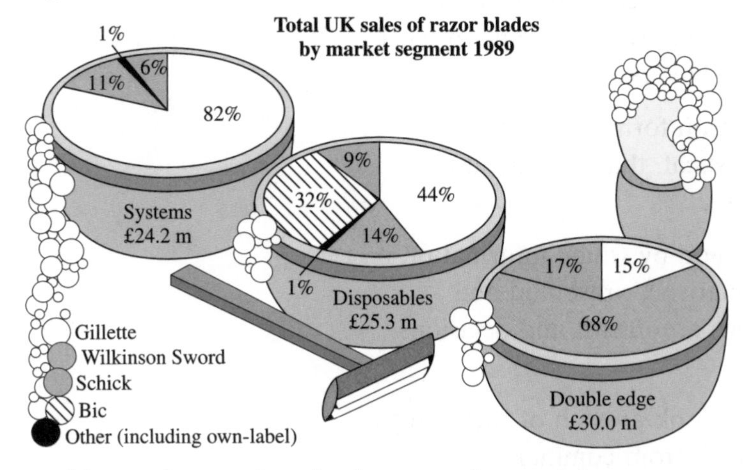

How could you change the pie charts to show a fairer representation of the different types of razor blades sold?

3. The diagram shows the reported non-collections of refuse as a percentage of the total number of households.

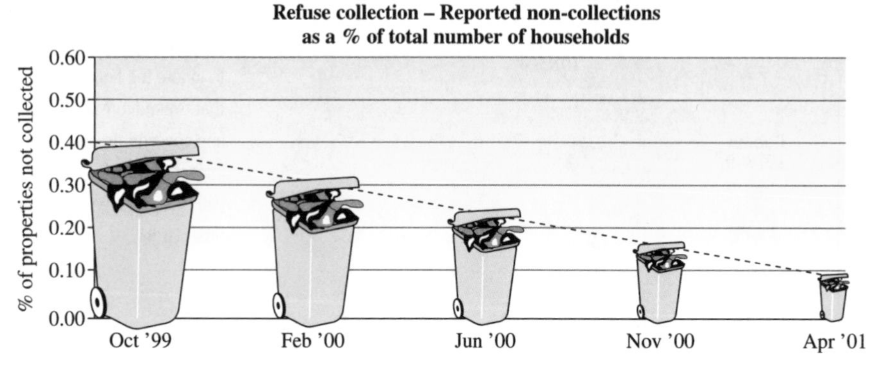

Critically comment on the diagram.

Summary of key points

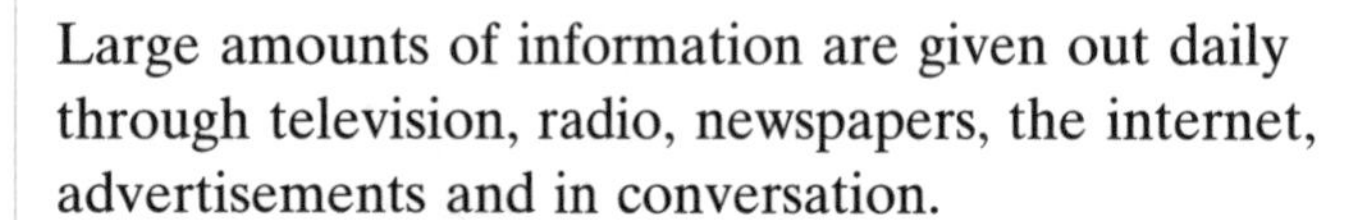

✦ Look at axes, titles and choice of graph to decide if it represents data fairly

Links to the Real World

Large amounts of information are given out daily through television, radio, newspapers, the internet, advertisements and in conversation.

We need to absorb data quickly, reject it or select it, and maybe act upon it. When driving or cycling we need to process road sign information; in supermarkets we need to compare prices and decide what to buy; in finance we need to compare interest rates and at work we need to understand our pay and tax.

Everyone is confronted with information, much of which is numerical or statistical, that they need to interpret if it is to be of use.

Statistics is a scientific method by which information is collected, organised, summarised, presented and analysed before conclusions are drawn and decisions are made.

The following chapters will look at each of these steps in turn using real data drawn from commerce and government concerning real situations.

Revision Exercise 1

1. Expectation of life is the further number of years which a person of a certain age and gender may expect to live.

The table gives this information for United Kingdom residents in the years 1931 and 1991.

	Men		Women	
Age \ Year	1931	1991	1931	1991
At Birth	59	71	62	77
1	62	71	65	77
10	56	62	59	68
20	47	53	50	58
30	38	43	41	48
40	30	34	32	39
50	22	25	24	30
60	14	17	16	21
70	9	10	10	14
80	4	6	5	8

Source: adapted from *Social Trends*

For example, in 1931 a man aged 30 could expect to live another 38 years.

(a) (i) Write down how many years a woman aged 30 in 1931 could expect to live.
(ii) Compare the data for men with that for women. What conclusion can you draw?

(b) The expectation of life of both men and women in 1991 is longer than in 1931. Give a possible reason for this.

(c) (i) Comment on the life expectancy in 1931 of children at birth and at 1 year old.
(ii) Give a possible reason for this. [AQA]

2. An estate agent has one house for sale at £100 000 and one at £150 000.
The diagram has been drawn to represent this information.

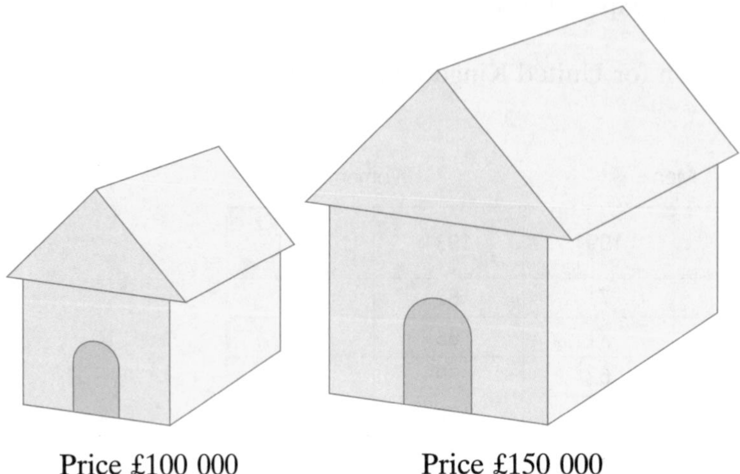

Price £100 000 Price £150 000

(a) Explain why the diagram is misleading in representing these house prices.
(b) The agent decides to represent the houses using a two dimensional diagram.

The width representing the £100 000 house is 3 cm. Calculate the width representing the £150 000 house. [AQA]

3. Fifty pupils were asked about the type of accommodation they stayed in on holiday last year.
Some of the results are shown in the table.

	Hotel	Caravan	Tent	Total
Boys	12	9		24
Girls			14	26
Total	20		17	50

(a) How many girls stayed in a hotel?
(b) Copy and complete the table. [AQA]

4. The table shows the percentage by age for each ethnic group of the UK population 2001–2002.

Ethnic group \ Age	Under 16	16–34	35–64	65 and over
White	19	25	40	16
Mixed	55	27	16	2
Indian	22	34	38	6
Pakistani	35	36	25	4
Bangladeshi	38	38	21	3
Other Asian	22	36	38	4
Black Caribbean	24	25	42	9
Black African	33	35	30	2
Other Black	35	34	26	5
Chinese	20	40	35	5
Other	20	37	39	4

Source: *Adapted from Office for National Statistics, Summer 2003*

(a) Which ethnic group had the largest percentage of its population under 16 years of age?
(b) What was the difference between the percentages of Chinese ethnic group and Black African ethnic group aged 35–64 years?
(c) Give one similarity and one difference between the age profiles of the White ethnic group and the Indian ethnic group. [AQA]

5. The table gives the size of households in Great Britain between 1971 and 2001. For example, in 1991, 34% of households consisted of two people.

	1971	1981	1991	2001
One person	17	22	27	28
Two people	33	32	34	35
Three people	19	17	16	16
Four people	17	18	16	14
Five or more people	14	11	8	7

Source: *Adapted from Social Trends 2005*

(a) What percentage of households in 1981 consisted of four people?
(b) Throughout the period 1971–2001 what size household accounted for about a third of the households?

(c) The total of the percentages for 1991 is 101%.
Give a possible reason for this.

(d) The composite bar chart shows the data from the table for 1971–1991.

Complete the chart by drawing the axes and the bar for 2001.

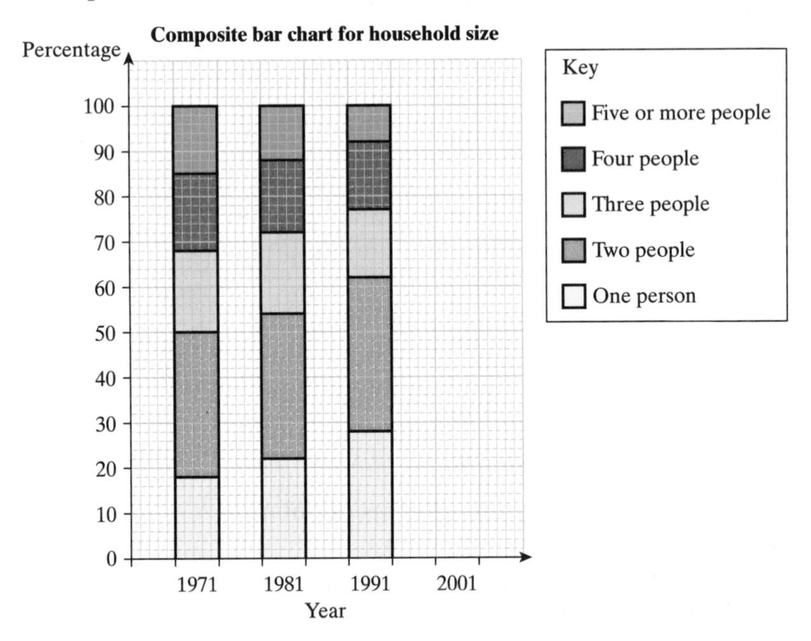

(e) Use the composite bar chart to identify one similarity and one difference in the data for the year 1971 and the year 2001. [AQA]

6. (a) The diagram shows the population of Hong Kong from 1993 to 1999.

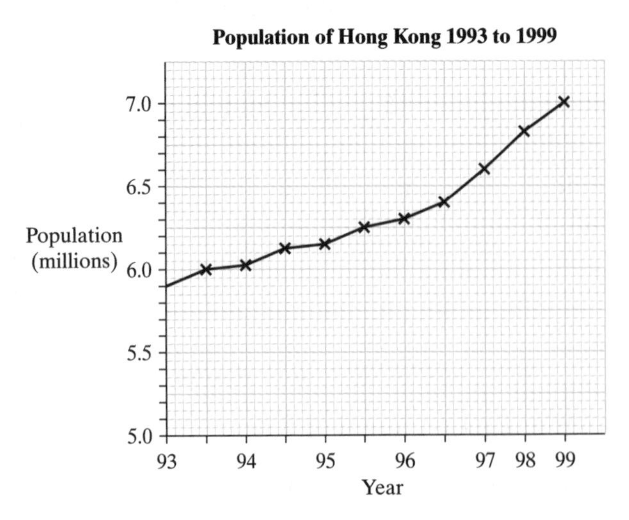

Give two reasons why this diagram is misleading.

(b) Explain why this graph does **not** show that drivers aged over 79 years are the safest on the roads.

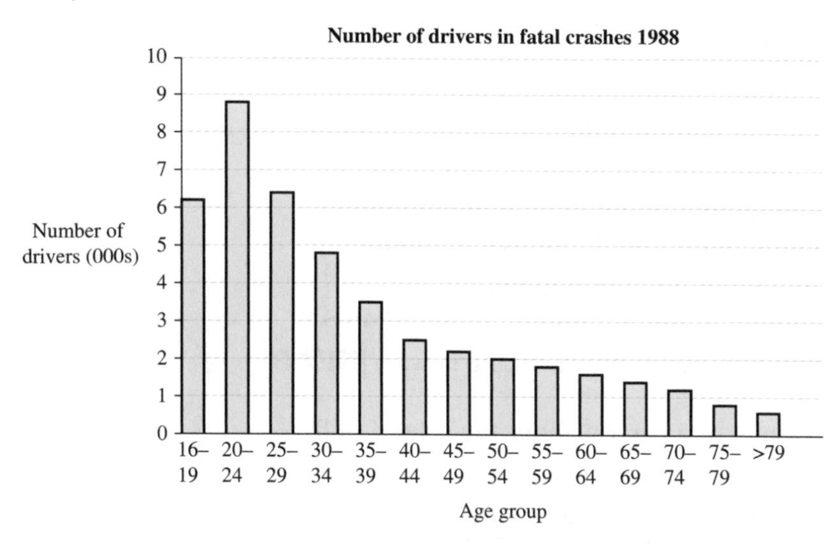

[AQA]

7. The Government produced the following accounts for the year 1995–96.

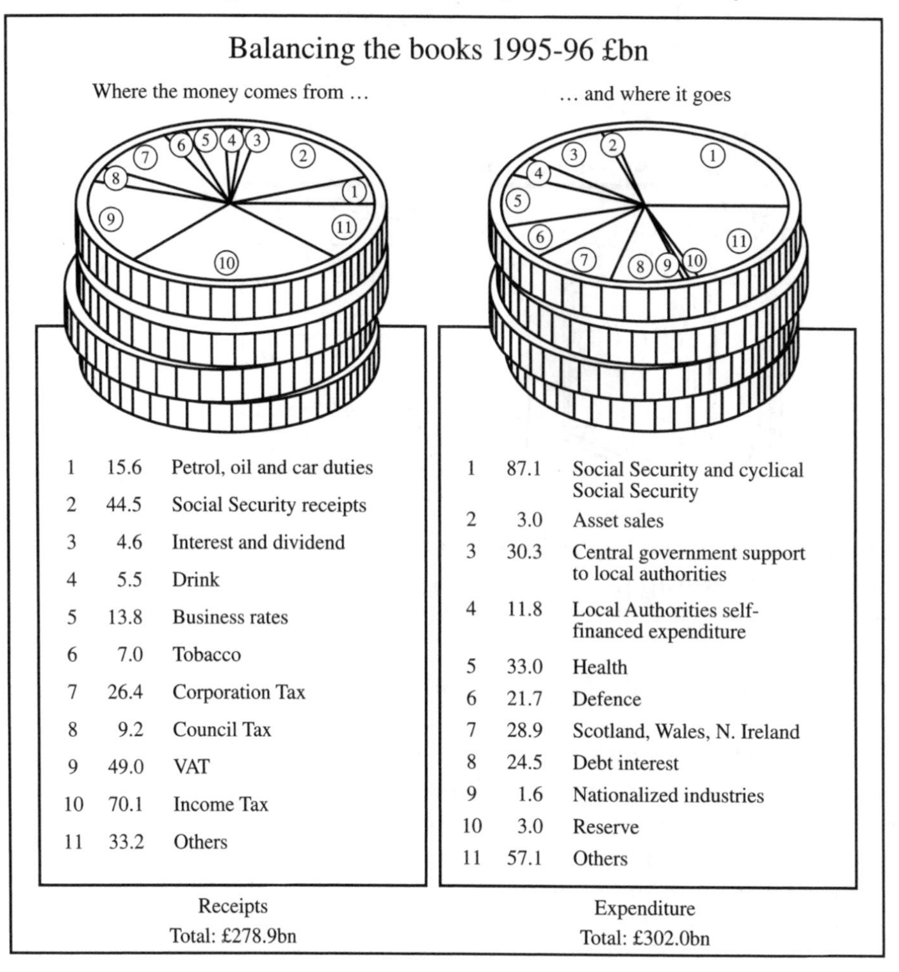

(a) Where does the largest amount of money come from?
(b) How much did the Government spend on Defence?
(c) How much did the Government need to borrow to meet the expenditure total of £302.0bn? [SEG]

8. The following headline was taken from a newspaper.

> **SHOCKING NEWS. 40% OF CHILDREN IN BRITISH SCHOOLS GET LESS THAN THE AVERAGE NUMBER OF MARKS FOR MATHEMATICS**

Explain in your own words why this is **not** shocking news. [NEAB]

9. The diagram shows the results of a survey about the sale of milk.

Source: *The Times* 24.3.95

(a) In 1990, what percentage of milk was delivered to the doorstep? Give your answer to the nearest 10%.
(b) In which year did the sale of milk at supermarkets equal the sale of milk at the doorstep?
(c) In 1993, what percentage of milk was not sold at supermarkets or at the doorstep?
(d) Which region had the cheapest milk delivered to the doorstep?
(e) What is the cost of a 4-pint container of milk in the supermarket?
(f) How much would be saved by a family in Wales if they bought a 4-pint container of milk from a supermarket instead of having 4 pints delivered to the doorstep? [NEAB]

10. The following diagram was produced to give information about cereal production in Morocco.

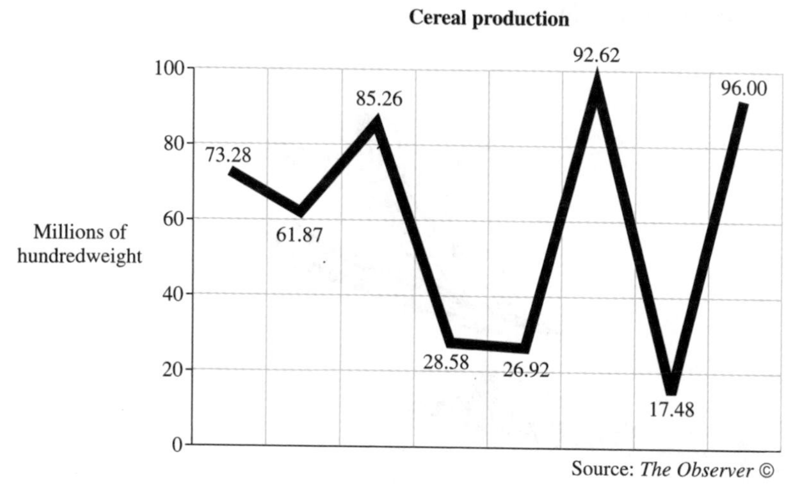

Make **three** comments saying why the diagram could be misleading. [SEG]

11. The table below shows the results of a survey about the three basic skills.

BASIC SKILLS

2875 people were asked about any difficulties they had experienced with basic skills since leaving school.

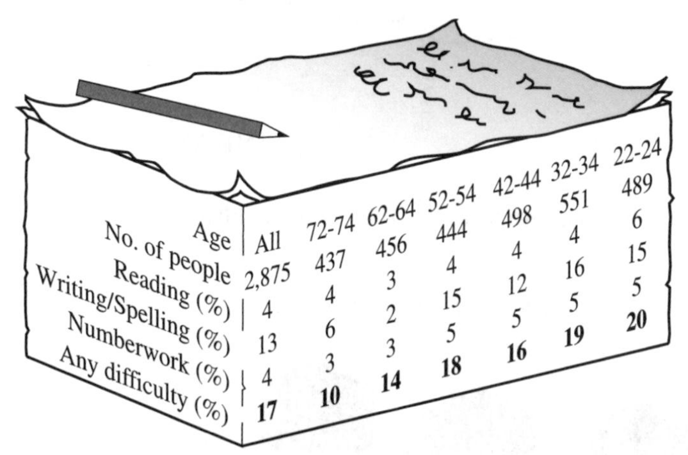

Age	All	72-74	62-64	52-54	42-44	32-34	22-24
No. of people	2,875	437	456	444	498	551	489
Reading (%)	4	4	3	4	4	4	6
Writing/Spelling (%)	13	6	2	15	12	16	15
Numberwork (%)	4	3	3	5	5	5	5
Any difficulty (%)	**17**	**10**	**14**	**18**	**16**	**19**	**20**

Source: *ALBSU* 1994

(a) What percentage of 22–24 year olds found reading difficult?
(b) 16% of which age group had difficulty with writing/spelling?
(c) Some people had difficulty with more than one basic skill. How can you tell this from the table?
(d) There is a mistake in the 62–64 column. How can you tell?

[NEAB]

12. Criticize the diagram below.

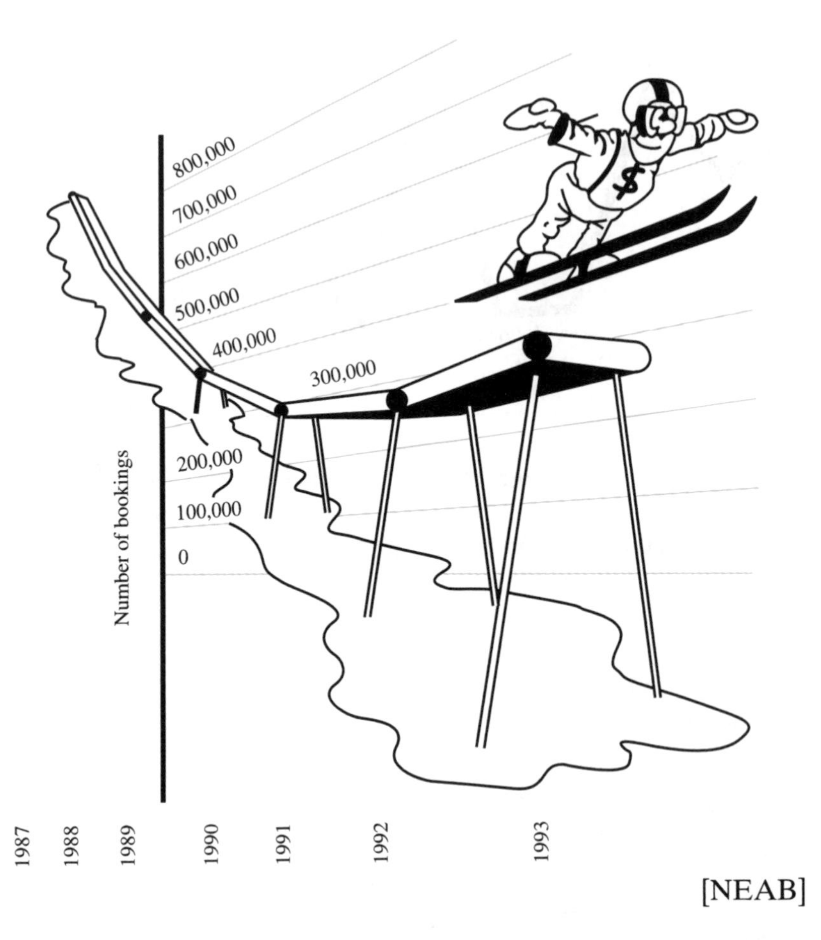

[NEAB]

13. The diagram below shows the percentage of British people who own their own house.

State **two** ways in which the diagram is misleading. [NEAB]

14.

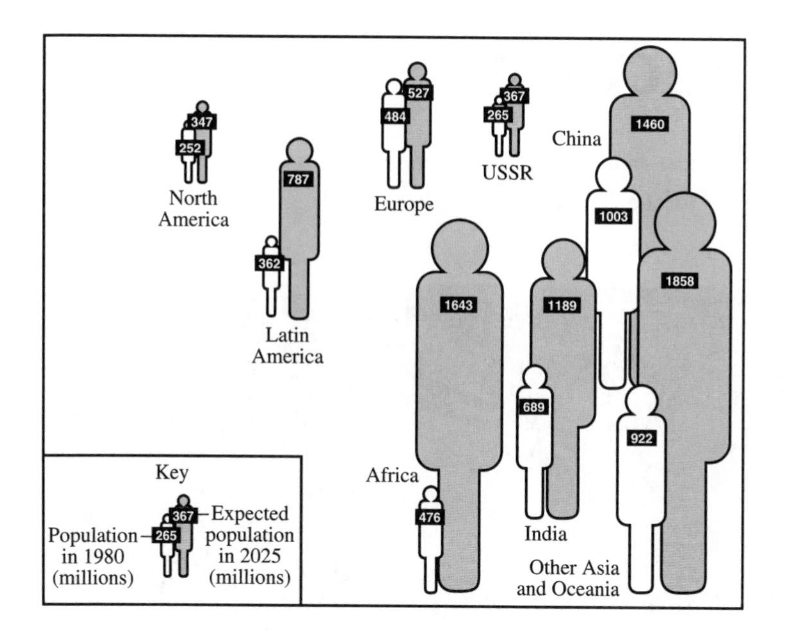

Give **one** reason why the way of representing the data shown above could be misleading. [SEG]

15. A car manufacturer produces two makes of car, Rodeo and Siesta. They sell twice as many Rodeos as Siestas.

(a) The diagrams have been drawn to represent this information. Explain why the diagrams are misleading.

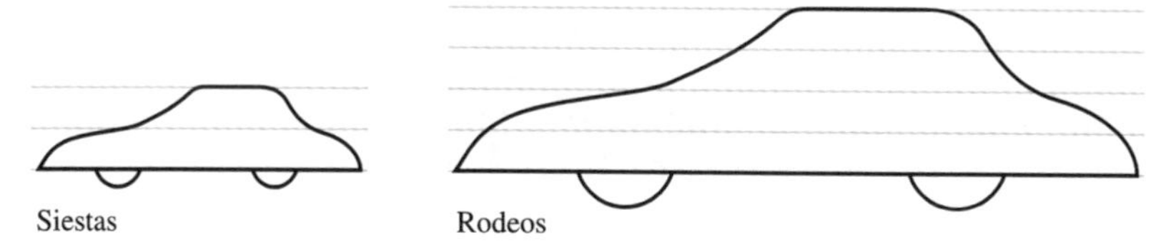

The manufacturer decides to make models of the two cars in proportion to their sales.
The model of the Rodeo will be twice the volume of the model of the Siesta.

The model of the Siesta will be 4 cm long.

(b) Calculate the length of the model of the Rodeo. [SEG]

2 Data collection

We are just statistics, born to consume resources
Horace (65–8 BC) Epistles Book 1

This unit will show you how to

- ✦ Classify data
- ✦ Take a sample of data
- ✦ Design questionnaires and carry out a survey
- ✦ Conduct experiments
- ✦ Draw tables to collect data

Before you start

You should be able to answer these questions

1 (a) How much is
(i) 𝍸 𝍸 𝍸 𝍸 ||| (ii) |||| (iii) 𝍸 𝍸

(b) Write using tally marks
(i) 6, (ii) 14, (iii) 20, (iv) 2, (v) 5

2 Round to the nearest whole number
(a) 4.1, (b) 18.9, (c) 23.0,
(d) 10.5, (e) 33.3, (f) 66.6

3 A bag of 40 marbles has 10 green, 7 purple, 8 yellow, 3 white, 6 blue and 6 red.
What proportion of the marbles are
(a) red, (b) green,
(c) white, (d) yellow,
(e) yellow or white, (f) blue or green,
(g) not purple?

Every day a new flood of data is brought to us by newspapers, leaflets, television, radio, the internet and so on. This data may be in the form of measurements, observations or lists of facts.

2.1 Types of data

Vast amounts of raw data are being collected all the time.

Raw data is information that has not been ordered or processed in any way.

Data can be

- **qualitative** (non-numerical)
  For example: the texture and colour of a fabric are properties that are not numbers.
- **quantitative** (numerical)
  For example: the number of books in a room or the height of a person are numbers.

Qualitative data is sometimes called categorical data

Qualitative data describes a quality that cannot be counted.

Quantitative data describes a quantity that can be counted or measured.

Quantitative data can be

- **discrete** (countable)
  For example: the number of rooms in a house or a person's shoe size.
- **continuous** (measurable)
  For example: length, weight and time are all measured on a continuous scale.

Discrete data is usually concerned with a limited number of countable values.

Continuous data is measured on some scale and can take any value within that scale.

Continuous data may sometimes seem discrete. For example, you may record time to the nearest second.

You usually collect data on a particular **variable**.

> A variable is a property able to assume different values.

For example, temperature is a variable and data can be collected on it.

Example

Imogen buys a new dress.
Write down two variables associated with a dress that illustrate the following data types: (a) qualitative, (b) discrete and (c) continuous.

(a) Colour and texture of the material are qualitative.

(b) The size of the dress and the number of buttons it has are discrete.

(c) The length of the sleeves and the diameter of each button are continuous.

Exercise 2A

1. Robert is spending the summer hiring out deckchairs at the beach.
   (a) Is the number of deckchairs hired out each day a discrete or continuous variable?
   (b) Describe a qualitative variable associated with the deckchairs.

2. Sheena is buying a wig for a fancy dress party.
   Describe a qualitative variable associated with the wig.

3. Adam takes 23 minutes to complete a jigsaw puzzle.
   Is this a discrete or continuous variable?

4. Give an example of (i) a qualitative and (ii) a quantitative measure associated with each of the following.
   (a) A toy car.
   (b) A shoal of fish.
   (c) A computer game.

5. Sort the following into (i) discrete and (ii) continuous data.
   (a) How long you take to finish in a cross-country race and your finishing position in the race.
   (b) The weight of a parcel and the cost of its postage.
   (c) The number of eggs and the amount of sugar needed in a cake recipe.

6. David attended a job interview. His communication skills were rated as either 1 – good, 2 – average or 3 – poor.
   Why is this qualitative and not quantitative data?

7. Gareth is looking at the night sky through a telescope. Is the number of stars in the galaxy discrete or continuous data?

2.2 Collecting data

Before you collect data you should have an aim in mind.

You then need to decide what sort of data to collect and the most appropriate and efficient method to obtain it.

Secondary & primary data

You can use data that someone else has collected and published or you can collect it yourself.

Secondary data sources include: Social Trends, Economic Trends, Annual Abstract of Statistics, Monthly Digest of Statistics, newspapers and the Internet.

Primary data is data that you collect yourself.

Secondary data is obtained from published statistics. It is data that already exists, so it is second hand.

The table shows the main advantages and disadvantages of using primary and secondary data.

Data	Advantages	Disadvantages
Secondary	Cheap Easy to obtain May give a starting/reference point for a survey or experiment.	Could be unaware how it was collected, who it was collected from, how it was collated. May be out of date.
Primary	You know how it was collected. You know who it was collected from.	Expensive Time-consuming

Experiments, observations & surveys

You can use an experiment to collect data.

Experiments and observations range from very controlled environments to more natural situations with less or even no control.

Scientific experiments conducted in a laboratory are examples of a highly controlled environment. Data collected from observed behaviour is an example of data collected 'in the field' where there may be no control and the subjects studied may not even be aware they are being observed.

In an experiment, at least one of the variables is controlled – this is called the **explanatory** or **independent variable**. The effect is observed – this is called the **response** or **dependent variable**.

There may be many other variables that might affect the experiment. These are called extraneous variables.

Extraneous variables might be gender, time of day, background noise, etc.

Example

Edith carries out an experiment to find out which age group at a school is best at estimating a minute.

Suggest independent and dependent variables for her experiment.

She chooses the age groups so the age is the independent variable. She records the responses, so the time estimated is the dependent variable.

You can use a survey to collect data.

Surveys are particularly useful for collecting personal data.

The main survey methods are:

- Observation, which involves monitoring behaviour or information.
- Personal interviews, which are widely used in market research.
- Telephone surveys, which are a special type of personal interview.
- Postal surveys in which the survey is sent to an address.
- Online surveys in which the survey is sent by email or found on a website.

When more than one person observes the same thing, but they perceive and record observations differently, inter-observer bias occurs. This can be minimized by giving guidance on what to focus on and record.

The table outlines the main advantages and disadvantages of these survey methods.

Survey method	Advantages	Disadvantages
Observation	Systematic & mechanical.	Results are prone to chance.
Personal Interview & Telephone Survey	High response rate Many questions can be asked.	Expensive The interviewer may influence the replies.
Postal Survey & Online Survey	Relatively cheap Large amount of data can be collected.	Poor response rate Limited in the type of data that can be collected Only part of the survey may be completed.

Example

A car design company wishes to design and market a new sports car.

(a) Explain how and why they could use both secondary and primary data.
(b) Which method of collecting primary data could be used?

(a) Secondary data – you could refer to published data on human body measurements, to decide on roof height, seat/gear stick distance etc.
Primary data – conduct a survey to find out which features in a car would be most attractive to your market.
(b) The survey could be conducted by personal interview or by post.

Exercise 2B

1. To improve the road safety in Dangercity the council propose to install speed restriction humps. They study the accident rates for the busiest roads.
Are they using primary or secondary data?

2. Darryl and Jason want to predict next season's football league champions. Darryl looks at the football results from 2000. Jason looks at the results from 1995 to 1999.
(a) What type of data are they using?
(b) Whose opinion is likely to be more reliable and why?

3. Choc-u-like is a confectionery company. They want to produce a new chocolate bar.
Should they collect primary data or use secondary data?
Give a reason for your answer.

4. Coftea is a manufacturer of kettles.
How could they use secondary data in designing a new kettle?

5. Jasmine is convinced that people with longer legs run faster in sprint races. She conducts an experiment to test her theory.
What are the explanatory and response variables she should measure?

6. Richie Vanson, a businessman, is considering building a leisure centre in Tintown.
What method of collecting primary data should he use to help him decide whether to build?
Give a reason for your answer.

7. A survey is carried out to investigate the cost of heating newly built houses.
Give one reason why this survey should be carried out by post.

2.3 Sampling

It depends on who is included in a survey as to the picture the survey gives.

When you want to collect data you must first identify your **population**, that is, who or what you want to include in your survey.

A **population** is everything or everybody involved in the study.

Census data

Census data obtains information from every element of a population.

An example of a census involving a large population is the Government National Census conducted every ten years.

- A census is usually only practical when the population is small and known, for example when studying the working conditions of a small firm or the television preferences of a class of pupils.
- A census is not always possible, for example if you wanted to find the weight of all the tea in China.

Census information is used by central and local government, health authorities and many other organisations to allocate resources and plan services for everyone.

Sample data

When a census is not practical or possible you need to take a sample of the population.

The purpose of sampling is to collect data from some of the population and use it to make conclusions about the whole population.

Two samples drawn from the same population are likely to give different results.

To collect sample data, you take information from part of the population.

You should try to ensure that the sample you choose is free from **bias**.

In statistics, bias means a distortion of results.

Bias in sampling may arise from:

- Misidentifying the population.
- Choosing an unrepresentative sample.
- Non-response to a survey.
- Asking ambiguous or leading questions.
- Dishonesty of those sampled.
- Errors in recording answers.
- Not controlling external factors in experiments, such as the effect of noise on the ability to complete a task requiring concentration.

An external factor is also called an extraneous variable.

The main advantages and disadvantages of using census data or taking a sample from a population are outlined in the table.

	Advantages	Disadvantages
Census	Accurate Unbiased Includes every item in the population	Expensive Time-consuming Difficult to ensure the whole population is surveyed
Sample	Cheaper Less time-consuming Reduces the amount of data to be collected and analysed	May be biased Not totally representative

Exercise 2C

1. Citsale, elastic band producers, conducted an experiment to see how much a new elastic band would stretch.
   Identify the population to use in the experiment.
   Give a reason why a census should not be carried out.

2. A new canteen was being built at a small factory.
   Give a reason for the management to conduct a census survey to determine the factory canteen's menu.
   Identify the population for this survey.

3. For the following studies, decide whether you would conduct a census or a sample survey. Give a reason for your choice.
   (a) A study of house prices in England and Wales.
   (b) A study of house prices in the village of Smallbury, population 105.

4. A school proposes to install floodlights on their football pitch.
   Identify the population affected by their proposal.

2.4 Sampling methods

To ensure each item in the population has an equal chance of being selected, you take a **random sample** from the whole population.

Usually, the larger the sample the more representative the statistics are of the whole population.

A random sample is one chosen without conscious decision.

A **sampling frame** is used to identify the population. It consists of all items in the population and ensures that they all have a chance of being sampled.

Often there has to be a balance between practical convenience and ideal conditions. To obtain a true random sample you use simple random sampling.

Simple random sampling

Every item in the population has an equal chance of being chosen. You assign a number to each item and then use random number tables, a calculator or computer to choose a sample, ignoring duplicate numbers.

Although using random numbers is free from (personal) bias, there is no guarantee that the actual sample chosen is unbiased.

This method is more suited to a relatively small population where the sampling frame is complete.

Example

Below is an extract from a table of random numbers.

Use the numbers to identify a sample of 5 from a population of 50.

67485 88715 45293 59454 76218 78176
87146 99734 35555 76229 00486 64236
74782 91613 53259 79692 47618 20025
16022 27081 00058 58042 67833 23539
37668 16324 97243 03199 45435

- ✦ Assign a number to each member of the population from 00 to 49.
- ✦ Choose any point in the table to start and read pairs of numbers in a direction of your choice.
- ✦ Ignore repeated numbers and numbers above 49.

- ✦ For example, start here and read across.
- ✦ Then the pairs you read are:
  ~~70~~ ~~81~~ 00 05 ~~85~~ ~~80~~
  42 ~~67~~ ~~83~~ 32 35
- ✦ The crossed out numbers are too big for the question, so your sample of 5 would be:
  0, 5, 42, 32 and 35.

Activity

A calculator can generate random numbers using the RAND or RAN# key.

Assign numbers to the database in Appendix 1 and using your calculator choose several samples of 5 students. Are the results identical for each of the samples?

What if you chose a larger sample, size say 10 or 15. Do your results become more similar as the sample size increases?

Multi-stage sampling

This involves a series of samples taken at successive stages. First the population is divided up. For example, if the population consisted of all the people in Great Britain you may divide the population by geographical area. A number of these, say three or four areas, are chosen. Each of these will be divided again into smaller areas. A few of these smaller areas are then chosen at random. Finally individuals are selected at random from each of these smaller areas.

Multi-stage sampling is used to save time and money when the population is very spread.

Stratified sampling

The population is divided into categories (strata) by age, gender, social class . . . , then a random sample is chosen from each category. The size of each sample is in proportion to the size of each category within the population.

Stratified sampling ensures you have a fair proportion of responses from each group of the population.

Example

At an infant school there are 113 Reception year pupils, 133 Year 1 and 136 Year 2.
A sample of size 60 stratified by year group is chosen.
How many pupils from each year will be chosen?

Total number of pupils = 382
Multiply proportion by sample size.

Reception year	Year 1	Year 2
$\frac{113}{382} \times 60 = 17.7$	$\frac{133}{382} \times 60 = 20.9$	$\frac{136}{382} \times 60 = 21.4$

Round the answers to give whole numbers. (This total should equal the sample size.)

18 pupils	21 pupils	21 pupils

Systematic sampling

A regular pattern is used to choose the sample. Every item in the population is listed, a starting point is randomly chosen and then every *n*th item is selected.

For example every fiftieth packet of seeds from a production batch is tested for germination starting with the eighth.

This is a simpler and quicker method to select a (random) sample, but may be unrepresentative if a pattern exists in the list.

Cluster sampling

The population is divided into groups or clusters. A random sample of clusters is chosen and every item in the chosen cluster is surveyed.

A large number of small clusters minimizes the chances of this being unrepresentative.

This method is used for example by biologists to study flora and fauna.

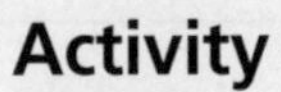

Activity

Discuss how you would use cluster sampling to estimate

- ✦ The number of blades of grass on a football or hockey pitch.
- ✦ The amount of wood in an area of woodland.

Quota sampling

Instructions are given concerning the amount (quota) of each section of the population to be sampled.

A disadvantage is that the actual people or items chosen are left to the discretion of the surveyor which could lead to bias.

An advantage of this method is that no sampling frame is required.

This method is commonly used in market research.

If there are n items in the population, an appropriate sample size is $\sqrt{n}$.

To quarter ($\frac{1}{4}$) the variability you use $4^2 = 16$ times the sample size.

Convenience sampling

The most convenient sample is chosen which, for a sample of size sixty, could mean the first sixty people you meet.

It is highly likely that this sample would be biased and unrepresentative.

Opinion polls

Large-scale opinion polls often use a combination of cluster and quota sampling.

An example of this is the accurate estimates of the outcome of general election for public office.

The criteria for selection of a sample in national opinion polls are: geographical area, age, gender, social and economic background.

The sample size may be **large** but is often based on a very small proportion of the population.

A major disadvantage of conclusions drawn from opinion polls is that opinions may change over time.

Example

Nyree wanted to investigate whether people measured their height using metric or imperial units. She went to her local supermarket and asked the first twenty people she saw how tall they were.

(a) For this survey state the sampling frame, the sampling method used and why it might be biased.

(b) Outline a better method to use to choose the sample.

(a) The sampling frame could be the whole population of this country (or the whole population in the world).

The sampling method used is convenience sampling. It is biased as everyone chosen most probably lives in the same area and so may not provide a cross-section of social class. Also the sample is very small.

(b) A better method could be to use quota sampling, ensuring for example that men and women across all ages, children, different ethnic groups and different social classes were all represented.

If Nyree had wanted to know how people in her town measured their height, then she could have used stratified sampling as the sampling frame would be every person living in that town.

Exercise 2D

For each of questions 1 to 8:

(a) identify the population (sampling frame),
(b) explain why the sample may be biased,
(c) explain a better method to use to choose the sample.

1. John was carrying out a survey to find how far, on average, residents in his town travel to work. He asked all the people at his local railway station one Monday morning.

2. Hazel thinks that boys at her school get more pocket money than girls. There are 300 children at the school, 120 boys and 180 girls. In her survey she asks 30 boys and 30 girls.

3. To find out attitudes on abortion, an interviewer stopped people in a local shopping centre one weekday morning and asked shoppers their views.

4. Pedro wanted to find out how much people in Britain were prepared to spend on holidays abroad. He asked people on the street where he lives.

5. Catriona believes that more people in Scotland get married in church than in a registry office. She asks all the people attending a church service where they got married.

6. To investigate the statement 'children no longer do enough sport', all the children at one school in Downtown were surveyed.

7. Glowalot, a light bulb manufacturer claimed that their light bulbs lasted for more than 200 hours. Gina thought it would be a good idea to test their claim by lighting all the bulbs produced in one month.

8. Joanne wanted to find out if rich people in England smoked more cigarettes than poorer people. She chose 200 households at random and sent them a 40 page questionnaire which they had to pay postage to return.

9. A sample of size 50 stratified by gender is to be chosen from a population of 422 women and 638 men. How many women and how many men should be chosen?

10. A sample of size 40 stratified by year group is to be chosen from a junior school with 122 Year 3, 117 Year 4, 93 Year 5 and 90 Year 6 pupils. How many from each year group should be chosen?

11. A university campus has all its first year students living on site. There are 22 accommodation blocks each of which is divided into 8 flats. There are between 5 and 8 students in each flat. Josh carries out a survey to find out what the students think of Freshers' Week. Describe how he could use multi-stage sampling to choose a sample of 60 students from 12 flats.

2.5 Questionnaires

You often need to use a **questionnaire** to collect data.

> A questionnaire is a set of questions used to obtain data from individuals.

The questions can ask for factual information, for example 'how many radios do you own?' or for opinions, for example 'which radio station do you prefer to listen to?'

People who answer questionnaires are called **respondents**.

The questionnaire itself should:

- ✦ Be clear as to who should complete it.
- ✦ Start with easy questions as this encourages the respondent to continue.

- Be clear where and how the answers should be recorded.
- Be able to be answered quickly.
- Be as brief as possible.

Individual questions should:

- Be short.
- Use simple and clear language.
- Be unambiguous.
- Be free from bias.
- Not be leading (not be questions of the type 'do you agree that...' as this leads respondents to agree).
- Be useful and relevant to your survey.

There are different questioning techniques you can use.

Open questions

> An open question has no suggested answers and allows a respondent to reply with a single word or a long explanation.

Open questions may reveal responses or opinions that you have not considered.

Closed questions

> A closed question has a set of suggested answers to choose from.

The advantage of using closed questions is that it is easier to summarize all the data obtained and make comparisons.

Tick box choices for closed questions

The choices offered in a closed question should not overlap or leave gaps.

For example if you wanted to find out the age group of your respondent and the choices were:

☐ under 10 ☐ 11–20 ☐ 21–30 ☐ 30–40 ☐ over 40

- a 10-year-old would not be able to answer.
- a 30-year-old will have two answer boxes.

Opinion scales

If you use an opinion scale, responses tend to cluster around the middle of the scale as people do not want to appear extreme.

For example if the answer choices were given as tick boxes:

☐ strongly disagree ☐ disagree ☐ no opinion ☐ agree ☐ strongly agree

or respondents were asked to mark on a scale:

disagree |————————————| agree

the majority of respondents would choose the middle options.

One way to avoid this is to provide an even number of options so that there is no middle choice.

Pilot surveys

A pilot survey is a small replica of the actual survey (or experiment) that is to be carried out.

A pilot survey may also give an estimate of the non-response rate and a guide as to the adequacy of the sampling frame.

The pilot should help you identify potential problems with the wording of the questions, and so limit the errors in expensive full-scale surveys.

If you ask closed questions in a survey, you must ensure that the choices of answers reflect the typical answer of the respondents.

To do this, use open questions in a pilot survey to find out the kinds of responses you will get. Then use closed questions in the actual survey.

Sensitive questions

Few people willingly provide intimate facts about themselves and many resent being asked such questions.

If you need to ask highly personal questions, you should leave them to the end of a questionnaire.

To ensure truthful answers to sensitive questions you can use the 'random response' technique.

Example

'Toss a coin. If it shows heads tick the yes box; if it shows tails answer the question:

Have you ever used class A drugs? ☐ yes ☐ no'

If 20 people answer the question then the expected number of 'heads' is 10. If 13 of the people answer 'yes' the proportion who 'genuinely' answer 'yes' is $\frac{3}{10}$.

There is more about expected outcomes on page 239.

Activity

The database in Appendix 1 contains data collected on objects recalled by a sample of students. In groups, write a questionnaire for a survey to find out what people think of their memory, whether memory can be improved etc.

Exercise 2E

Comment critically on questions 1 to 6.
Suggest how they could be improved, either by rephrasing the question or by giving a choice of answers.

1. Do you watch a lot of television?

2. Do you agree that the teachers at your school are superb?

3. Approximately how tall are you?
   ☐ under 1 metre ☐ over 1 metre, but less than 5 feet
   ☐ 2 metres or more

4. (a) What do you think of the facilities at the new leisure centre?
   (b) Have you visited the new leisure centre? ☐ yes ☐ no

5. How old are you? ☐ young ☐ middle-aged ☐ old

6. How many times during the last week did you take a bath or shower?
   ☐ once ☐ twice ☐ every day

7. Write a questionnaire to find out the most popular flavour of crisps for different age groups in your school.
   State (a) the sampling frame
   (b) the sample size and how you would obtain the sample.
   Describe how you could use a pilot survey.

8. A manufacturer of CD players has asked you to find out the features people would want on a portable personal CD player and how much they would be prepared to pay.
   Write a questionnaire for a pilot enquiry to find this information.
   State (a) the sampling frame for the whole survey
   (b) how you would choose the sample for the pilot enquiry.

2.6 Experimental design

If you carry out an experiment as part of your investigation, here are some methods that you should consider.

Data logging is a mechanical or electronic method of collecting primary data. You programme a machine to take readings at set intervals.

You use data logging to measure rates such as your pulse rate after exercise.

You use a **control group** when you want to test the effect of different factors in an experiment. A randomly chosen group, the control group, is not subjected to any of the factors that you wish to test.

To test how nutrients affect the growth of plants you should have a control group that is not given any nutrients.

You can use **matched pairs**, using two groups, to investigate the effect of a particular factor. Both groups to be tested need to have everything in common except for the factor to be studied.

In the 1930s, Newman investigated the effect of the environment on personality through studying two identical twins reared apart, from an early age, in different environments.

You could conduct a **before-and-after experiment** to help judge the influence that a factor could have.

Schools determine the effect of the long summer break on childrens' education by testing at the end of one school year and then again at the start of the following year.

You can use a **capture–recapture method** to estimate the size of a self-contained population. A sample is taken and tagged and then returned to the population. Some time later a second sample is taken and the number of tagged members is noted. An estimate of the total population can then be made.

For the estimate to be reliable, there needs to be extensive intermingling of the first sample within the whole population.

Example: capture–recapture method

Forty ducks are caught, tagged and returned to a bird sanctuary. In a second sample of sixty ducks, twelve are found to have tags from the first sample.

Estimate the number of ducks in the sanctuary.

The proportion $\frac{12}{60}$ is estimated to be the same as $\frac{40}{n}$ where n is the number of ducks in the sanctuary.

$$\frac{12}{60} = \frac{40}{n}$$

$$n = \frac{40 \times 60}{12}$$

$$n = 200$$

Simulation

It is not always possible to carry out an experiment or survey. For example, studying how quickly a house could burn down when set on fire.

Simulation mimics the conditions of a situation in order to carry out a theoretical study. Simulation is a fairly quick, cheap method to collect data. One or more variables from the original theory can be easily altered and the study repeated. A coin, dice or random numbers are used to help the study be more realistic.

Example

Six different books are included inside crisp multipacks. You want to find out how many multipacks you need to buy to collect the set of six books. Explain how you would carry out the simulation if

(a) there are equal numbers of each book in the multipacks.
(b) there are five times as many book A than each of the others.

(a) Assign numbers on a fair dice to each of the books. Roll the dice until at least one of each number has occurred once. The total number of rolls of the dice is the number of multipacks you need to buy.
(b) Assign digits 0, 1, 2, 3, 4 to book A; assign one digit 5, 6, 7, 8, 9 to each of the other books. Use random number tables, calculator or computer to generate single digits until each of 5, 6, 7, 8, 9 and one of 0, 1, 2, 3, 4 has occurred. The total number of digits generated is the number of multipacks you need to buy.

Activity

When queuing in line is it better for many people to receive quick service while a few wait a long time or for everyone to wait a moderate, but roughly equal amount of time?

A human simulation can determine the best method of queue to use at a bank.

- Queue method A: Separate queues for each bank teller – switch queues if you want!
- Queue method B: One queue in which to wait for the first available teller.

This simulation can be carried out as a whole class activity (20 or more students works well)

Give each student a card on which is written a random arrival time and a transaction time. (Use random numbers to generate arrival time and transaction time).

The times on the card are to be used in both simulations to model queue method A and queue method B in order to analyse the differences in the waiting time to the queuing method used.

Students need to record their **waiting time** for each queuing method simulation.

(You may need a practice attempt at this, keep the data to analyse, find measures and draw diagrams in chapters 3 and 4)

For any experiment that involves two groups, you need to make sure that all the extraneous variables are held constant to both groups e.g. same number of boys and girls in each group.

Exercise 2F

For each of the experiments numbered 1 to 7, decide which experimental method could be used.

1. A new treatment for malaria is to be tested for effectiveness.
2. The heart rate of a sample of people of differing ages is to be monitored as they perform a particular physical exercise.
3. A dormant volcano is monitored for activity.
4. The growth of a genetically modified crop is monitored.
5. An estimate is to be made of the number of deer in a particular area of woodland.

6. An assessment is to be made on the effects of alcohol on driving ability.

7. The population of Jackass penguins, an endangered species, is monitored for change in population.

8. Fifty fish are caught, tagged and returned to a particular pond. In a second sample of thirty fish, five are found to have tags.
Use the capture–recapture method to estimate the number of fish in the pond.

9. There was a population explosion at a rabbit sanctuary. 140 rabbits were caught, tagged and returned to the sanctuary. A second sample of 80 rabbits were snared. 28 of these were tagged.
Estimate the number of rabbits in the sanctuary.

10. At a set of traffic lights 25% of cars turn left, 25% of cars turn right and 50% go straight on.
(a) Describe how you would (i) use coins and (ii) use random numbers to simulate the direction of travel for the cars passing through these lights.

The percentages are thought to be incorrect and that 30% turn left, 10% turn right and 60% go straight on.
(b) Describe how you would carry out a simulation of the direction of travel.

2.7 Presentation of data

You collect raw data by counting or by measuring. It is useful to collect the data in a frequency table so that it is easier to analyse.

You can use tally marks to record data in a frequency table.

Ahmet wanted to find out the pets owned by his classmates.
Here is part of his frequency table:

Pet	Tally	Frequency
Dog	||||	4
Cat	~~||||~~	5
Goldfish	~~||||~~ |||	8
......		...

Add up the tallies to find the frequency

List the categories on the left, leaving space for unusual responses.

Collect the responses in 5s to make the data easier to count.

Exercise 2G

1. Draw frequency tables to find
   (a) the frequency of type of pet owned in your class
   (b) the colour of bicycle owned by your classmates.

2. A survey was carried out to find the number of gel pens owned by each member of a class, with the following results:

   9 8 12 15 9 13 14 13 13 11 12 10 9 9 14 8 11 10 9 12

   Draw a tally chart to summarize this data.

3. Throw a dice 30 times and record the outcomes in a tally chart.

4. Draw a tally chart to record the number of times each vowel – a, e, i, o and u – appears on page 18 of this book.

2.8 Limits of accuracy

When you collect continuous data it will be rounded to the nearest sensible measurement.

Age is an exception to this rule. If you are 15 years and 8 months you are still aged 15 despite being closer to 16 years old.

The **upper bound** is the largest value that a measurement could be.
The **lower bound** is the smallest value that a measurement could be.

Example

The width of my computer screen is 37 cm.

This measurement is given as a whole number (to the nearest integer).

The *actual* measurement of my computer screen must be in between 36.5 cm and 37.499 999 ... cm.

36.5 cm is the lower bound and 37.499 999 ... cm is the upper bound.

If you measure more accurately and find the width of the computer screen is 36.7 cm:

the lower bound is 36.65 cm and the upper bound is 36.749 99 ... cm.

In practice, you would say that the upper bound is 36.75 cm.

Exercise 2H

Find the upper and lower bounds for questions 1–6.

Remember that the smallest unit of money is 1p.

1. The cost of a CD player given as £120 to the nearest pound.
2. The cost of a CD player given as £120 to the nearest £10.
3. The weight of a box of cereal given as 750 g to the nearest gram.
4. The weight of a box of cereal given as 750 g to the nearest 10 g.

5. The weight of a bag of flour given as 1 kg to the nearest 20 g.
6. The distance between two towns given as 45 km to the nearest 5 km.

What are possible upper and lower bounds for questions 7–10?

7. The waistband of a skirt labelled as 26 cm.
8. A garden path measured to be 40 m long.
9. A tree measured to be 9.7 m high.
10. A beetle weighed as 35 g.

2.9 Grouped frequency tables

You can use a grouped frequency table to record your data.

To record data on foot length, part of it may look like this:

Foot length in cm	Tally	Frequency
......		
22		
23		
......		

The foot length 22 cm is measured to the nearest cm and so actually represents all foot lengths from 21.5 cm to 22.5 cm.

> In a grouped frequency table you collect data using class intervals (the lower and upper bounds).

Foot length in cm	Tally	Frequency
......		
21.5 and up to 22.5		
22.5 and up to 23.5		
......		

You can write the class intervals just using the lower or upper bounds, that is

Foot length in cm	or	**Foot length in cm**
......		......
21.5 –		– 22.5
22.5 –		– 23.5
......		......

> Once you enter a tally mark in a class, the raw data (the actual measured length) is lost.

When you design a grouped frequency table you need to decide on the size of each class interval.

Note that:

- ✦ Each class interval does not have to be the same width.
- ✦ There should be no gaps or overlaps between the class intervals.
- ✦ You will always lose some detail when combining two or more categories.
- ✦ A grouped table may be more difficult to read.
- ✦ Discrete and continuous data can be collected in a grouped frequency table.

Collecting raw data in a grouped frequency table

When you collect raw data in a grouped frequency table you can decide on the width of the class intervals. However,

- ✦ Over-simplification (data falling into too few groups) effectively loses trends.
- ✦ Under-simplification loses detail without highlighting trends.

The first or last class interval in a table could be open-ended (that is it has no lower bound or upper bound respectively), but this may make some calculations impossible to perform and some diagrams difficult to draw.

The most common reason to leave a class open-ended is because to specify a limit may be misleading.

Activity

Design grouped frequency tables for each of the following situations and use them to record:

- ✦ The weight of each crisp in a bag of crisps.
- ✦ The height of each member of your class.

Exercise 2I

1. The lifetime in hours of 40 electric bulbs was recorded as follows:

   34 48 76 56 58 64 30 72 63 58 76 51 50 43 44 67 78 64 32 39
   61 78 65 43 48 59 42 64 57 51 78 30 79 67 64 39 44 53 55 42

   Draw a grouped frequency table using equal class widths 30–39, 40–49, . . . , 70–79.

2. The times taken, in seconds, for a group of children to swim 25 metres were:

   25.4 31.1 19.7 26.0 29.9 32.2 21.7 24.1 28.6 27.1 19.2 27.2 25.9 23.8
   25.5 30.1 20.4 26.1 28.7 21.4 29.6 30.5 33.1 26.9 27.0 21.9 24.6 26.9

   Draw a grouped frequency table using equal class widths 19–21, 22–24, . . . , 31–33. (Think about the lower and upper bounds of the class intervals.)

3. Draw a grouped frequency table to record these heights, in cm, of these students.

114 134 114 116 138 110 112 116 132 126 108
116 118 115 122 137 123 119 106 127 133 101

4. Draw a grouped frequency table to record the masses in grams for this sample of 21 sweets.

1.15 0.82 0.91 1.44 1.03 1.39 0.88
0.99 0.73 1.11 0.98 1.21 0.79 1.14
1.19 1.08 0.94 1.06 1.12 0.81 0.98

2.10 Bivariate data and two-way tables

In many surveys and experiments you look at links between variables and so data is collected for two variables, for example height and weight, age and reaction time.

This type of data is **bivariate** and can be summarized in a **two-way table**.

Example

The following table shows the distribution of numbers of brothers and sisters from a survey of a group of children.

One variable is listed vertically

One variable is listed horizontally

Number of sisters

Number of brothers	0	1	2	3
0	4	6	3	1
1	7	5	3	0
2	1	0	2	0
3	1	0	0	0

3 people have 2 sisters and 1 brother

(a) How many children took part in the survey?
(b) How many children have (i) no brothers or sisters?
(ii) one brother, but no sisters?
(c) How many children are there in the largest family?

(a) To find how many children took part in the survey, you need to find the sum of each of the entries in the table, that is

$4 + 6 + 3 + 1 + 7 + 5 + 3 + 1 + 2 + 1 = 33$

(b) (i) There are 4 children who have no brothers or sisters, you look for the number in row 0 and column 0.

(ii) To find the number of children who have one brother, but no sisters you need to look in row 1 and column 0. The answer is 7 children.

(c) The largest family is the one where there are the most brothers and sisters. In two families there are 4 siblings (2 brothers and 2 sisters). There are 5 children in these families.

Exercise 2J

1. The principal of a music school posted letters to all of his students. The number of days it took for the letters to arrive is summarized in the following table:

Postage type \ Number of days	1	2	3	4	5
First Class	12	4	2	0	1
Second Class	0	5	6	4	3

(a) How many students are there at the music school?
(b) How many of the first class letters took more than one day to arrive?
(c) How many letters took 3 days to arrive?

2. The weight and mint year of a sample of ten pence pieces are listed below.

1998–10.3 g 1996–9.8 g 1996–10.0 g 1998–10.5 g 1999–11.0 g
1999–10.8 g 1997–9.9 g 1997–10.2 g 1999–10.9 g 1996–9.6 g
1997–10.5 g 1996–9.8 g 1996–20.2 g 1998–10.3 g 1998–10.4 g

The weights were measured to the nearest tenth of a gram.
Why do you think that the 1996 coin weighing 20.2 g may have been incorrectly recorded?
Ignoring this coin, copy and complete the table.

Weight in g	Year			
	1996	1997	1998	1999
9.6–10.0				
10.1–10.5				
10.6–11.0				

Comment on the results.

3. Clues in a crossword puzzle are given for words that are written across or down. The number of letters in the shortest answer is 3 and in the longest answer it is 8. Design a two-way table to record the number of letters and type of clue.

4. Design a two-way table to find the types of music boys and girls in your class have bought in the last three months.

5. A book of poems has poems that are one to four verses long, where each verse contains 8 to 12 lines. Design a two-way table to record the number of verses and the number of lines in each poem in the book.

Summary of key points

- Quantitative data is numerical, qualitative data is not numerical.
- Discrete data is countable, continuous data is measurable.
- Data can be collected using a survey or experiment.
- A pilot survey is small scale replica of the actual survey.
- Census data contains information about every member of the population.
- Sample data contains information from only a part of the population, but is used to draw conclusions about the whole population.
- A questionnaire is used to gather information.
- A frequency table is used to record raw data.
- A two-way table shows information about two variables at the same time.

Links to the Real World

Governments collect numerical information about all aspects of life. This numerical information is as diverse as the number of prescriptions issued by the NHS for each drug on the market, for different age groups by area of the country, and what agricultural produce is farmed, where and in what quantity.

The 10-yearly census collects population data in order to monitor population changes and demographic movement and to plan for future housing, schools, hospitals, roads and so on.

Market researchers collect numerical information and opinions from samples of the population from which conclusions are drawn about the whole population. At election time their conclusions are constantly in the media and may well influence the 'floating voter'. They also conduct research with small groups and often stop people in the streets to ask opinions and complete questionnaires.

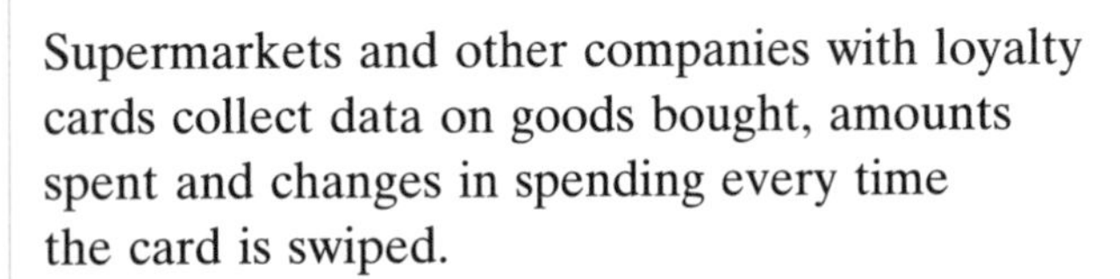

Supermarkets and other companies with loyalty cards collect data on goods bought, amounts spent and changes in spending every time the card is swiped.

Numerical data on its own does not provide any sense of the information it could convey. A set of numbers, say 4% 3% 2.8% 4.9%, mean very little. If you know they are interest rates for a savings account over a year or inflation figures for four consecutive months then you can begin to process and interpret them.

In the next chapter you begin this process with calculations to summarise and interpret information. Calculations on their own have little value if you do not know what they mean.

Revision Exercise 2

1. Peter receives a questionnaire in the post about a new local radio station. Three of the questions are shown below.

   Give **one** criticism of each question.

   Question 1
   How many hours have you listened to the radio during the past six months?

   Question 2
   How much do you earn each year? Please tick one box.

   Less than £10000 £10000 up to £20000 More than £20000

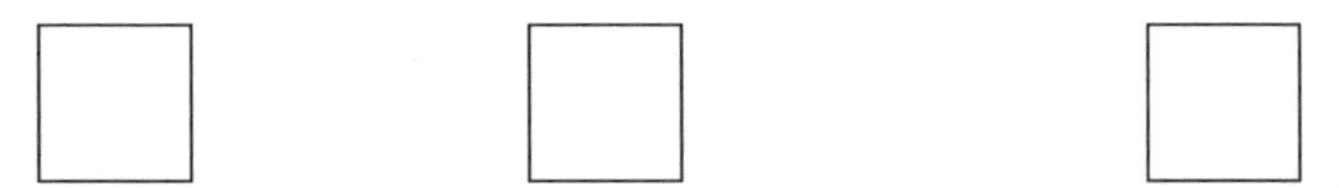

   Question 3
   If you have already heard our new radio station, give one reason why you enjoyed listening to it. [AQA]

2. A travel agent decides to survey all existing customers using a postal questionnaire.

   (a) One question is shown here.

   'How much do you spend each year on holidays abroad?'
   Please tick one box.

   £1000–£1500 ☐

   £1500–£2000 ☐

   £2000–£3500 ☐

   £3500–£6000 ☐

   £6000 and over ☐

   Give **two** distinct criticisms of the response section of this question.

   (b) Of 2000 questionnaires posted out, only 93 were returned.
   Give **two** ways in which the response rate could be increased. [AQA]

3. A youth club has 72 members. The leader decides to select six members at random to go on a sailing course.
He numbers the members 01 to 72 and uses the random number table below to make his selection.

29	44	76	56
44	51	38	00
07	21	92	17

(a) Starting with 29 and reading across each row, write down the number of each of the six members that he selects.
(b) The youth club has 48 boys and 24 girls as members.
Calculate the number of boys and girls the leader should include in a stratified sample of six members. [AQA]

4. Martin downloads music onto his computer.
The computer records information about each track.
It records:
the length of each track
the type of music of each track
the download speed.

Give an example of
(a) a discrete variable that the computer records
(b) a continuous variable the computer records. [AQA]

5. In a questionnaire, Niles was finding out about pupils' taste in music.
(a) Why might he carry out a pilot survey first?
(b) Explain how he could obtain a systematic sample.
(c) He decides to use a quota sample.
Explain how he could obtain a quota sample.
(d) Give **one** advantage of using a systematic sample over a quota sample.
(e) Give **one** advantage of using a quota sample over a systematic sample. [AQA]

6. A group of scientists wants to estimate the number of fish in a lake.
They catch and ring 100 fish.
They return and 100 fish to the lake.
They then catch 300 fish
Of these 300 fish, 14 are ringed.

(a) Estimate the number of fish in the lake.
(b) What could the scientists do to improve the accuracy of their estimate? [AQA]

7. The table shows how many students are in a school.

Lower School	Upper School	Sixth Form
720	480	400

Chelsey wants to survey 100 students from the school using a stratified sample.

(a) Work out how many students Chelsey should include in her survey from the Lower School.

(b) 25 students from the Sixth Form are to be chosen. Describe a method of choosing a random sample of these Sixth Form students. [AQA]

8. A company proposes to build a large wind turbine close to a village. Ben designs a questionnaire to obtain opinions on the proposal from the villagers.
One of his questions is

Do you agree that the wind turbine will be a disaster for our village?

Yes, definitely ☐ No ☐

(a) Give **two** distinct criticisms of Ben's question.

(b) Rewrite Ben's question to make it more appropriate. [AQA]

9. The diagram shows a factory layout divided into four different work areas. The numbers of male and female staff in each area are also given.

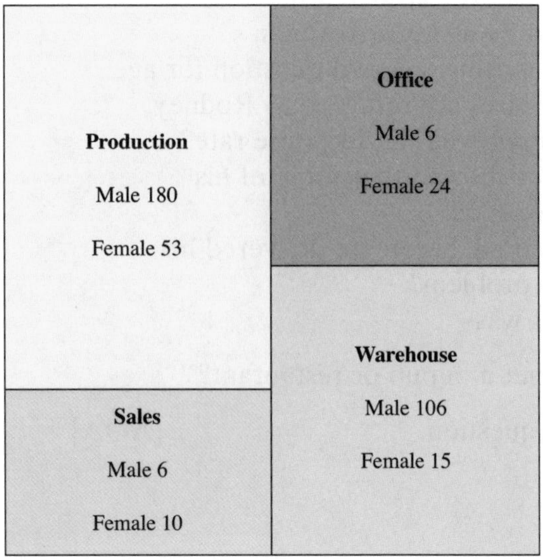

Production
Male 180
Female 53

Office
Male 6
Female 24

Sales
Male 6
Female 10

Warehouse
Male 106
Female 15

The factory owner wishes to undertake a survey to find the reaction of the staff to the introduction of a new bonus payment scheme.
He decides to take a systematic sample of 20 male production staff.

(a) Explain how this sample could be selected.
(b) Give **two** reasons why this sample would be unrepresentative of the whole staff.
(c) As an alternative the owner is advised to take a sample, stratified by sex and work area, of 50 of the 400 staff.
  (i) Calculate the number of sales staff to be included in the sample.
  (ii) Calculate the number of female office staff to be included in the sample.
(d) Part of the survey will involve interviewing staff to find their views on plans to change the number of hours worked each week in the factory.
One of the questions to be asked will be

> *What is your opinion of the proposal to increase the number of hours worked each week to 39?*

Describe two types of scale could be used to measure the opinions in this case. [AQA]

10. Rodney is considering opening a small restaurant in the village where he lives.
To find out the views of local people he delivers a questionnaire to every house in the village.

(a) Included in the questionnaire is a closed question asking for people's age.
  (i) Explain what is meant by a *closed question.*
  (ii) Give one advantage of using a closed question for age.
(b) Only 12% of the questionnaires are returned to Rodney.
How might Rodney have improved the response rate?
(c) The returned questionnaires showed that some of his questions had been badly worded.
What should Rodney have done before he delivered his questionnaire to avoid this problem?
(d) One of Rodney's questions was

"How often do you eat out at a pub or restaurant?"

Give two criticisms of this question. [AQA]

11. Mr and Mrs Jones were carrying out a survey.
They asked members of their sports club how much money they spent on sport, how many children they had and how long it took them to travel to the sports club.

(a) What kind of data source is this?
(b) Give an example of a **discrete** variable that Mr and Mrs Jones collected.
(c) Give an example of a **continuous** variable that Mr and Mrs Jones collected. [SEG]

12.

The picture shows some of the ingredients needed for making a fruit cake.

Give **one** example of **each** of the following to do with making a cake:

(a) a continuous variable (b) a discrete quantitative variable
(c) a qualitative variable [SEG]

13. At a pilot training centre, twenty new pilots were given reaction time tests and graded as follows.

Grade	Reaction time in seconds	Tally	Frequency
A	0–		
B	0.2–		
C	0.4–		
D	0.6–0.8		

The following times were recorded:

0.1, 0.2, 0.3, 0.16, 0.23, 0.71, 0.19, 0.24, 0.3, 0.31,
0.35, 0.38, 0.31, 0.39, 0.62, 0.51, 0.44, 0.59, 0.4, 0.5.

(a) Complete the tally and grouped frequency distribution on a copy of the above table.
(b) After training, all pilots previously in grades *B*, *C* and *D* improved their times by 0.05 seconds.
How many pilots are now in the *C* grade range? [SEG]

14. Amanda wants to choose a sample of 500 adults from the town where she lives.
She considers these methods of choosing her sample.

Method 1: Choose people shopping in the town centre on Saturday mornings.
Method 2: Choose names at random from the electoral register.
Method 3: Choose people living in the streets near her house.

Which method is **most** likely to produce an unbiased sample?
Give a reason for your answer. [NEAB]

15. A school needed planning permission to construct an all-weather playing surface with floodlights.
The school planned to distribute questionnaires in order to find the level of local support.

(a) State **one** advantage of using a sample to obtain the required information.

Questionnaires were given to the families of pupils in the school.

(b) Explain why this method of selecting the sample was unsuitable.
(c) Describe a better way of obtaining the sample of people to be given questionnaires.

The school wished to know the ages of the people completing the questionnaires.

(d) Write out a question suitable for obtaining this information, exactly as it should appear on the questionnaire. [SEG]

16. (a) What is the main difference between obtaining information by census and by sampling?
(b) Why is it necessary to use sampling in a survey to find the lifetime of electric bulbs?
(c) Why is it usual to use sampling for an opinion poll? [NEAB]

17. To improve sales it is necessary to find out what the public think of all kinds of products and services.
Questionnaires are often used to obtain this information.

(a) Write down **two** important points which should be remembered when designing a questionnaire.

Questionnaires are often sent by post.

(b) (i) Give **one** advantage of using the postal system.
(ii) Give **one** disadvantage of using the postal system.

A food company intended to ask the following question in a questionnaire:

'How heavy are you?'

(c) (i) Why is this question unacceptable?
(ii) Rewrite the question to make it acceptable. [SEG]

18. A market research company is conducting a survey to find out whether most people had a holiday in Britain, elsewhere in Europe or in the rest of the world, last year. It also wants to know if they stayed in self-catering accommodation, hotels or went camping.

Design **two** questions that could be used in a questionnaire to find out all this information. [NEAB]

19. A report in a medical journal says that people are taller in the morning than in the evening. Describe a simple statistical experiment to test this assertion. [NEAB]

20. A dentist wishes to investigate the effectiveness of a new brand of toothpaste.
He chooses 50 boys and 50 girls at random from his patients.
The girls are given the new brand of toothpaste and the boys are given a different brand.
After 6 months the dentist compares the boys' and girls' teeth.

(a) Give **two** reasons why this is not a reliable experiment.
(b) Give **two** ways in which the experiment could be improved.
[NEAB]

21. A new brand of 'slim-fast' milk has been introduced for sale into a store. It is claimed that users will achieve significant weight loss after using the product for a period of seven consecutive days.

A statistical experiment is to be set up to test this claim.
The experiment will involve using 50 members each in both experimental and control groups. These participants are to be selected from the first 200 shoppers entering the store on a given day.

Explain briefly

(a) why a control group should be used in this case,
(b) how members of the control and experimental groups should be selected if paired comparisons are to be made,
(c) what procedures should be followed to ensure valid conclusions are reached from this experiment. [NEAB]

22. One of the questions from a questionnaire used in a survey is shown.

Are you tall?	Please tick	Yes	☐
		No	☐

Out of 100 people who took part in this survey 20 ticked 'Yes' and 30 ticked 'No'.
There was a non-response of 50.

(a) What proportion of those that answered this question ticked 'Yes'?
(b) Give two reasons why the 'non-response' category cannot be ignored.
(c) Rewrite the question in a more suitable form. [SEG]

23. The number of pupils in each Year Group of a school is given in the following table.

Year Group	7	8	9	10	11
Number of pupils	100	75	125	100	100

(a) Describe how a **simple random** sample of 80 pupils should be selected.
(b) Describe how a **stratified** sample of 80 pupils should be selected.
(c) Describe how a **quota** sample of 80 pupils should be selected.
[SEG]

24. A car rental firm intends to conduct a survey to help improve its service to the public. Before employing a consultancy firm to conduct the survey, the car rental firm decides to carry out its own small survey.

Arriving at the local station at 11 am, employees of the car rental firm spend an hour questioning travellers.

(a) Give **two** different reasons why this survey is unsatisfactory.
(b) The consultancy firm recommends either a systematic or a stratified sample.
  (i) How might the **systematic** sample be taken?
  (ii) How might the **stratified** sample be taken?
  (iii) What is the main difference between these sampling methods?
(c) Write a question to find the age of the people likely to use the firm. [SEG]

25. The number of workers on the three floors of a factory are shown.

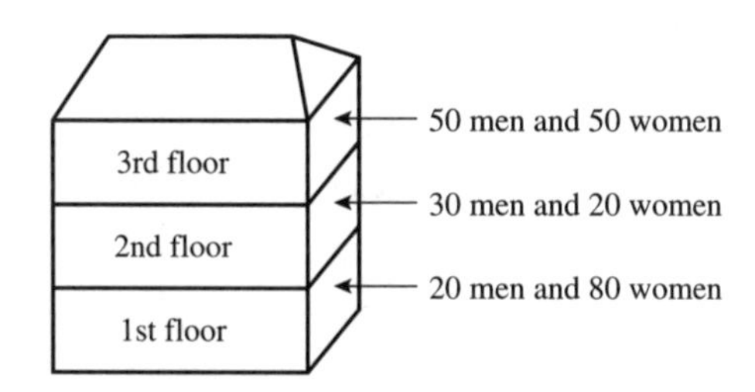

A different type of work is done on each floor.
The owner wants to ask 50 workers what they think of their working conditions.

(a) Give **one** advantage of taking a sample of the workforce to obtain this information.

(b) Explain why a **random** sample is considered to be an unsuitable way of selecting this sample.

It was decided to obtain a **stratified** sample according to the number of workers on each floor.

(c) Calculate the number of workers that should be questioned from each floor.

(d) How many women should be included from the 2nd floor to make the sample a fair representation of that floor?

(e) Explain how you would finally make a systematic selection of the women who would represent the 2nd floor. [SEG]

Question 26 over page

26. A teacher wishes to select a representative sample of five pupils from a class of 18 boys and 12 girls. The class register is shown below. (B) indicates a boy and (G) indicates a girl.

Number	Name	Number	Name
1	C Baker (G)	16	N Jewell (G)
2	P Brown (B)	17	T Kennedy (B)
3	H Cant (G)	18	G Lomas (B)
4	H Curtis (B)	19	L Manors (G)
5	E Daly (G)	20	M Monet (B)
6	W Diamond (B)	21	K Nutt (B)
7	L Edwards (B)	22	F Oliver (B)
8	P Fletcher (G)	23	H Patel (B)
9	T Flynn (G)	24	D Peters (B)
10	W Ghani (B)	25	B Quarishi (B)
11	A Glade (G)	26	H Rayson (G)
12	B Hale (G)	27	C Rogers (B)
13	X Hatcher (B)	28	L Stonor (B)
14	F Isaacs (G)	29	P Taylor (B)
15	J Jacobs (B)	30	K Wood (G)

The teacher selects the five pupils by using the random numbers below. She starts at the top left of the random numbers and goes along the rows selecting two-digit numbers. If the random number is a register number the corresponding pupil is accepted. Otherwise the number is ignored. For example, the first two pupils selected are C Rogers and M Monet.

27 74 87 94 57 38 94 20 29 70 53 33 24 95 49
49 74 25 44 52 92 51 86 10 02 38 66 59 18 23

(a) Write down the names of the other three pupils selected.
(b) Why is the choice of pupils **not** satisfactory in this case?
(c) Suggest a better way to select a representative sample of five pupils. [NEAB]

3 Summary statistics

It is a capital mistake to theorize before one has data
Sir Arthur Conan Doyle,
The Memoirs of Sherlock Holmes

Lies, dammed lies and statistics
Benjamin Disraeli

Complex machinery needs to be monitored using statistical measures.

This unit will show you how to

- Calculate measures of location
- Calculate measures of dispersion
- Compare data sets using skew and measures of location and dispersion
- Calculate standardised scores
- Use quality assurance to analyse measures

Before you start

You should be able to answer these questions

1 Find midpoint of
(a) 12 and 18, (b) 1 and 6, (c) 8 and 9

2 Find the midpoint of class interval
(a) $5 < x \leqslant 10$, (b) 20–30

3 What is $\frac{1}{4}$ and $\frac{3}{4}$ of these numbers
(a) 80, (b) 200, (c) 230

4 Find
(a) $\sqrt{729}$, (b) $\sqrt[3]{64}$

The aim of summary statistics is to condense a large quantity of numbers, the data, into just one or two numbers that together describe the essence of the data.

The two main types of summary statistics are **measures of location** and **measures of dispersion**.

Measures of location describe the size of the numbers in the data.

Measures of dispersion describe the variation between the numbers in the data.

3.1 Measures of location

Measures of location are often referred to as average. The word 'average' is used all the time:

"The average rainfall ..." "Average house prices have fallen."

The three most commonly used types of average are mode, median and arithmetic mean (often just referred to as the mean).

Mode or modal value is the value that occurs most often in the data.

Median is the middle value from an ordered set of data.

The mean is found by calculating the sum of all the values divided by the number of values.

Example

The examination marks for a group of 11 students were

45 64 72 43 43 38 56 21 65 43 64

Find the mode, median and mean of this data.

Mode = 43
There are more marks recorded at 43 than any other score.

Median = 45
First arrange in order
21 38 43 43 43 45 56 64 65 72 72

There are 11 values so the middle value is the 6th.
45 is the 6th value when arranged in order.

Mean = 51.1
First add up the numbers
$21 + 38 + 43 + 43 + 43 + 45 + 56 + 64 + 65 + 72 + 72 = 562$
Then divide by how many values there are:

$562 \div 11 = 51.1$

Suppose a twelfth mark was recorded as 72. There would be two **modes** 43 and 72.

A twelfth mark of 72 would give two middle values, 45 and 56. The **median** would then be 50.5, half-way between the two middle values.

The **mean** may **not** be an integer.

Activity

Suppose every student in the example above were awarded an extra 5 marks so that the marks were: 50 69 77...
Then what would the mean mark be? Can you find a quick way of calculating the mean?
Suppose instead the original numbers represented the salary, in £1000's of 11 employees:
£45 000 £64 000 £72 000...
Then what would the mean salary be? Can you find a quick way of calculating this mean?

Why have three averages?

Average	Advantages	Disadvantages
Mode	Use with all types of data Not affected by extreme values Mode is always an actual value	Not easy to use for further analysis There is not always a mode There can be many modes
Median	Not affected by extreme values Straightforward to calculate	Not always an actual value Not easy to use for further analysis
Mean	Uses all the values	Not always an actual value Distorted by extreme values

Exercise 3A

1. For the following data sets find the (i) mode (ii) median (iii) mean.
(a) 3, 6, 3, 9, 7, 8, 3, 4, 5
(b) 4, 7, 16, 17, 14, 9, 12, 17
(c) 6, 8, 14, 19, 11, 8, 15, 21, 21, 1, 9, 13, 24, 25, 8
(d) 26, 28, 52, 35, 45, 66, 36, 28, 20, 45
(e) 4.3 4.7 5.4 5.1 5.0 4.6 4.3

2. For each of the following sets of data write down, with reasons, which average (mean, median or mode) is the most appropriate measure and find this average.
(a) 14. 6 19.3 11.0 15.7 41.7
(b) 2003 2005 2008 2011 2006 2003 2008 2003 2003
(c) 101 102 102 102 108 108 108 109
(d) 49 44 44 47 38 36 44 44 49 44 43

3. (a) Find the mean, median and mode of 7, 7, 24, 5, 2
(b) One number is added to the data set. What could that number be if
(i) the mode remains the same (ii) the median remains the same
(iii) the mean remains the same (iv) the mean is increased by 2?
(c) One number is removed from the data set. What could that number be if
(i) the median remains unchanged (ii) the mean is increased by 1?

4. A sample of 12 dogs have a mean weight of 68.7 kg. What is the total weight of all 12 dogs?

5. (a) The mean weight of six letters is 54.2g. Two further letters are added. Their weights are 40g and 58g. Find the mean average weight of all eight letters.
   (b) The mean height of a group of four girls is 154cm. The mean height of a different group of five girls is 162cm. Find the mean height of the whole group of nine girls.

3.2 Finding averages from frequency distributions

A large amount of discrete data is often presented in a frequency distribution.

Frequency tables

Example

The numbers of peas in each of 100 pods are given in the table. Find the mode, median and mean of the data.

Number of peas in a pod	Frequency	Peas x Frequency
4	15	60
5	29	145
6	23	138
7	13	91
8	12	96
9	8	72
Total	**100**	**602**

All the averages will fall within the range of values in the 1st column.
The frequency column just tells you how many of each value there are.

Mode = 5 Highest frequency 29

Median = 6 Middle value would be 50th & 51st
Adding the frequencies: 15 + 29 = 44 not enough;
44 + 23 = 67 so 50th & 51st value are both 6.
The median is 6.

Mean = 6.02 Add a column to the table to find the sum of all the peas. Mean = 602 ÷ 100 = 6.02

Mean = $\sum fx \div \sum f$
$\sum$ means 'the sum of'.
f is the frequency.
x is the variable.

Activity

"The majority of people have more than the average number of legs."
Can you explain why this statement may be correct?

Grouped frequency tables

Continuous data or large amounts of discrete data may be presented as a grouped frequency distribution.

Example

The times taken for a group of 40 people to solve a Sudoku puzzle are given in the table.
Find the modal class, the median and an estimate of the mean.

Time, t, minutes	Frequency
$1 < t \leqslant 4$	11
$4 < t \leqslant 7$	8
$7 < t \leqslant 10$	9
$10 < t \leqslant 13$	5
$13 < t \leqslant 16$	4
$16 < t \leqslant 19$	3
Total	**40**

Mid-point	Midpoint × frequency
2.5	2.5 x 11 = 27.5
5.5	5.5 x 8 = 44
8.5	8.5 x 9 = 76.5
11.5	11.5 x 5 = 57.5
14.5	14.5 x 4 = 58
17.5	17.5 x 3 = 52.5
	316

The averages will be either a class interval or a value within those intervals.

Modal class = $1 < t \leqslant 4$ Look for the highest frequency – this is 11.

Class containing median $7 < t \leqslant 10$ Middle values are 20th and 21st;
$\frac{1}{2}(40 + 1) = 20\frac{1}{2}$
Adding frequencies: $11 + 8 = 19$
So 20th and 21st are both in class $7 < t \leqslant 10$

Mean = 7.9 Add two columns to the table.
Record the midpoint of each class to represent that class.
Find sum of all the times and divide by the total frequency.
Mean = $316 \div 40 = 7.9$.

Because you have used midpoints your mean will only be an estimate.

Activity

Suppose one of the people never finished the Sudoku puzzle. Could you find values for each of the three averages? What would they be?

Arithmetic mean and linear transformations

Mistakes are easily made when entering large amounts of data, very large values or very small values into a calculator. A linear transformation of the values is used to simplify the arithmetic and make the values easier to handle.

Refer back to the activity/discussion on page 62.

Can you use a linear transformation to make the calculation easier?

> Adding/subtracting a number, adds/subtracts that number to the mean

> Multiplying/dividing by a number, multiplies/divides the mean by that number

Example

Find the mean gap for the sample of 25 spark plugs given in the frequency table.

Gap, mm	0.80	0.81	0.82	0.83	0.84
Frequency	2	5	8	6	4

Using the transformation:

Gap → × 100 → − 80 →

Gap, mm	0	1	2	3	4
Frequency	2	5	8	6	4

Mean = $\sum fx \div \sum f =$
$\{(0 \times 2) + (1 \times 5) + (2 \times 8) + (3 \times 6) + (4 \times 4)\} \div 25 =$
$55 \div 25 = 2.2.$

Reversing the transformation: Mean → + 80 → ÷ 100 →

Mean = $\sum fx \div \sum f = (2.2 + 80) \div 100 = 0.822$

Exercise 3B

1. The data sets give information about the length of words in two crosswords. For each data set find the
(i) mode (ii) median (iii) mean.

(a)

Word length	Frequency
4	6
5	3
6	5
7	4
8	2
9	5
10	2

(b)

Word length	Frequency
3	5
4	4
5	6
6	7
7	7
8	4
9	2

2. Jo had 24 boxes of matches. The table gives information about the number of matches in each box.

Number of matches	Frequency
40	5
41	7
42	8
43	3
44	1

Work out the mean number of matches in a box.

3. The table shows the number of sweets in each of 30 mini-boxes of sweets.

Number of sweets	Frequency
8	5
9	4
10	7
11	6
12	8

(a) Find the (i) mean (ii) mode (iii) median number of sweets in the boxes.
(b) Which average is best to use? Explain why.

4. The data sets give information about the times taken to solve two crosswords. For each data set find
(i) the modal class (ii) the class containing the median
(iii) an estimate of the mean.

(a)

Time, t minutes	Frequency
$0 < t \leqslant 10$	3
$10 < t \leqslant 20$	6
$20 < t \leqslant 30$	4
$30 < t \leqslant 40$	5
$40 < t \leqslant 50$	2

(b)

Time, t minutes	Frequency
$5 < t \leqslant 10$	8
$10 < t \leqslant 15$	5
$15 < t \leqslant 20$	7
$20 < t \leqslant 25$	4
$25 < t \leqslant 30$	0
$30 < t \leqslant 35$	1

5. Alfie kept a record of his monthly mobile phone bills for one year.

Phone bill, £ (B)	Frequency
$0 < B \leqslant 12$	6
$12 < B \leqslant 24$	2
$24 < B \leqslant 36$	3
$36 < B \leqslant 48$	1

(a) Write down the class interval that contains the median.
(b) Calculate an estimate for the mean cost of Alfie's mobile phone bill.

6. The table shows the amount of discount given to staff at a store during one week.

Monies spent, £ (M)	Frequency
$0 < M \leqslant 20$	7
$20 < M \leqslant 40$	9
$40 < M \leqslant 60$	11
$60 < M \leqslant 80$	2
$80 < M \leqslant 100$	1

(a) Calculate an estimate for the mean discount given.
(b) Write down the class interval that contains the median.
(c) Write down the modal class for the amount spent.
The manager of the store did not include his own discount in the calculation. That week he received £110 in discount.
(d) If this amount were included, which of the averages would change and which would not. Explain your answer.

7. Use a linear transformation to find the mean for the following data sets.

(a) The masses, in milligrams, of a sample of 18 pebbles.

169	178	164	182	194	204	186	192	201
182	164	175	179	173	182	172	180	171

(b) The waist measurement, to the nearest millimetre, of a sample of size 10 jeans.

Waist Measurement, mm	277	278	279	280	281	282
Frequency	3	5	12	27	11	2

(c) The men's winning times of the New York marathon from 1976 to 1992, in hours minutes and seconds.

2:10:10	2:11:29	2:12:12	2:11:42	2:09:41
2:08:13	2:09:29	2:08:59	2:14:53	2:11:34
2:11:06	2:11:01	2:08:20	2:08:01	2:12:39
2:09:24	2:09:29			

3.3 Geometric mean

The geometric mean is used for a data set of values that are meant to be multiplied together or are exponential in nature, such as data on population growth or interest rates.

Example

£1 is invested and earns 10% the first year, 30% the second year, and 50% the third year.

What is the average rate of return?

The average rate of return for these three years means finding the constant factor the investment needs to be multiplied by each year.

These interest rates mean in the first year the £1 is *multiplied* by 1.10, in the second year the total is multiplied by 1.30, and in the third year the total is multiplied by 1.50. After three years the £1 is now £2.145 (£1 $\times$ 1.1 $\times$ 1.3 $\times$ 1.5 = £2.145), which you round to £2.15.

Geometric mean = $(1.1 \times 1.3 \times 1.5)^{\frac{1}{3}} = 1.29$ (2dp) so this is an average rate of 29%.

(Note that the arithmetic average $(10 + 30 + 50) \div 3 = 30\%$ and would, if applied to £1 for 3 years, give £2.197 (£1 $\times$ 1.3 $\times$ 1.3 $\times$ 1.3) which is not the correct answer.)

Geometric mean of *n* numbers is the *n*th root of the product of those numbers.

Example

Find the geometric mean of the numbers 5, 6, 2, 8, 7

Geometric mean $= \sqrt[5]{5 \times 6 \times 2 \times 8 \times 7} = \sqrt[5]{3360} = 5.07$

Exercise 3C

1. The annual rates of interest for two consecutive years are 6.2% and 5.5%.
   (a) Calculate the single rate for two years that would pay the same amount of interest.
   (b) In the third year the interest rate was 6.45%. Calculate the single rate of interest that could be applied across all three years to pay the same amount.

2. The population of a village increased by 2% in 2005, 5% in 2006, 7% in 2007 and 12% in 2008. Calculate the average annual increase in the population of the village from 2006 to 2008.

3. The value of a car fell by 24% after one year, 15% in its second year and 10% in its third year. Calculate the single rate of loss for the three years that would be equivalent to the three separate annual losses. (Hint: A loss of 24% means the value of the car is 76% of what it was worth.)

4. In a town the average house prices decreased by 8% in 2007 and 18% in 2008.
   Calculate the average change in house prices in the town in 2007 and 2008.

5. Average house prices in a big city rose in 2007 by 20% and fell in 2008 by 12%. Calculate the average decrease in house prices in the city across those two years.

6. Find the geometric mean of these sets of values:
   (a) 4, 3, 7
   (b) 2, 9, 8, 6, 5
   (c) 1.8, 2.9, 3.7, 2.3

7. Explain why it would not be sensible to find the geometric mean of these values:
   2, 5, 0, 6

3.4 Measures of dispersion

Measures of dispersion are sometimes referred to as measures of spread.

In a spelling test five women scored marks of 2 9 11 11 17 and five men scored marks of 8 9 11 11 11. Both data sets have mode 11 median 11 and mean 10, but the data sets are clearly different. Measures of dispersion help explain that difference.

Range

The range is the difference between the highest and lowest values. It is a crude measure of dispersion based on two values, its advantage being that it is easy to calculate. A disadvantage of using the range is that a single very large or very small value would give a misleading impression of the spread of data.

For a grouped frequency distribution, the exact values of the data are unknown so the range cannot be found accurately.

Interquartile range (IQR)

The IQR is the difference between the upper quartile (UQ) and the lower quartile (LQ).

UQ and LQ are values at top quarter and bottom quarter of the data set. Find $\frac{1}{4}(n + 1)$th values from the lowest and from the highest in the data set.

The IQR is more useful than the range as it describes the middle 50% of the data. However the IQR is still based on only two values that may not be representative.

Example

For the raw data set of examination marks below, find the range and the interquartile range.

21 38 43 43 43 45 56 64 65 72 72

Highest value = 72 Lowest value = 21 72 – 21 = 51
Range = 51

11 values $\frac{1}{4}(11 + 1) = 3$ 3rd value from the top UQ = 65
3rd value from bottom LQ = 43
IQR: 65 – 43 = 22
IQR = 22

Example

Find the range and interquartile range for the frequency distribution for peas in a pod.

Number of peas in a pod	Frequency
4	15
5	29
6	23
7	13
8	12
9	8

Highest value = 9 Lowest value = 4   9 − 4 = 5
Range = 5

Total frequency 100 values; $\frac{1}{4}$ of 100 = 25
25th value from top UQ = 7 (8 + 12 = 20, 20 + 13 = 33 so 25th value is 7)
25th value from bottom LQ = 5 (15 + 29 = 43 so 25th value is 5)
IQR = 7 − 5 = 2

Use the 1st column and *not* the frequency to find the range.

With a large frequency use $\frac{1}{4}$ n^{th} value instead of $\frac{1}{4}(n+1)^{th}$ value.

Activity

Can you find the range of the middle 80% of the data?
When might this interpercentile range be more useful than say the range or IQR?

The **IQR** range and other interpercentile ranges can be estimated from a cumulative frequency graph. See page 115.

Exercise 3D

1. Find the range and interquartile range for the following data sets.
   (a) 6, 8, 14, 19, 11, 8, 15, 21, 21, 1, 9, 13, 24, 25, 8
   (b) 26, 28, 52, 35, 45, 66, 36, 28, 20, 45, 32, 37, 54, 15, 32, 63, 17, 28, 36
   (c) 169 178 164 182 194 204 186 192 201
   182 164 175 179 173 182 172 180 171
   168 172 169 185 182 200 166 198 170
   (d) 47 54 68 39 32 57 54 44 60
   56 53 48 62 38 58 38 46 58
   36 48 62 54 64 66 42 44 50
   (e) 281 283 287 278 279 277 286 276 279
   290 277 276 280 281 282 288 290
   291 292 276 270 271 280 277 280
   (f) 49 44 44 47 38 36 44 44 49 44 43 45 50 39 32 19 36

2. Find the range and interquartile range for the following frequency distributions.

(a)

Word length	Frequency
4	6
5	3
6	5
7	4
8	2
9	5
10	2

(b)

Word length	Frequency
3	5
4	4
5	6
6	7
7	7
8	4
9	2

(c)

Sweets in a box	Frequency
14	2
15	7
16	18
17	12
18	7
19	1

(d)

Goals scored	Frequency
0	3
1	12
2	7
3	5
4	4
5	1
7	1

3.5 Variance and standard deviation

Suppose you are given these two sets of data, Set A and Set B:

Set A: 10 49 49 50 50 50 50 50 51 51 90
Set B: 10 10 49 49 50 50 50 51 51 90 90

You will see that both data sets have 11 values and the same values for
Mean = 50 **Mode** = 50 **Median** = 50 **Range** = 80 **IQR** = 2
UQ = 51 LQ = 49

However set B has four extreme values compared with only two extreme values in set A. This extra variability can be quantified by finding the differences between each value and the mean for that data set:

Set A: –40 –1 –1 0 0 0 0 0 1 1 40
Set B: –40 –40 –1 –1 0 0 0 1 1 40 40

In each case the sum of the differences is zero. (This will always happen. Why?)

Squaring these differences (and so making the negatives positive) and then finding their sum will give a measure of variation that is not zero.

This is represented by $\sum_{i=1}^{n}(x_i - \bar{x})^2$ x_i represents each value; where $\bar{x}$ is the mean.

The more variation there is in the data the larger $\sum_{i=1}^{n}(x_i - \bar{x})^2$ becomes.

However the sum of the squares of the deviations may be large simply because of the amount of data and so an average of the sum of the squares of the deviations is used. This is the **variance**.

Variance $\sigma^2 = \frac{1}{n}\sum(x - \bar{x})^2 = \frac{\sum x^2}{n} - \bar{x}^2$

Multiplying out and simplifying the 1st formula will give the 2nd formula.

Standard deviation σ is defined as being the **square root of variance.**

Standard deviation shows the dispersion of values around the arithmetic mean.

$$\sigma = \sqrt{\frac{\sum x^2}{n} - \bar{x}^2}$$

It is essential to learn how to use your calculator to find σ and σ^2

For set A:
$\sum x^2 = 30704 \quad \bar{x} = 50 \quad \sigma^2 = \frac{1}{11}(30704) - 50^2 = 291.27 \quad \sigma = 17.1$

For set B:
$\sum x^2 = 33904 \quad \bar{x} = 50 \quad \sigma^2 = \frac{1}{11}(33904) - 50^2 = 582.18 \quad \sigma = 24.1$

The greater number of extreme values in set B is reflected in the larger value for σ, the standard deviation.

An advantage of using standard deviation is that it uses all the data.
A disadvantage is that it is affected by extreme values.

Activity

Check that both formulae above give the same answers by calculating the variance for set A and set B using the 1st formula.

For a frequency distribution $\sigma^2 = \frac{\sum fx^2}{\sum f} - \bar{x}^2$ and $\sigma = \sqrt{\frac{\sum fx^2}{\sum f} - \bar{x}^2}$

For a grouped frequency distribution, use the midpoints of the classes for x values.

Exercise 3E

1. Find the variance and standard deviation for the following sets of data.

   (a) 4, 7, 16, 17, 14, 9, 12, 17
   (b) 6, 8, 14, 19, 11, 8, 15, 21, 21, 1, 9, 13, 24, 25, 8
   (c) 26, 28, 52, 35, 45, 66, 36, 28, 20, 45
   (d) 4.3 4.7 5.4 5.1 5.0 4.6 4.3

2. Find the variance and standard deviation for the following frequency distributions.

(a)

Word length	Frequency
4	6
5	3
6	5
7	4
8	2
9	5
10	2

(b)

Sweets in a box	Frequency
14	2
15	7
16	18
17	12
18	7
19	1

3. Find the variance and standard deviation for the following grouped frequency distributions.

(a)

Time, t minutes	Frequency
$0 < t \leqslant 10$	3
$10 < t \leqslant 20$	6
$20 < t \leqslant 30$	4
$30 < t \leqslant 40$	5
$40 < t \leqslant 50$	2

(b)

Phone bill, £(B)	Frequency
$0 < B \leqslant 12$	6
$12 < B \leqslant 24$	2
$24 < B \leqslant 36$	3
$36 < B \leqslant 48$	1

4. Find the variance and standard deviation from the following summary information.

   (a) $\sum t = 20.2$ $\quad \sum t^2 = 82.58$ $\quad n = 5$
   (b) $\sum v = 1373$ $\quad \sum v^2 = 89761$ $\quad n = 22$
   (c) $\sum w = 10.4$ $\quad \sum w^2 = 7.0372$ $\quad n = 16$
   (d) $\sum y = 457$ $\quad \sum y^2 = 7553$ $\quad n = 30$
   (e) $\sum (x - \bar{x})^2 = 26$ $\quad n = 5$
   (f) $\sum (s - \bar{s})^2 = 293$ $\quad n = 12$

3.6 Using summary statistics: Box and whisker plots and skewness

When used together the measures of location and dispersion give a numerical summary. They allow comparisons to be made between two or more sets of data by comparing like with like; that is median with median or mean with mean and so on.

Box and whisker plots

The median is the middle value of the data. The IQR = UQ – LQ; these quartiles are the middle values of each half of the data. It is sensible to use median and IQR together to compare data sets.

Comparisons can be made pictorially. A **box and whisker plot** is drawn using the median, UQ, LQ, lowest and highest values.

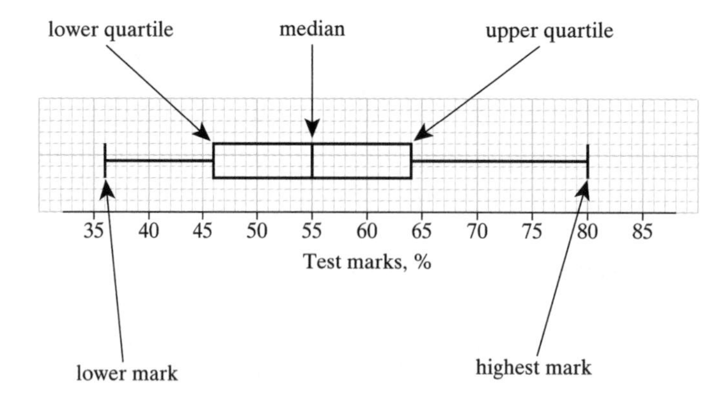

Use graph paper. Scale and label the axis.

You can draw box and whisker plots using Autograph. First open a 1-D statistics page. Click Object and choose between Enter raw data and Enter box and whisker diagram.

Use Enter box and whisker diagram if you know median, quartiles and so on, enter them and click OK.
Use Enter raw data to enter your own data or to import data from a spreadsheet. To enter your own data add all the values and click OK. To import data from a spreadsheet highlight the data you want and copy (use Ctrl+C or Edit Copy) open enter raw data and import (use Ctrl+V or Edit Paste) and click OK.

Click on the graph to move the diagram up and down the graph.
Use Edit axes to change scales and change to graph paper.
Add a text box to label the diagram.
Repeat to show more than one diagram on the same axes.

Example

The box and whisker plots summarise the heights of a sample of boys and a sample of girls aged 13 and 14 at a school.

Boys
Median = 1.6 m;
IQR = 0.18 m

Girls
Median = 1.63 m;
IQR = 0.13 m

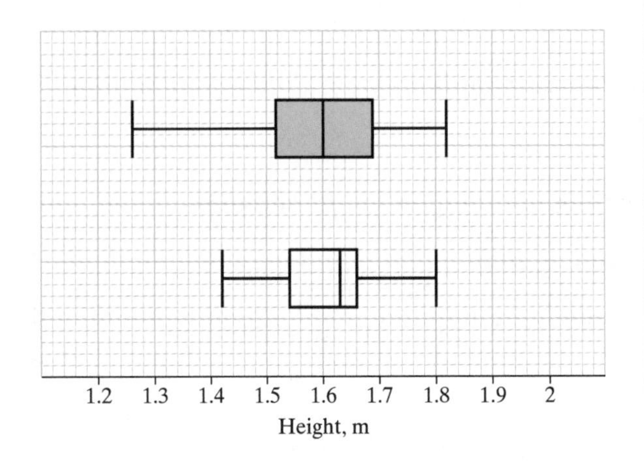

Write down two comparisons between the heights of the boys and the girls

Girls' median is greater than boys' so on average the girls are taller than the boys.

IQR for boys is greater than IQR for girls so the middle 50% of heights is more varied for boys than for girls.

The range for boys is greater than the range for girls and the lowest value for the boys appears to be very low, but is it extremely low?

For boys: $1.5 \times \text{IQR} = 1.5 \times 0.18 = 0.27$ LQ = 1.51
$1.51 - 0.27 = 1.24$
The boys' lowest value = 1.26 > than 1.24; this low value is not considered an **outlier**.

An **outlier** is a value less than $1.5 \times$ IQR below LQ or greater than $1.5 \times$ IQR above UQ.

Skewness

In the previous example the boys' median is central in the box whereas the girls' median is nearer the UQ than the LQ.
The boys' heights are not skewed whereas the girls' heights are negatively skewed.
A distribution that is not symmetrical is skewed. Skewness describes the shape of a distribution.

Skewness will be revisited in data representation; see pages 124.

A median central in the box shows the distribution is likely to be **symmetrical.**
A median closer to the LQ than the UQ shows the distribution has **positive skew.**
A median closer to the UQ than the LQ shows the distribution has **negative skew.**

A measure of skewness can be calculated from measures of location and dispersion.

Pearson's coefficient of skewness $= \dfrac{\text{mean} - \text{mode}}{\text{standard deviation}}$ or $\dfrac{3(\text{mean} - \text{median})}{\text{standard deviation}}$

Quartile coefficient of skewness $= \dfrac{\text{UQ} + \text{LQ} - 2\text{Median}}{\text{UQ} - \text{LQ}}$

A positive result means positive skew; a negative result, negative skew. The greater the value of the coefficient the greater the degree of skew.

For the example above of boys' and girls' heights the quartile coefficients of skewness are

$$\text{Boys} = \frac{1.69 + 1.51 - (2 \times 1.6)}{1.69 - 1.51} = 0$$

$$\text{Girls} = \frac{1.67 + 1.54 - (2 \times 1.63)}{1.67 - 1.54} = -0.385$$

This confirms no skew for boys' data and a small negative skew for girls' data.

Activity

Use the data you obtained from the simulation of different ways to queue on page 40 to find appropriate measures of location and dispersion for the data sets and, if appropriate, draw a box and whisker plot to compare the data.

Exercise 3F

1. The number of completed years of the reigns of Kings and Queens of England from 1066 are:

21	13	35	19	35	10	17	56	35	20	50
22	13	9	39	22	0	2	24	38	6	0
5	44	22	24	36	3	13	6	12	13	33
59	10	7	63	9	25	0	15			

   (a) Draw a box and whisker plot for these data.
   (b) Comment on the skewness shown by your plot.

   (c) Calculate a measure of skewness using the quartile coefficient of skewness and compare your answer with your answer to part (c).
   (d) Determine whether any of the lengths of reign are outliers.

2. (a) On the same graph draw box and whisker plots for the times taken, to the nearest minute, for a group of students to solve two Sudoku puzzles.

Puzzle X:	13	17	19	10	8	22	31	11	24	27
	6	37	18	12	29	14	8	17	9	
Puzzle Y:	28	21	29	15	12	9	32	17	18	11
	19	16	8	33	24	14	25	17	23	

   (b) Write down as many comparisons as you can between the times taken to solve the two puzzles.

   (c) Determine the values of the measures of skewness using (i) Pearson's coefficient using the mode (ii) Pearson's coefficient using the median (iii) quartile coefficient.

3. At a health centre patients can see a doctor or dentist. The graphs show the waiting times for patients during one week.

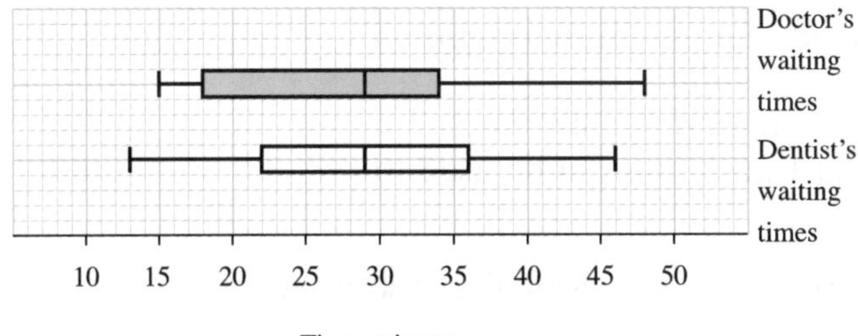

   (a) Write down as many similarities and differences as you can find between the two waiting times.

   (b) Are there any outliers in the waiting times for the doctor or the dentist?
   (c) Determine the value of a measure of skewness using the quartile coefficient.

4. The graph shows the systolic blood pressure for a sample of smokers and non-smokers.

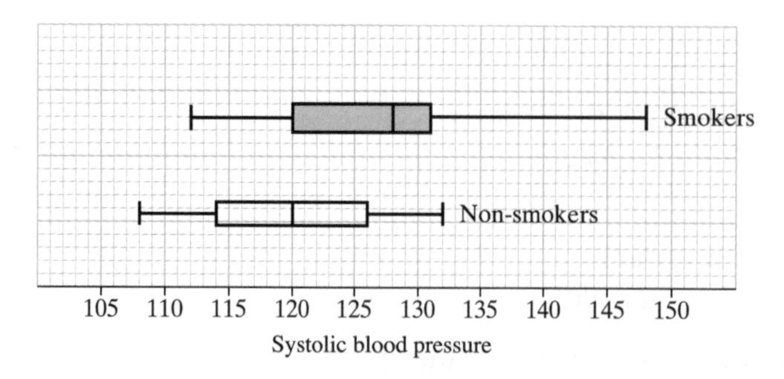

   (a) Write down as many similarities and differences in the systolic blood pressure that you can find.
   (b) Are there any outliers in the systolic blood pressure for either group of people?
   (c) Calculate a measure of skewness using the quartile coefficient of skewness.

5. The number of minor errors scored in a driving test by 17 year olds taking their test for the first time are summarised as having mean 2.6, median 2 and standard deviation 2.33. Calculate Pearson's coefficient of skewness using the median and use your answer to describe the shape of the distribution.

6. The reaction times, in seconds, for a sample of students is summarised as having mean 3.6, mode 4.2 and standard deviation 1.25. Calculate Pearson's coefficient of skewness using the mode and use your answer to describe the shape of the distribution.

3.7 Using summary statistics: Normal distribution and standardised scores

The mean is used as part of the calculation to find the standard deviation. Together the mean and standard deviation can be used to compare data sets.

Mean and standard deviation can be represented on a **normal distribution curve**.

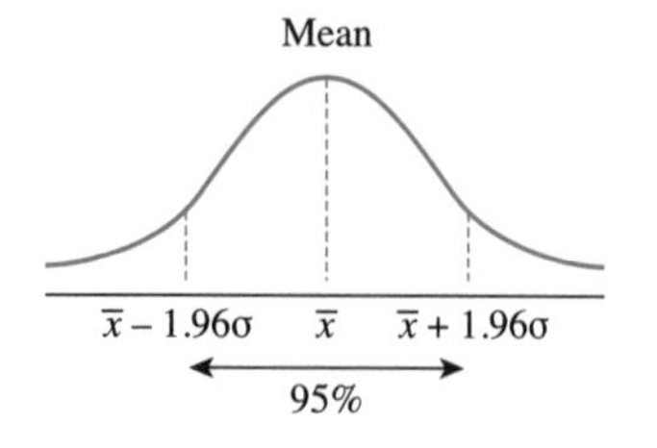

The normal curve is symmetrical about the mean. Approximately 95% of its values lie within 1.96 standard deviations of the mean.
Almost all values are within 3.09 standard deviations of the mean.

Two distributions with the same mean, but different standard deviations would peak at the same place, but the curve with the greater standard deviation would be more spread out and less peaked.

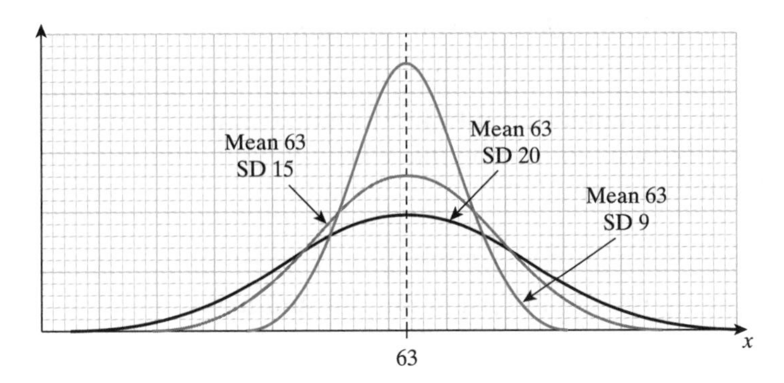

The normal distribution is a probability distribution. The total probability is the area under the curve. This means the area under curve = 1

Two distributions with the same standard deviation, but different means would be the same shape but at different positions on the x-axis.

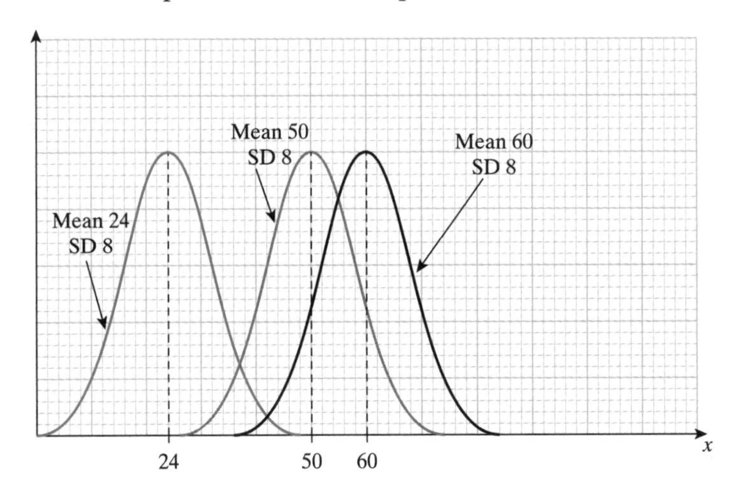

Activity

Using a suitable computer package draw several normal distribution curves. Explore the effect of changing the mean and standard deviation.

In Autograph to draw a normal curve open a 1-D statistics page then go to Object and Enter Probability Distribution. Click on Normal and OK. Enter the mean and standard deviation and click OK. You can repeat this to draw more than one distribution on the same axes.

For any set of data if the mean and standard deviation are known:

- Subtracting the mean from all values moves its graph to have a mean = 0
- Dividing values by the standard deviation gives its graph a standard deviation = 1

Taken together all data sets can be standardised to have mean 0 and standard deviation 1 and allow comparisons to be made by **standardising scores** in different data sets.

Example

Students take two maths papers, paper A and paper B. The summary statistics are:

	Mean mark	Standard deviation
Paper A	52	12
Paper B	45	8

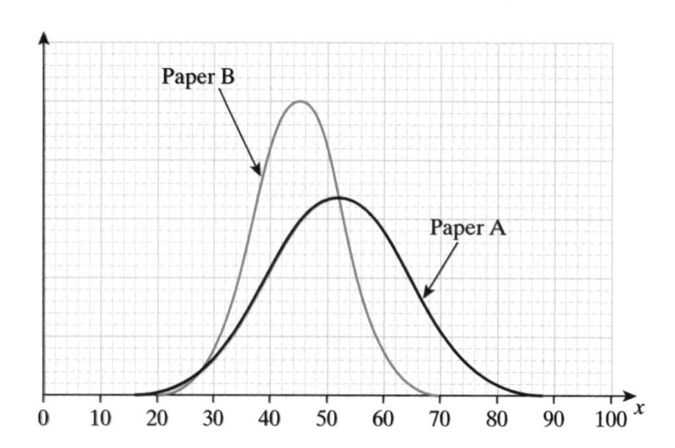

Karl achieved a score of 55 in paper A and 54 in paper B. In which paper did he do best?

Paper A: $\dfrac{55-52}{12} = 0.25$ Paper B: $\dfrac{54-45}{8} = 1.125$

Standardised score Paper B > standardised score Paper A. Although his paper B actual mark is less, Karl did better relative to the other candidates.

Standardised score, $z = \dfrac{\text{score} - \text{mean}}{\text{standard deviation}}$

Exercise 3G

1. (a) Which of these normal distributions has
   (i) the smallest mean?
   (ii) the greatest standard deviation?

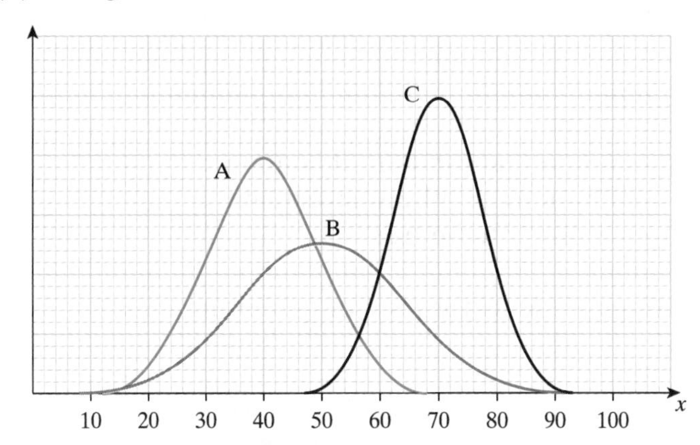

   (b) Write down the median and the mode for each distribution. What do you notice?

2. On the same axes sketch the following distributions
   A: mean 60 standard deviation 12
   B: mean 45 standard deviation 4
   C: mean 72 standard deviation 6.

3. One month, the mean height of applicants for the Royal Marines was 1.78m. The standard deviation of their heights was 0.06m.
   (a) Estimate the height of (i) the shortest applicant (ii) the tallest applicant.
   (b) Work out an estimate of the heights within which 95% of the applicants are likely to be.

4. Students sat two examination papers. Paper 1 had a mean mark of 52 and standard deviation of 9.4. Paper 2 had a mean mark of 60 and standard deviation of 2.5.
   Julia achieved a mark of 70 in one of the papers. Using a sketch of the distributions or otherwise explain in which of the papers this mark is more likely to have been achieved.

5. A proof-reader checks two manuscripts, from Josh and from Ryan. The table shows the mean and standard deviation of the number of errors per page.

	Josh	Ryan
Mean	2.4	1.7
Standard deviation	0.12	0.58

A page from one of the scripts was chosen at random. It contained 3 errors. Using a sketch of the distributions or otherwise explain which of the manuscripts this is most likely to be from.

6. The table shows the marks for three students for each of two exam papers.

	Jenny	Karen	Louise	Mean	Standard deviation
Physics	61	60	74	64	5
Chemistry	55	60	72	56	8

(a) Calculate the standardised scores for all six papers.
(b) Who did equally well in both papers?

3.8 Using summary statistics: Quality assurance

Machine production of commodities, such as packets of sweets, does not produce packets absolutely identical in weight and size. The machine produces the packets to a target weight or size, but there will always be variation from packet to packet. Changes to targets set could be caused by machine malfunction or a poor machine operator.

Activity

A normal distribution curve of weights or sizes should show they lie within 3.09 standard deviations of their mean. Where should the target weight be for a machine producing a packet of sweets labelled as containing 250g?
Why does it matter if the target weight is too low or too high?
Who might need this information?

Quality control takes samples of the products at different times. Means, medians and/or ranges of these samples are calculated and plotted on a **quality assurance graph**.

The graphs are checked for any trend in the measurements and that the variation from its target is within limits.

Quality assurance graphs for means and medians

The diagram shows a quality assurance chart for the mean weights of samples of 50g bars of chocolate.

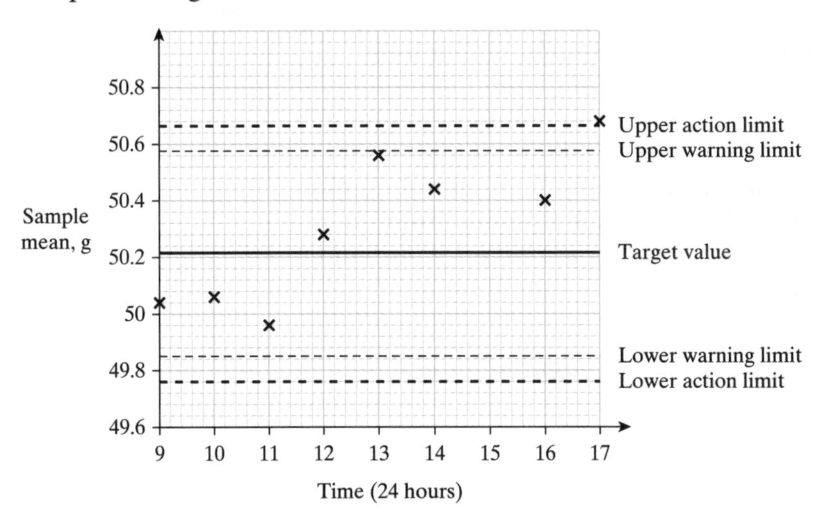

Questions in the exam will only give the target value on quality assurance graphs drawn for mean and median.

If the sample means all lie within the warning limits, the product is accepted.

If a sample mean value is within both the warning and action limits a further sample is immediately taken and checked.

If a sample mean lies outside of the action limit production is stopped and investigated.

Activity

Warning limits are set so that 95% of the samples should lie within them.

Action limits are set so that almost all the samples lie within them.

What target value, warning and action limits would you set for a 100g bar of chocolate?

(Hint: Use what you have learnt about the normal distribution.)

You can define your own standard deviation for your machine.

Quality assurance graph for range

If the range of the sample data is checked you would expect it to be very small, ideally zero. The quality assurance graph for range has no target value, but does have an action limit.

The diagram shows a quality assurance graph for the ranges of weights of samples of 50 g bars of chocolate.

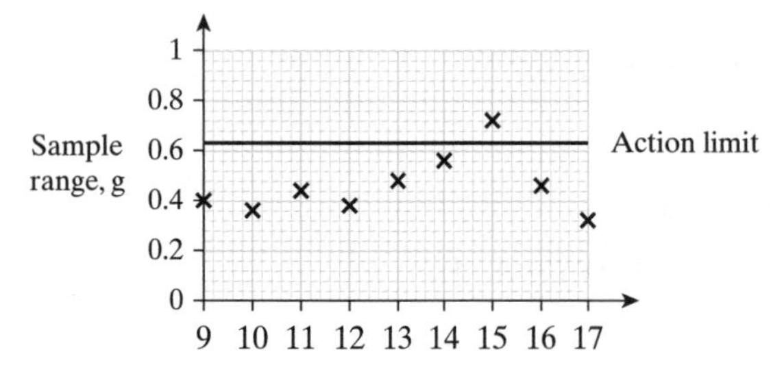

As the sample taken at 15:00 hours is greater than the action limit, further samples would have been checked.

Exercise 3H

1. The manager of a clothes factory carries out quality control checks on five machines. He takes samples from each machine from the production line of size 10 trousers. These should have a waistband size of 27cm. The action limit for the range is 0.8cm.

   For each machine's samples:
   (i) Look at the quality control graphs and comment on the variability shown.
   (ii) What action, if any, would you advise?

   Machine A

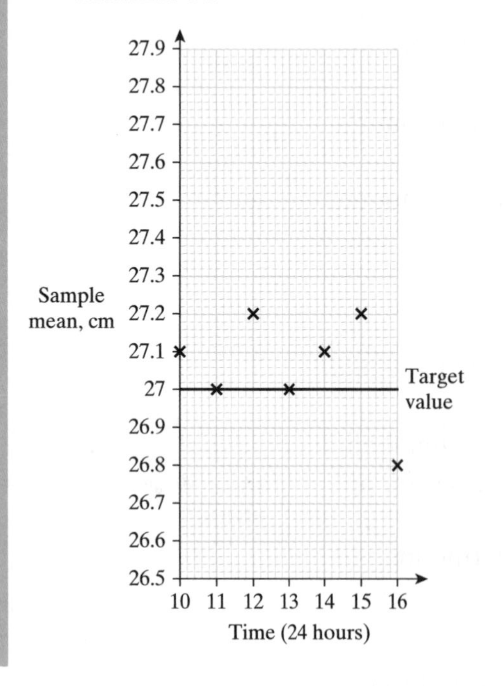

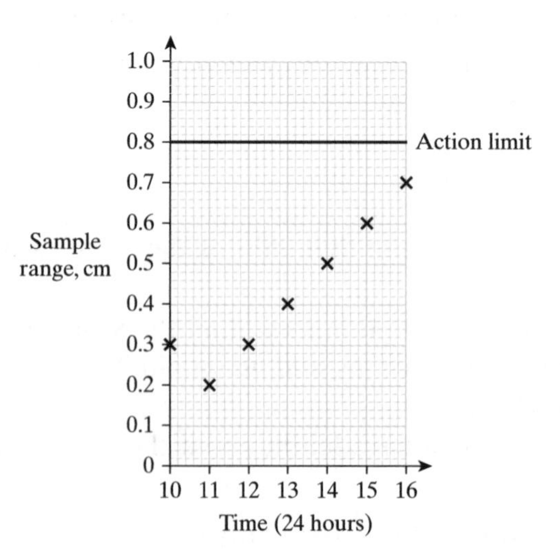

Machine B

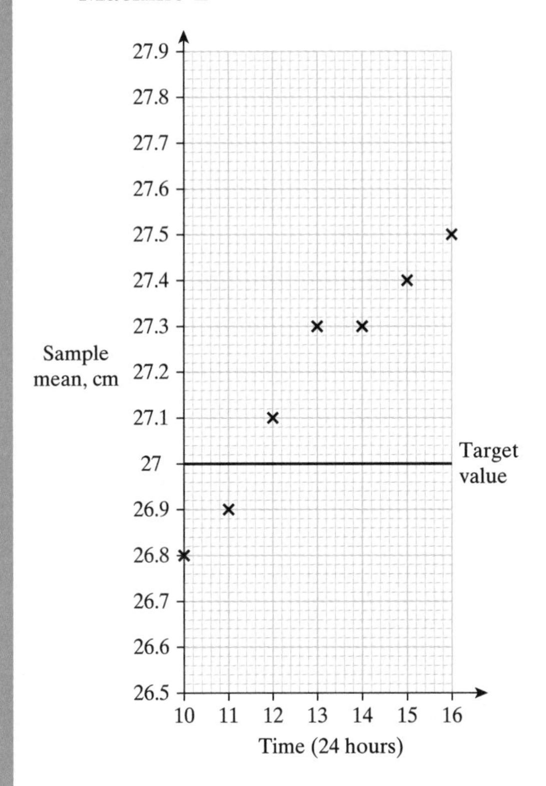

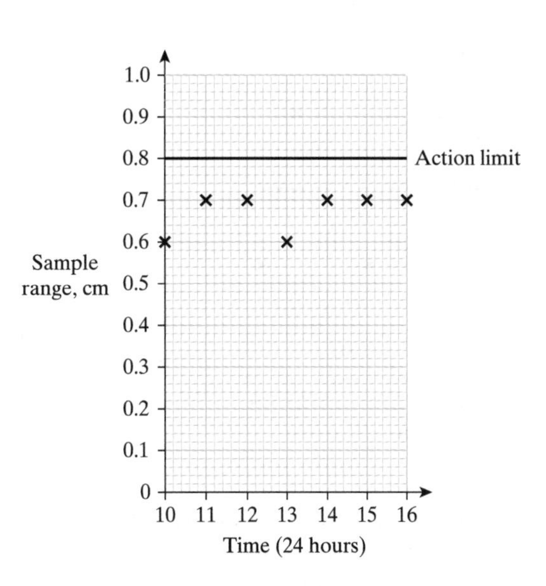

Machine C

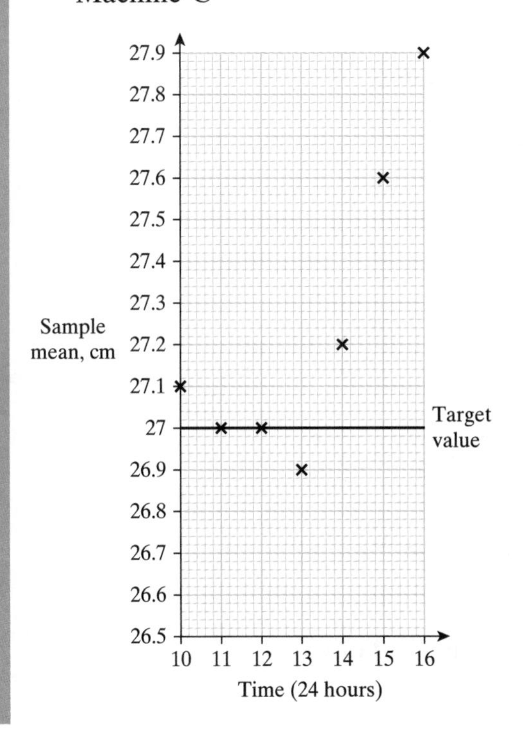

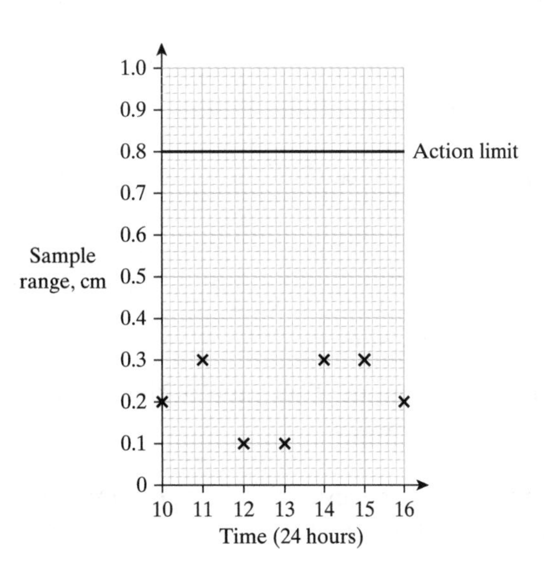

Machine D

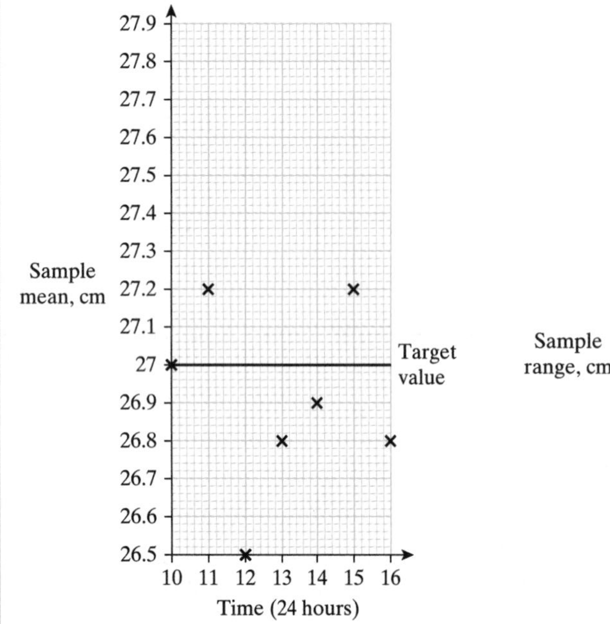

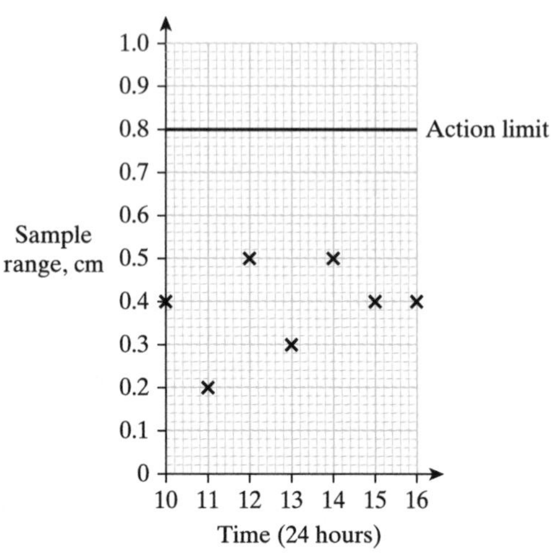

2. Boxes of washing powder were filled by a machine. The boxes should contain 4 kg of powder. The target amount of powder is 4.1 kg. The action limit for the range is 100 g.

(a) Explain why the target amount of powder is greater than the amount the box should contain.

The diagrams show the mean and range of samples of powder taken at regular intervals from one machine on one day. The machine was reset after the third sample was taken.

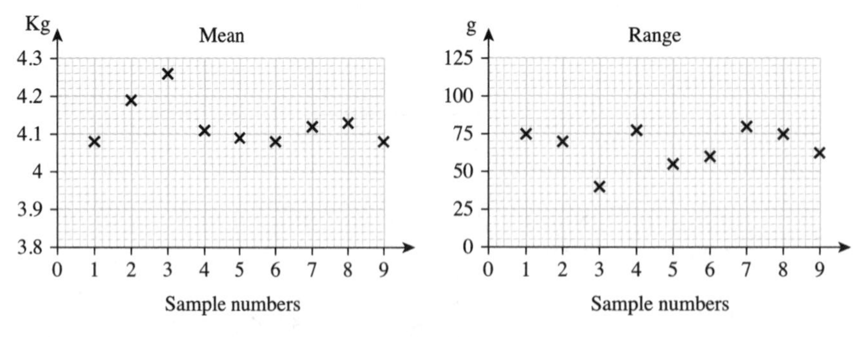

(b) Make one comment on each of the graphs in relation to the production process.

3. Explain why it is necessary to have quality control graphs for both an average and the range.

Summary of key points

A measure of location or average is a single value used to describe a set of data.

- Mode is most common value
- Median is middle value of an ordered set of data
- Mean is calculated as sum of all values divided by the total number of values
- Geometric mean of a set of n values is the nth root of the product of those values.

A measure of dispersion describes the spread of the data.

- Range is the difference between the highest and lowest values
- Interquartile range is the difference between the upper quartile and lower quartile
- Standard deviation is a measure of differences of values from the mean.

Together a measure of location and a measure of dispersion are used to compare data sets.

- Use median with IQR; represent these on a box and whisker plot
- Use mean with standard deviation; use standardised scores to compare data sets
- Skewness measures the shape of the distribution.

Quality assurance is used to study trends in the mean, median and the range.

Links to the Real World

The internet is a rich source of tables of information. For many people the only complicated tables of numbers that are used and understood are those for sport, such as football league tables or batting averages in cricket. In general the media tends to avoid tables of information and instead presents us with a summary that can often form part of the headline.

Summary statistics, in particular mean, standard deviation and normal distribution, are used extensively to design and make products that the majority of the population will be able to use. Combining data on human measurements such as height, arm length or hand span, with the knowledge that 95% of a normal population lie within two standard deviations of the mean, manufacturers can design products to target almost all the population. For example, they would use this information to decide on the different positions for a car seat, mirror, pedals and so on.

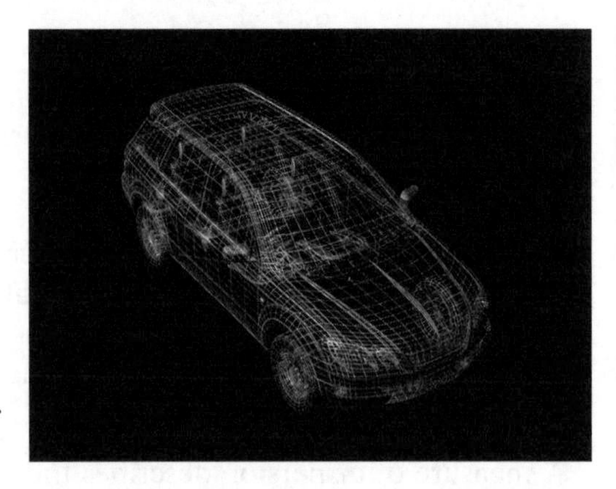

In industry summary statistics, along with mechanisms of quality assurance, are used to ensure that products do 'what they say on the tin'. Contents on jars or packages often state a minimum weight and trading standards would prosecute if the public were undersold.

Together with a numerical summary, a visual picture of the information can often convey more than words. The next chapter explores ways of displaying information.

Revision Exercise 3

1. In May 2001 an estate agent sold nine, three-bedroomed houses.
The sale prices in pounds were:

59 200	65 000	52 000
129 500	52 000	62 500
54 500	57 900	56 000

(a) Write down the mode of these prices.
(b) (i) Calculate the mean of these prices.
(ii) Give a **disadvantage** in using the mean to represent these prices. [AQA]

2. A firm produces tins of baked beans. For quality control purposes, a sample of five tins of baked beans is taken every hour and the mass of each tin is measured.
The mean mass and range of masses of each sample is calculated and plotted on separate graphs. The graphs below show the mean mass and range of masses of the first seven samples.
The eighth sample has tins of baked beans of the following masses:

1.072 kg 0.998 kg 1.024 kg 1.037 kg 1.046 kg

The mean mass of this sample is 1.0354 kg.

(a) Calculate the range of masses of this sample.
(b) Plot the values of the eighth sample on a copy of the appropriate graphs.

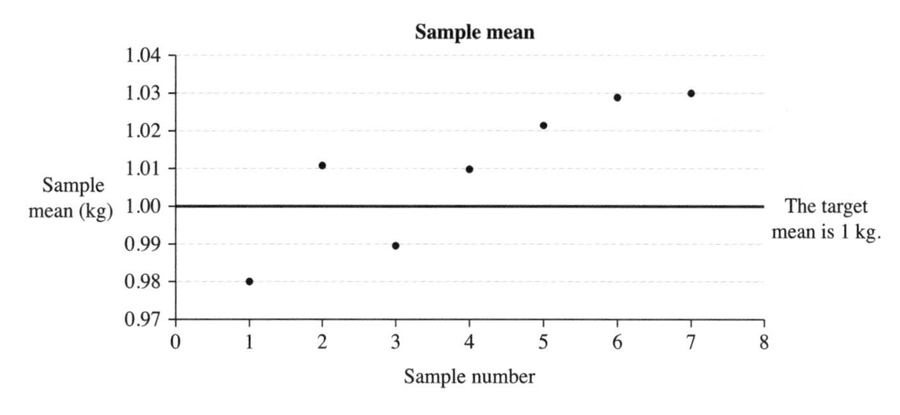

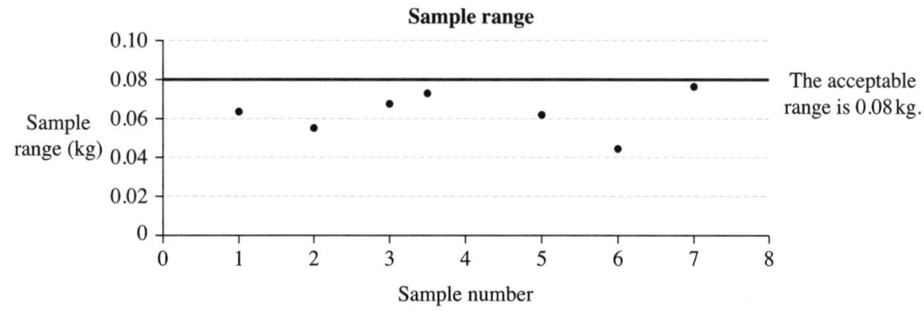

(c) Make **one** comment on each graph in relation to the production process. [AQA]

3. The duration, in minutes, of a sample of ten adventure films, is given in the table.

105	116	111	130	116
140	119	116	125	125

(a) Calculate the mean and standard deviation of the duration of the adventure films.

(b) Assume that the duration of all adventure films is normally distributed with a mean of 120 minutes and a standard deviation of 9.3 minutes.
Explain why a film is unlikely to last for more than 155 minutes.

(c) The duration of romance films has a mean of 130 minutes and a standard deviation of 7.53 minutes.
Compare the duration of adventure and romance films. [AQA]

4. A packet contains sweets. Some of the sweets are red.
A random sample of 3 sweets is chosen from the packet and the number of red sweets is recorded.
The sample is then replaced. Another sample is then taken.
The number of red sweets in each of 25 samples is given below.

1 2 2 1 2
1 2 2 2 2
2 0 2 0 1
1 0 0 1 1
1 1 1 1 3

(a) Copy and complete the frequency table below.

Number of red sweets in each sample	Frequency
0	
1	
2	
3	

(b) For this data
(i) write down the mode,
(ii) calculate the mean. [AQA]

5. The mean and standard deviation of the marks in a Mathematics exam and in a Statistics exam are shown.

	Mean	Standard deviation
Mathematics	63	6
Statistics	73	8

The marks in both exams are normally distributed.

(a) John scored 54 marks in the Mathematics exam and 57 marks in the Statistics exam.
John claimed that he was better at Mathematics.
By standardizing his marks decide if the data supports his claim.

(b) Sketch the distributions for both Mathematics and Statistics with an x-axis scale from 30 to 100. [AQA]

6. Ten pupils took an exam.
The sum of their marks was 315.
The sum of the squares of their marks was 10 829.

(a) Calculate the mean and standard deviation for these ten exam marks.

(b) One of the marks was 32 but was incorrectly recorded as 23.
Calculate the correct mean and standard deviation.

(c) Explain

(i) Why the mean has increased,

(ii) Why the standard deviation has decreased. [AQA]

7. Marie records the arrival times of buses into a bus station one Friday morning. She records how many minutes late each bus is, to the nearest minute.
Her results are recorded into this table.

Number of minutes late	Tally	Frequency
1	𝍸 𝍸 𝍸 𝍸 III	
2	𝍸 𝍸 𝍸 𝍸 𝍸 III	
3	𝍸 𝍸 𝍸 III	
4	𝍸 I	
5	III	
6	II	

(a) Copy the table and complete the frequency column.

(b) How many buses were there?

(c) What was the total number of minutes late?

(d) Calculate the mean number of minutes the buses were late by.

(e) What was the modal number of minutes the buses were late? [AQA]

8. Louise collects CDs.
She keeps records of her CDs.
The records she keeps are

the cost
the length of time each track lasts
the number of tracks on each CD.

(a) The length of time, t (seconds) of her favourite tracks is given in the table.

Time, t (seconds)	Frequency
$120 \leqslant t < 150$	12
$150 \leqslant t < 180$	17
$180 \leqslant t < 210$	21
$210 \leqslant t < 240$	8
$240 \leqslant t < 270$	2

Calculate estimates of the mean and standard deviation of these times.

(b) David wishes to calculate an estimate of the mean time of his favourite tracks.

He uses the same time intervals as Louise.
He codes the data using 135 seconds as 0, 165 seconds as 1, 195 seconds as 2 and so on.

David calculates the mean of the coded data as 3.6
Calculate the estimate of the mean time of David's favourite tracks. [AQA]

9. Two machines produce equal numbers of bottles of milk.
Bottles are filled with full-fat milk by one machine and with semi-skimmed milk by the other machine.
The distributions of the volumes of milk are both normal.
The mean and standard deviation of each distribution is shown in the table.

	Mean (ml)	Standard deviation (ml)
Full-fat milk	560	8
Semi-skimmed milk	570	2

A bottle is selected at random and contains at least 576 ml of milk.
Is it likely to contain full-fat or semi-skimmed milk?
You must support your answer with calculations. [AQA]

10. Reuben read all 12 Sharren Dan books.
He gave each book an enjoyment score out of 10.
The scores were
3 7 8 8 8 8 10 10 10 10 10 10

(a) For these scores work out
  (i) the range (ii) the mode
  (iii) the median (iv) the mean

(b) Reuben says the mean is the best average to use.
Give a disadvantage of using the mean in this case.

(c) Joshua also read all 12 Sharren Dan books.
He gave each book an enjoyment score out of 10.
The range of his scores was 2 and the median score was 6.
Write down **two** comparisons between the scores Joshua gave and the scores Reuben gave on the Sharren Dan books. [AQA]

11. A factory uses one machine to produce tins of food.
The Quality Control staff check the process by taking samples of 5 tins every half hour and recording the mean weight of each sample.
The target value for the mean weight is 410 g
The table shows the results of the first 8 samples taken from the machine.

Sample number	Sample mean weight (g)
1	410.30
2	409.65
3	410.25
4	410.30
5	410.50
6	410.95
7	410.30
8	409.70

(a) Copy these axes to draw a chart to show this data.

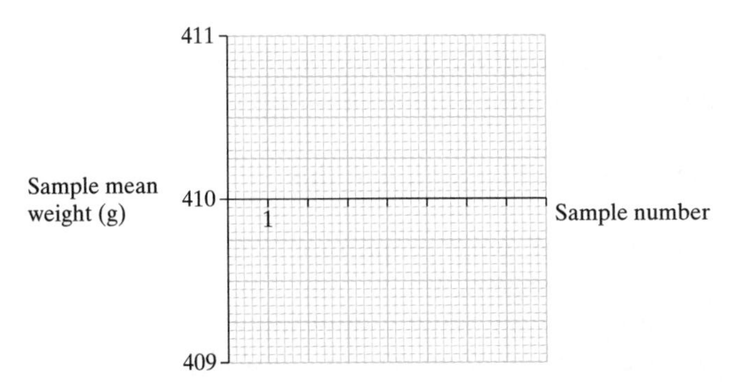

(b) At which point was the process stopped and the machine adjusted? Justify your choice. [AQA]

12. Joan is a Road Safety Officer for a City Council.

Part of her work involves recording the number of vehicles exceeding the speed limit as they pass local schools.

The following table gives the data recorded over a 120 day period e.g. on 42 days two vehicles per day exceeded the speed limit.

Number of vehicles per day exceeding speed limit	2	5	6	10	14	15	20
Number of days	42	28	18	14	10	5	3

(a) Calculate the mean and standard deviation of the number of vehicles per day exceeding the speed limit.
Give your answers to two decimal places.

(b) Due to a fault on the recording equipment, Joan's records did not show a further two vehicles **each** day which were exceeding the speed limit.
What effect will this error have on the values for
(i) the mean
(ii) the standard deviation?

(c) During the same period of time two other Road Safety Officers recorded equal numbers of actual traffic speeds at different locations in the city.
The speeds recorded by the first Road Safety Officer are normally distributed.
(i) Copy and complete the diagram for this distribution.

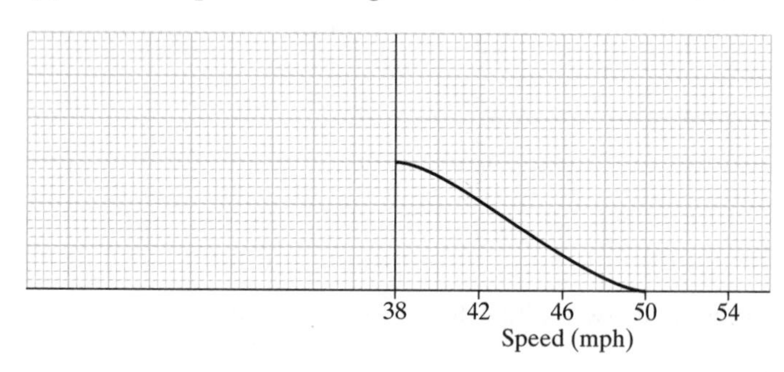

(ii) The speeds recorded by the second Road Safety Officer were also normally distributed. They had a mean of 44 mph and standard deviation of 2 mph.
On the same grid draw a diagram to represent this distribution.

(iii) For the first Road Safety Officer, what proportion of his records will show speeds of 38 mph or less?

(iv) For the second Road Safety Officer, what proportion of his records will show speeds above 52 mph? [AQA]

13. The amount of money spent by seven customers in a DIY shop was recorded.
The values were
£5 £12 £8 £225 £20 £14 £10

(a) Find the range of these values.
(b) Find the median of these values.
(c) Will the mean be higher or lower than the median?
Tick the correct box.
Higher ☐ Lower ☐
Give a reason for your answer. [AQA]

14. The weekly wages (in pounds) of the twenty workers in a factory are shown below.

85 90 90 90 85 85 120 85 85 85
90 120 160 220 85 90 120 335 160 120

Wage (in £)	Tally	Frequency
85		
90		
120		
160		
220		
335		

(a) Copy and complete the frequency distribution.
(b) The shop steward says that the average wage of the workers is £85.
Which average is he referring to, the mean, the median or the mode? [NEAB]

15. The number of goals scored by the 11 members of a hockey team in 1993 were as follows:

6 0 8 12 2 1 2 9 1 0 11

(a) Find the median.
(b) Find the upper and lower quartiles.
(c) Find the interquartile range.
(d) Explain why, for this data, the interquartile range is a more appropriate measure for spread than the range.
(e) The goals scored by the 11 members of the hockey team in 1994 are summarized in this box-plot.

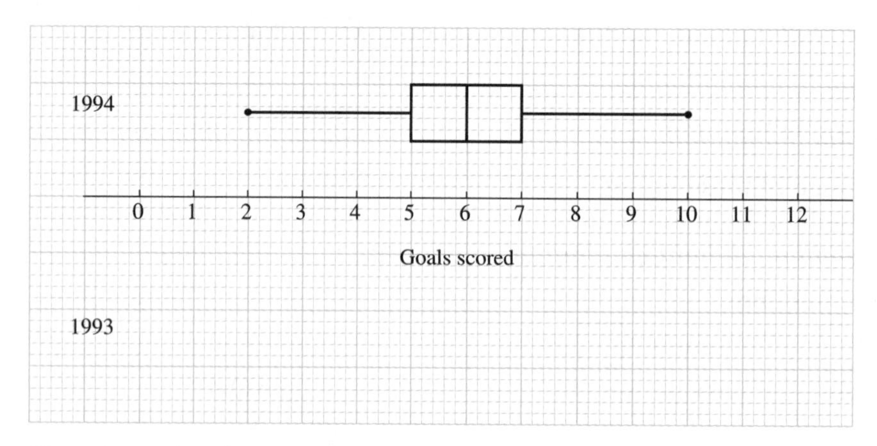

(i) Copy the diagram above and summarize the results for 1993 in the same way.

(ii) Do you think the team scored more goals in 1994? Explain your reasoning. [NEAB]

16. This histogram shows the alcohol consumption for a random sample of 100 adult males in the UK. The results show consumption in units of alcohol and relate to the week preceding the interview which formed the basis of the investigation.

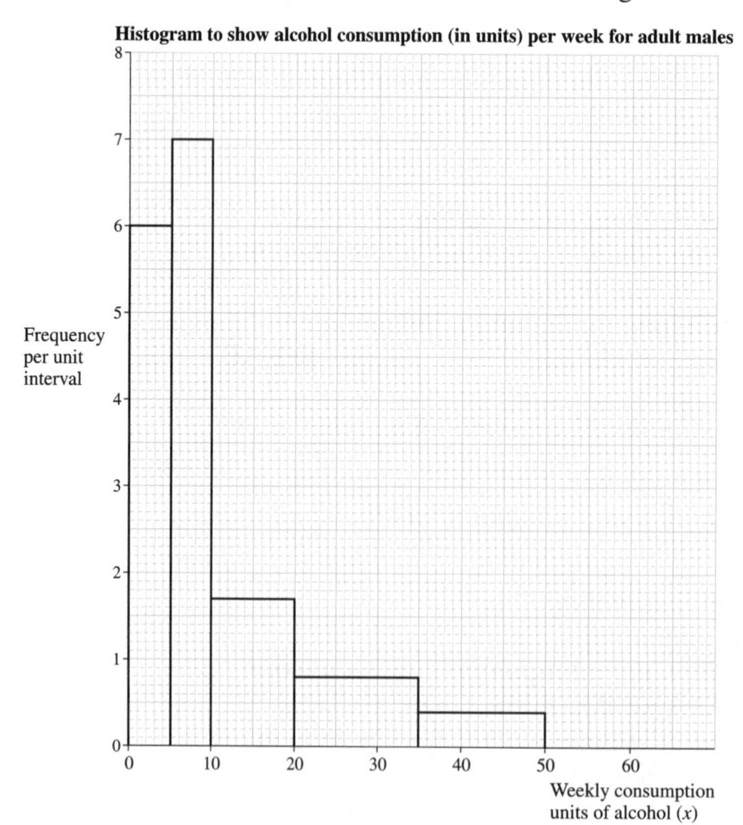

(a) Equivalent data for a sample of 100 females was:

Consumption units of alcohol (x)	Frequency
$0 < x \leqslant 5$	77
$5 < x \leqslant 10$	10
$10 < x \leqslant 20$	9
$20 < x \leqslant 35$	3
$35 < x \leqslant 50$	1

(i) Using the class mid-points 2.5, 7.5, 15, 27.5, 42.5 as (x), calculate, to one decimal place, estimates of the mean and standard deviation for female alcohol consumption per week.

(You may use the following formulae

Mean $= \dfrac{\sum fx}{\sum f}$ Standard deviation $= \sqrt{\dfrac{\sum f(x - \bar{x})^2}{\sum f}}$

or any suitable alternative, or the statistical functions on your calculator.)

(ii) Hence copy and complete the following table:

	Median	Mean	Standard deviation
Male	7.9	11.8	11.0
Female	3.3		

Comment on the key differences apparent in relation to alcohol consumption rates.

(b) (i) Use the following formula to calculate a measure of skewness for both male and female weekly consumption of alcohol.

$$\text{Measure of skewness} = \frac{3\,(\text{mean} - \text{median})}{\text{standard deviation}}$$

(ii) By reference to the results obtained in part (b) (i) and the histogram, describe the shape of the two distributions.

(c) Suggest a reason why the interviewer asked for alcohol consumption over the preceding week and not over a longer period.

(d) Indicate how the survey should be continued if the results are to be representative of changes in alcohol consumption throughout the year. [NEAB]

17. The length of 300 telephone calls from ordinary telephones is given in the table.

Time T (seconds)	$0 \leqslant T < 40$	$40 \leqslant T < 60$	$60 \leqslant T < 80$	$80 \leqslant T < 100$	$100 \leqslant T < 120$	$120 \leqslant T < 160$	$160 \leqslant T < 200$
Frequency	38	36	41	58	49	48	30

(a) Calculate an estimate of the mean and standard deviation of the length of calls.

The mean and standard deviation of the length of calls from mobile telephones are 64 seconds and 35 seconds respectively.

(b) Comment on the differences in the length of calls from mobile and ordinary telephones.

18. The number of flower buds on a sample of 10 azalea plants were recorded.

25 37 28 16 37 50 48 45 42 49

(a) Calculate the range of these data.
(b) Calculate the standard deviation of these data.

You may use the statistical functions on your calculator or the following formula.

$$\text{Standard deviation} = \sqrt{\frac{\sum x^2}{n} - \left\{\frac{\sum x}{n}\right\}^2}$$

The number of flower buds on the same 10 plants were recorded two years later. The second set of data had an increased range of 35 but a reduced standard deviation of 7.9.

(c) Write down two differences which you would expect to see in the values of the second set of data as compared with those of the first set of data.

Another type of plant had a positively skewed distribution with a mean of 50 buds per plant.

(d) Sketch this skewed distribution, clearly indicating possible positions of the mean, mode and median. [SEG]

19. (a) A machine is used to pack paper clips. In order to test the efficiency of the machine, twenty packets were taken at random and the contents counted.

Number of paper clips in a packet	Number of packets		
48	2		
49	2		
50	6		
51	5		
52	0		
53	1		
54	2		
55	2		

Calculate

(i) the mean number of paper clips in each packet,

(ii) the standard deviation.

(b) Another machine packs paper clips with a mean 51 and standard deviation 4.2. By comparing the machines give reasons why you would prefer one to the other for efficiency. [SEG]

20. The following table shows the profits (or losses) of 100 Retailing Companies and 100 Manufacturing Companies in 1999.

Profits (£000's)	Retailing	Manufacturing
$-10 \leqslant x < 0$	2	12
$0 \leqslant x < 10$	5	25
$10 \leqslant x < 20$	12	35
$20 \leqslant x < 30$	20	18
$30 \leqslant x < 40$	61	10

(a) Calculate the missing values in the following table.

	Retailing	Manufacturing
Mean profit		£13 900
Median profit	£33 606	£13 714
Standard deviation		£11 393

(b) A measure of skewness is given by the expression

$$3 \times \frac{(\text{mean} - \text{median})}{\text{standard deviation}}.$$

(i) Use the results from your completed table in part (a) to calculate to 2 decimal places a measure of skewness for each sector.

(ii) What do the measures of skewness indicate about the shape of the two distributions? [NEAB]

21. The number of traffic accidents recorded per day over a 200-day period at a busy road junction in the town of Fernlea were as follows.

Number of accidents per day, x	Number of days
0	24
1	88
2	61
3	20
4	5
5	2
	200

(a) Calculate for this data

(i) the mean ($\bar{x}$),

(ii) the standard deviation (s), to 2 decimal places.
(You may use the following formulae

$$\text{Mean} = \frac{\sum fx}{\sum f}$$

$$\text{Standard deviation} = \sqrt{\frac{\sum fx^2}{\sum f} - \bar{x}^2} \text{ or } \sqrt{\frac{\sum f(x - \bar{x})^2}{\sum f}}$$

or any suitable alternative, or the statistical functions on your calculator.)

An earlier study conducted over a similar time period at the same road junction produced the following summarized results.

Daily road accidents	
Mean ($\bar{x}$)	Standard deviation (s)
3.2	1.15

A comparison of the relative variation present in each of the two sets of data is to be undertaken using the following measure:

$$\frac{s}{\bar{x}}$$

(b) Calculate, to 2 decimal places, this measure for **each** data set.

(c) Comment on the results which you obtained in parts (a) and (b). [NEAB]

22. The table shows the mean and the standard deviation of the heights of a sample of adult males and a sample of boys aged nine.
The heights of both the adult males and the boys are normally distributed.

	Adult males	Boys aged nine
Mean	180 cm	135 cm
Standard deviation	18 cm	10 cm

David is a boy aged nine whose height is 120 cm.

(a) How many standard deviations below the mean is David's height?

It is believed that the height of a boy aged nine is a good indicator of his adult height.

(b) Estimate the height that David will be when he is an adult.

The diagram shows the distribution of the heights of the boys aged nine.

(c) Copy the diagram and sketch the distribution of the heights of the adult males.

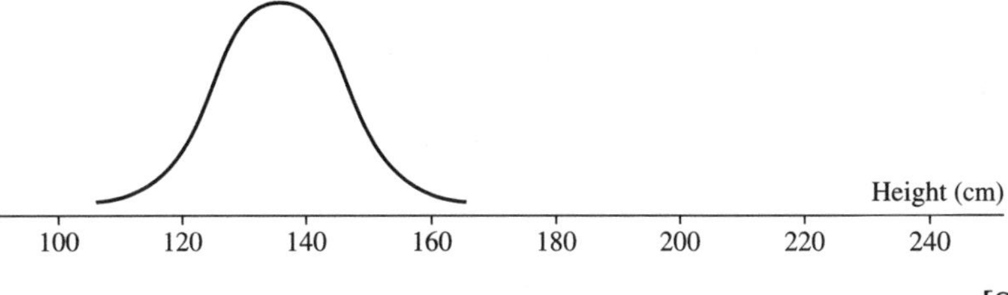

[SEG]

23. A class of students is given a History test and Physics test.

Both the History and Physics marks are approximately normally distributed.

The mean and the standard deviation of each distribution are shown in the table.

	Mean	Standard deviation
History	52	6
Physics	60	8

The graph shows a sketch of the distribution for the History marks.

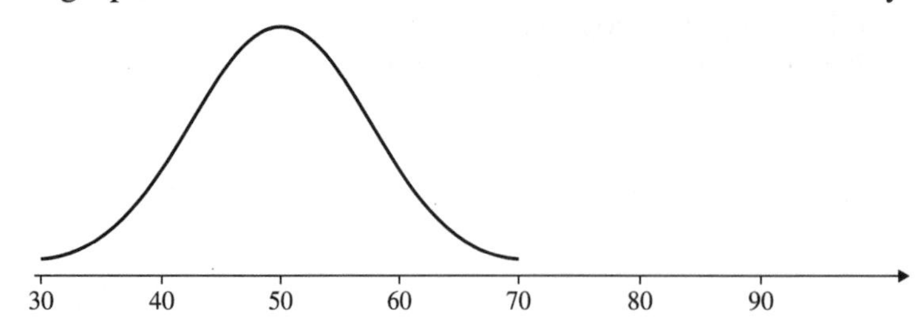

(a) Show, on a copy of the same graph, a sketch of the distribution of the Physics marks.

Kelly scores 64 in the History test and 72 in the Physics test, but she claims that she is better at History than at Physics.

(b) By standardizing her marks, find out whether her test results support her claim. [SEG]

24. The points awarded (out of a maximum of 6.0) by the 12 judges at a recent ice skating tournament were:

5.7, 5.9, 5.9, 5.7, 3.0, 5.8, 5.7, 5.7, 5.5, 5.8, 5.8, 5.5

(a) Calculate the mean points scored.

(b) Using the formula $\sqrt{\dfrac{\sum (x - \bar{x})^2}{n}}$ or the statistical functions on your calculator, or otherwise, calculate to two decimal places the standard deviation of the points scored.

(c) The points awarded by the judges are to be standardized by subtracting the mean from each of the values and then dividing the result by the standard deviation.

(i) What is the standardized value corresponding to a points score of 5.8?

(ii) Which of the original values corresponds to a standardized score of +0.263? [NEAB]

4 Representation of data

A judicious man looks at Statistics, not to get knowledge but to save himself from having ignorance foisted upon him
Carlyle

Diagrams can show clearly a wide range of information about a given population.

This unit will show you how to

- Draw diagrams to represent:
  Qualitative data; Discrete data; Continuous data
- Find summary statistics from diagrams
- Interpret the shape of diagrams
- Draw and interpret population pyramids
- Complete and interpret choropleth maps.

Before you start

You should be able to answer these questions

1 Find (a) $\frac{1}{4}$ of 360 (b) $\frac{1}{3}$ of 360 (c) $\frac{23}{90}$ of 360

2 Round
(a) to the nearest integer (i) 42.6 (ii) 59.4
(b) to the nearest tenth (i) 3.62 (ii) 0.87

3 The graph shows a currency conversion for Pounds and Euros.
Use the graph to find out
(a) How many euros you would get for
(i) £2 (ii) £4.50.
(b) How many pounds you would get for
(i) 4 euros (ii) 7 euros.

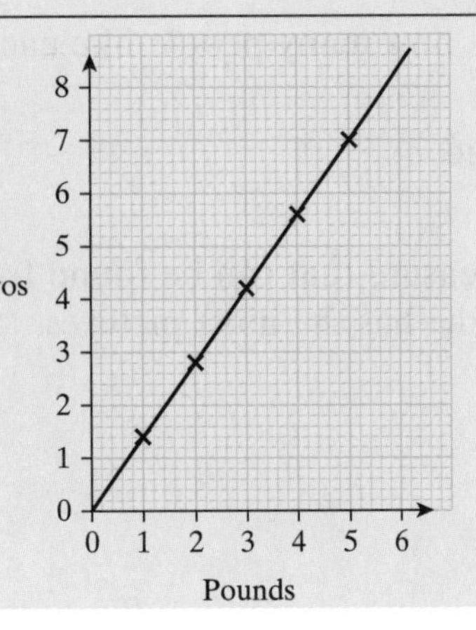

In newspapers, magazines and government reports, and in many business and scientific publications, data are presented in tables, charts and diagrams.

Data presented in tables doesn't convey the same instant impression as data presented in diagrams. However it can be easy to give a misleading impression with a diagram, and sometimes this may be intentional.

Good statistical diagrams should:

- Have axes clearly labelled, or a key, and a title and identify the source of the data
- Be clear and easy to understand and appropriate for the type of data.

4.1 Qualitative data: Pictograms and bar charts

Non-numerical data is represented by pictograms, bar charts and pie charts.

A **pictogram** uses symbols to represent a certain number of items.

This pictogram shows the favourite music for a group of 35 students

Favourite Music

Key: ○ = 4 people

Classic
Indie
Jazz
Pop
Rock

Use the key to work out how many people like each music type:

8 people like pop music
10 people like rock music
1 person likes classic.

The mode is the only measure that can be found from a pictogram. The mode is Indie as Indie has the most pictures.

A **bar chart** represents frequency by the height of the bar.

These bar charts show the same information as the pictogram.

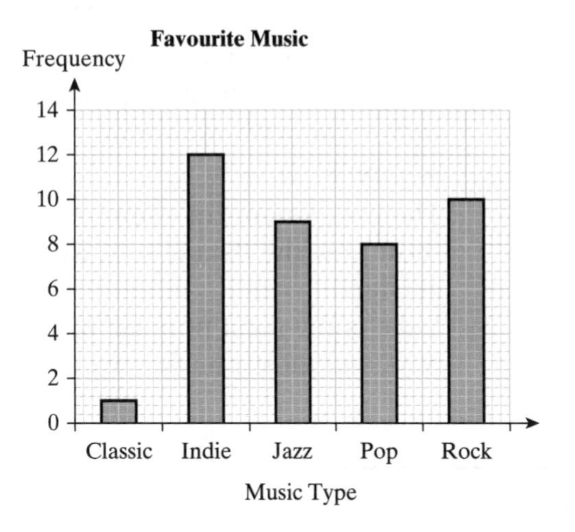

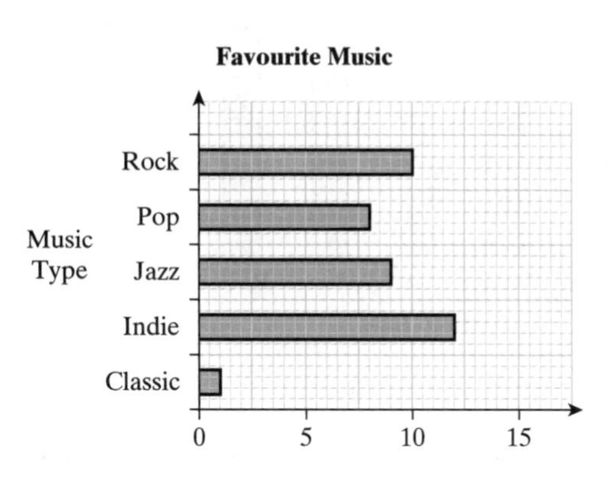

The bars can be vertical or horizontal.
The bars, and the gaps between the bars, should be the same width.

These data could be further split by gender and shown on a **multiple bar chart**.

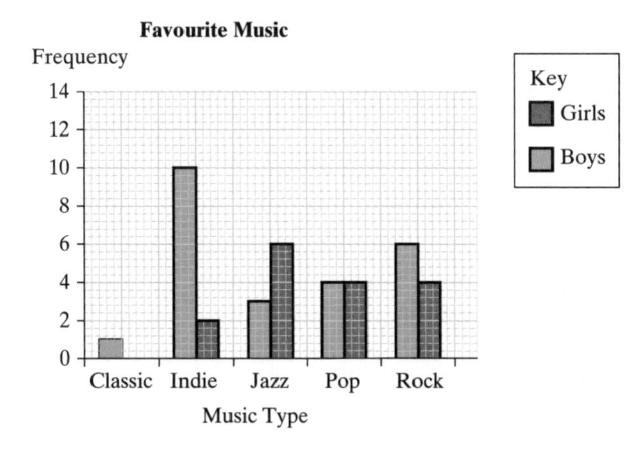

A multiple bar chart shows two or more data sets side by side.

This is a good chart to use to compare preferences between each data set.

Boys' and girls' preferences are easy to read.
Mode for boys: Indie
Mode for girls: Jazz
The same number of boys and girls chose Pop.

This is the same data shown on a **composite bar chart**.

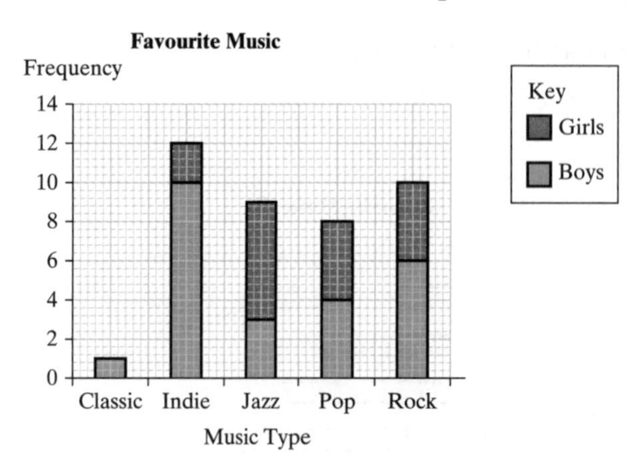

The total heights of each bar on a composite bar chart are the same as when the data is not split.

This is a good chart to use to compare the contribution of each value with each total across categories.

The components of each bar show how the data is split by gender.

Indie is the most popular with boys and most popular overall.

Exercise 4A

1. The pictogram shows the favourite type of newspaper in a survey of students.

Favourite Newspaper

Sunday	
Daily national	
Daily local	
Weekly local	

Key: = 10 people

(a) What is the preferred newspaper type?
(b) How many students preferred a daily local paper?
(c) How many more students preferred a Sunday paper to a weekly local paper?
(d) How many students in total were surveyed?

2. The table shows transport used by people visiting a sports centre one Saturday.

Transport	Car	Bus	Walk	Cycle	Other
Frequency	20	45	30	80	5

Draw a pictogram for this data. Remember to include a key.

3. (a) Write down three questions which could be answered by looking at this pictogram.

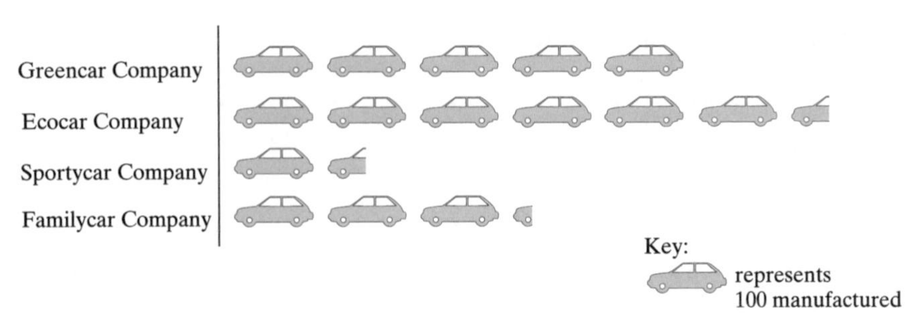

(b) Use the information in the pictogram to draw a bar chart.

4. (a) Write down three questions that could be answered by studying this bar chart.

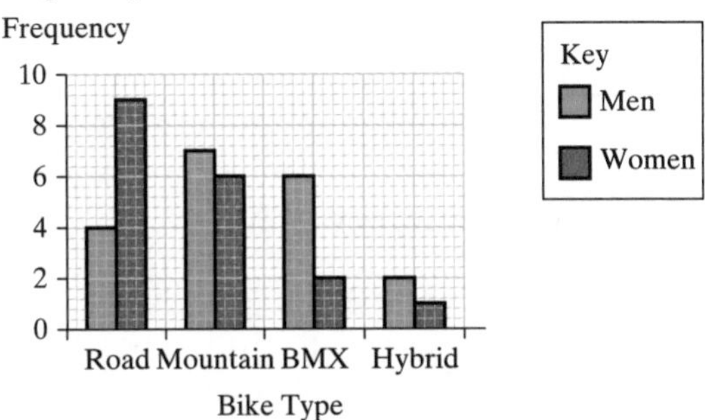

(b) Redraw the information in the bar chart as a composite bar.

5. The chart shows renewable energy sources.

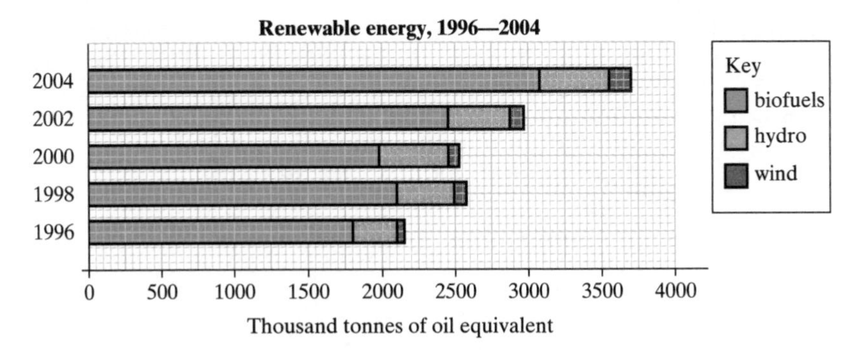

(a) Redraw this data as a multiple bar chart.

(b) Which energy source has remained approximately constant from 1998 to 2004?

4.2 Qualitative data: Pie charts

A pie chart represents data as proportions of a circle. It shows the contribution of each category to a total.
A pie chart is useful when there are only a few categories.

Example

Represent this data on a pie chart.

Music	Frequency	Working	Angle
Classic	1	$\frac{1}{40} \times 360$	9
Indie	12	$\frac{12}{40} \times 360$	108
Jazz	9	$\frac{9}{40} \times 360$	81
Pop	8	$\frac{8}{40} \times 360$	72
Rock	10	$\frac{10}{40} \times 360$	90
Total	40		360

To draw a pie chart, find the fraction of the total for each category. The angle on the pie chart will be the same fraction of 360°.

Favourite Music

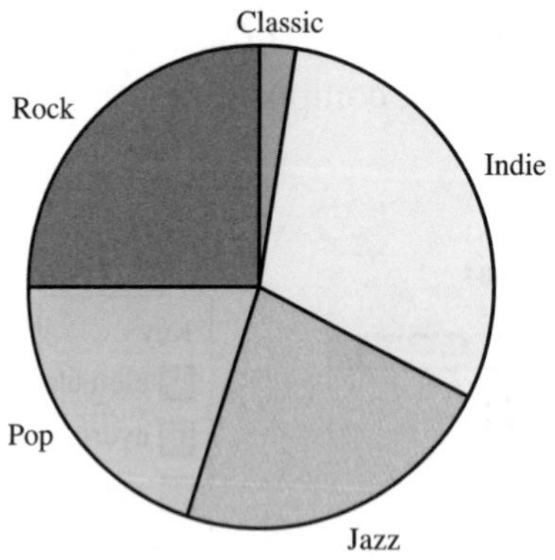

If needed round answers to the nearest degree and check that the total = 360.

Comparative pie charts

Comparative pie charts can be used to compare two sets of data. The **area** of each circle is in proportion to the total frequency in each of the data sets.
To draw the pie charts to fairly represent data sets you need to calculate the radius.

Example

Two pie charts to represent favourite music are drawn, one for boys and the other for girls. 24 boys and 16 girls took part in the survey. The pie chart for boys is drawn with a radius of 5 cm. What radius should the pie chart for girls be?

The ratio boys : girls = 24 : 16 = 3 : 2 and the area (not the radius) should represent this ratio.
Radius ratio boys : girls = $\sqrt{3} : \sqrt{2}$
If the radius for boys = 5 cm, radius for girls = $5 \times \frac{\sqrt{2}}{\sqrt{3}} = 4.1$ cm

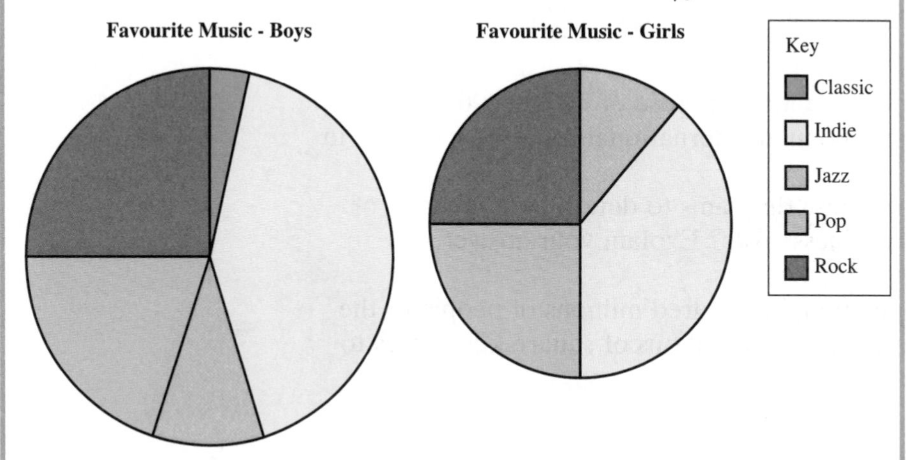

In this example, sectors are not labelled. A key is used to explain the pie charts sectors. The same colour is used for each type of music in both charts.

The sector for Rock in each pie chart is the same angle. However the larger radius in the boys pie chart means that although the angle is the same for Rock, the boys' Rock sector represents more people than the girls' Rock sector.

Exercise 4B

1. The pie chart shows the domestic water use in England and Wales for 2002.

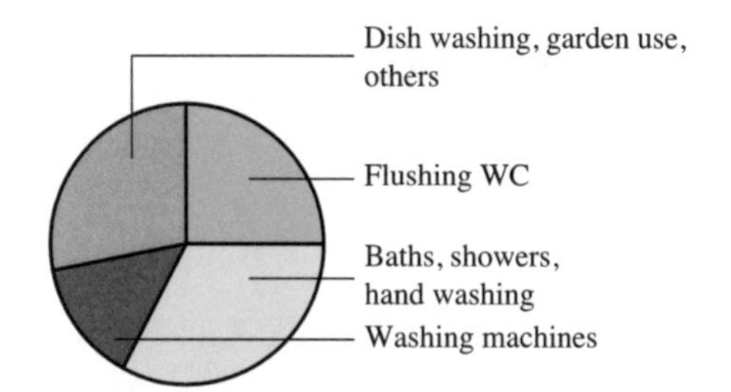

(a) What was the most common use of domestic water in 2002?
(b) How much water was used per day for flushing WCs?

2. These pie charts show aspects of international tourism in 2004.

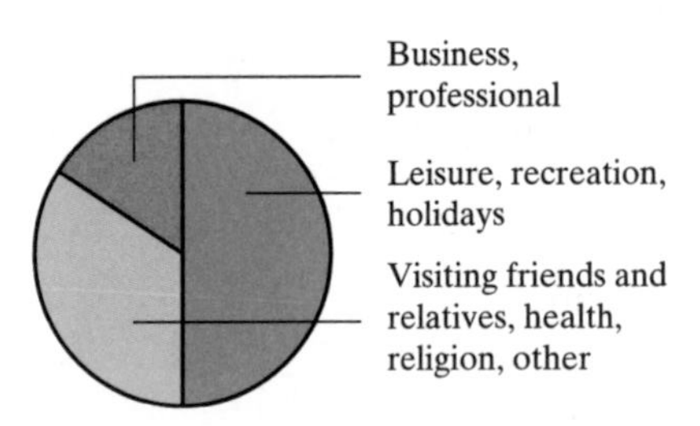

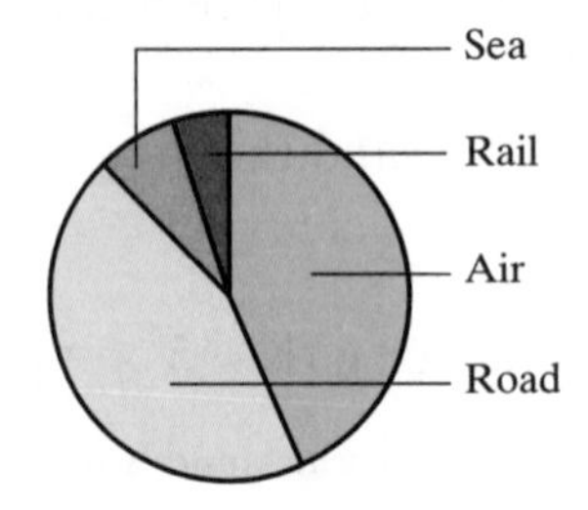

(a) What was the most common purpose of visit in 2004?
(b) What was the least popular international mode of transport in 2004?
(c) Is it possible from these diagrams to determine the mode of transport of the business visits? Explain your answer.

3. The tables show population, in hundred millions of people to the nearest million and land area, in millions of square kilometres to the nearest million.

Continent	Europe	Asia	Africa	North America	South America
Population	7	37	9	4	3

Continent	Europe	Asia	Africa	North America	South America	Antarctica
Land area	11	44	30	24	18	13

(a) Draw pie charts to represent these data (use the same colour for each country).
(b) Write three questions that you could ask by studying these pie charts.

4. School A has 1200 students, school B has 2400 students. Pie charts are to be drawn to represent the students at these two schools. The radius of pie chart for school A is 5 cm.

(a) Explain why it would be wrong to draw a pie chart for school B with radius 10 cm.
(b) Calculate the radius for the pie chart for school B.

5. The table gives the total number, in millions to the nearest million, of ethnic minority groups in some regions of England in 2001.

Region	East Midlands	Yorkshire & Humberside	South West
Frequency, Millions	27	32	11

If you were to draw comparative pie charts to compare these regions, and the pie chart for East Midlands had radius 6 cm, what radius pie chart would you draw to represent
(a) Yorkshire and Humberside
(b) South West?

Activity

IT can be useful to draw graphs quickly, however care should be taken to choose the correct graph for the data type you have.

Enter data into an Excel spreadsheet. Highlight the data and click on the chart wizard.

Explore the different types of graph that Excel can draw. Which graphs are really not useful and why not?

4.3 Discrete data: Stem and leaf diagrams

All types of bar charts and pie charts can be used to represent discrete data. A **vertical line graph** is also used to represent discrete data.

This graph shows the number of television sets in each of the households in Ash Road.

A vertical line graph looks like a bar chart, but vertical lines evenly spread, instead of bars, represent frequency.

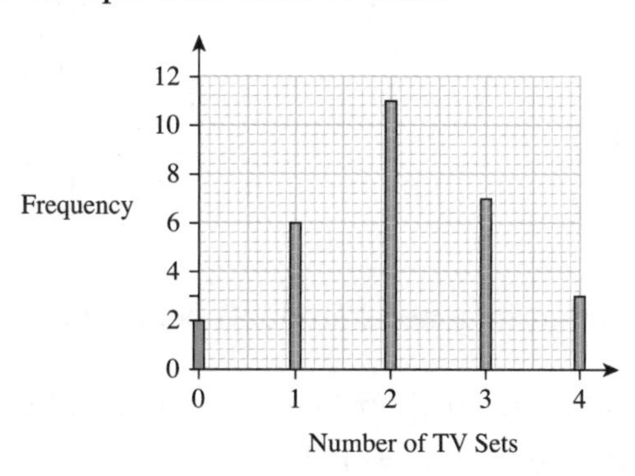

Very small discrete data sets can also be represented on a **dot plot**.
A dot plot is used to show overall trend.

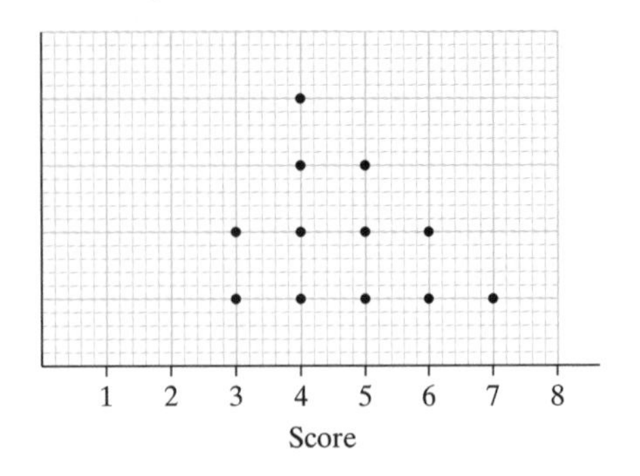

This dot plot shows positive skew.

Stem and leaf diagrams

A stem and leaf diagram is used to represent small data sets.

Example

These data are the percentages achieved in a test taken by 23 students.

58	54	78	66	67	40	45	38	58	73	51	49
47	53	41	36	59	64	52	43	39	80	37	

Plot a stem and leaf diagram and find the mode, median and interquartile range.

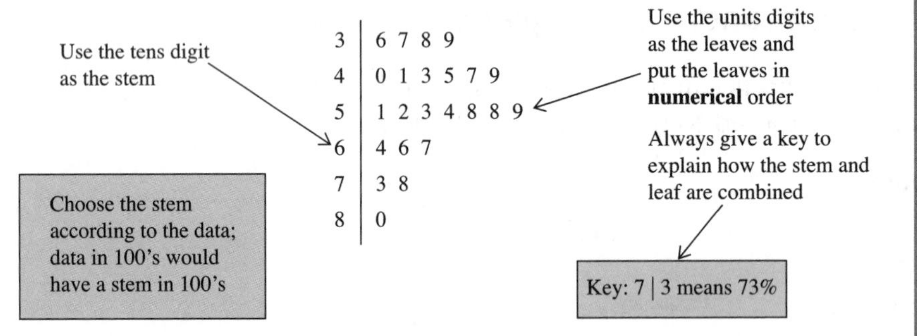

The trend shown is that in general students achieved a score below 60%.
Measures can found more easily from a stem and leaf diagram.

Mode	58%	Range 80 – 36 = 44%
Median	52%	data is in order; $\frac{1}{2}(23 + 1) = 12$, 12th value is median
LQ	41%	$\frac{1}{4}(23 + 1) = 6$, count up to 6th value for LQ
UQ	64%	count 6 values back from highest to find UQ
IQR	23%	IQR = UQ – LQ 64 – 41 = 23

Measures were explored in chapter 3

An ordered stem and leaf diagram shows all the data and the overall trend.

Measures found from an ordered stem and leaf diagram can be used to draw a box and whisker plot; refer back to page 74.

Back-to-back stem and leaf diagrams are used where you have two data sets to compare.

IQ scores for a class of girls and boys

Girls		Boys
5 4	9	9
9 7 7 6 1	10	3 6 7
8 7 4 2	11	2 4 6 8 9
	12	1 9

Key: 1 | 10 | 3 means 101 for girls, 103 for boys

In a back-to-back stem and leaf the data sets share a common stem.

The boys median IQ is higher than the girls median IQ; 114 compared with 107.
There is a greater range in IQ for the boys than for the girls; 30 compared to 24.
The IQR is the same for boys as for girls; both have IQR = 13.

Exercise 4C

1. The following scores were rolled with a dice.

   4 5 4 2 3 1 6 3 4

   Draw a dot plot and describe the trend shown.

2. The data gives the IQ scores of students in a school tutor group.

101	112	125	109	98	107	108	117	121	116	94
91	105	106	114	118	126	131	92	88	129	
89	116	103	108	127	110	117	104	119	133	

   (a) Draw a stem and leaf diagram to illustrate these data.
   (b) Find the median, UQ, LQ, highest and lowest value from your diagram and use them to draw a box and whisker plot.
   (c) Describe the skewness shown by your graph.

3. A survey of the number of lengths swum during the 'lane-swim only' session at a pool was carried out. These are the results.

32	23	28	21	12	18	16	33	39	42	13
50	47	31	33	25	19	26	16	14	10	15
35	23	21	37	35	40	30	10	48	10	40

   (a) Draw a stem and leaf diagram to illustrate these data.
   (b) Find the median, UQ, LQ, highest and lowest value from your diagram and use them to draw a box and whisker plot.
   (c) Describe the skewness shown by your graph.

4. The data gives the percentages achieved in two tests by the same sample of students.

Test A:	38	37	62	45	42	55	56	61	49	52
	47	58	43	51	44	56	41	44	53	
Test B:	65	72	57	79	66	48	53	54	41	75
	56	63	69	72	53	44	57	61	70	

(a) Draw a back-to-back stem and leaf diagram for these data.
(b) Find measures from both stem and leaf diagrams and use them to draw two box and whisker plots on the same axis.
(c) Write down a similarity and a difference between the two test results.

4.4 Discrete data: Step cumulative frequency diagrams

Using a step cumulative frequency diagram is a good way to display a large amount of discrete data. It can show trends as the data accumulates or grows.

Example

The table gives the number of objects remembered by 160 girls in a memory test.

Number of objects	5	6	7	8	9	10	11	12
Frequency	8	13	24	39	28	22	19	7

Construct a step cumulative frequency diagram.
First work out the cumulative frequency.

Number of objects	$\leqslant 5$	$\leqslant 6$	$\leqslant 7$	$\leqslant 8$	$\leqslant 9$	$\leqslant 10$	$\leqslant 11$	$\leqslant 12$
Cumulative Frequency	8	8 + 13 21	21 + 24 45	45 + 39 84	84 + 28 112	112 + 22 134	134 + 19 153	153 + 7 160

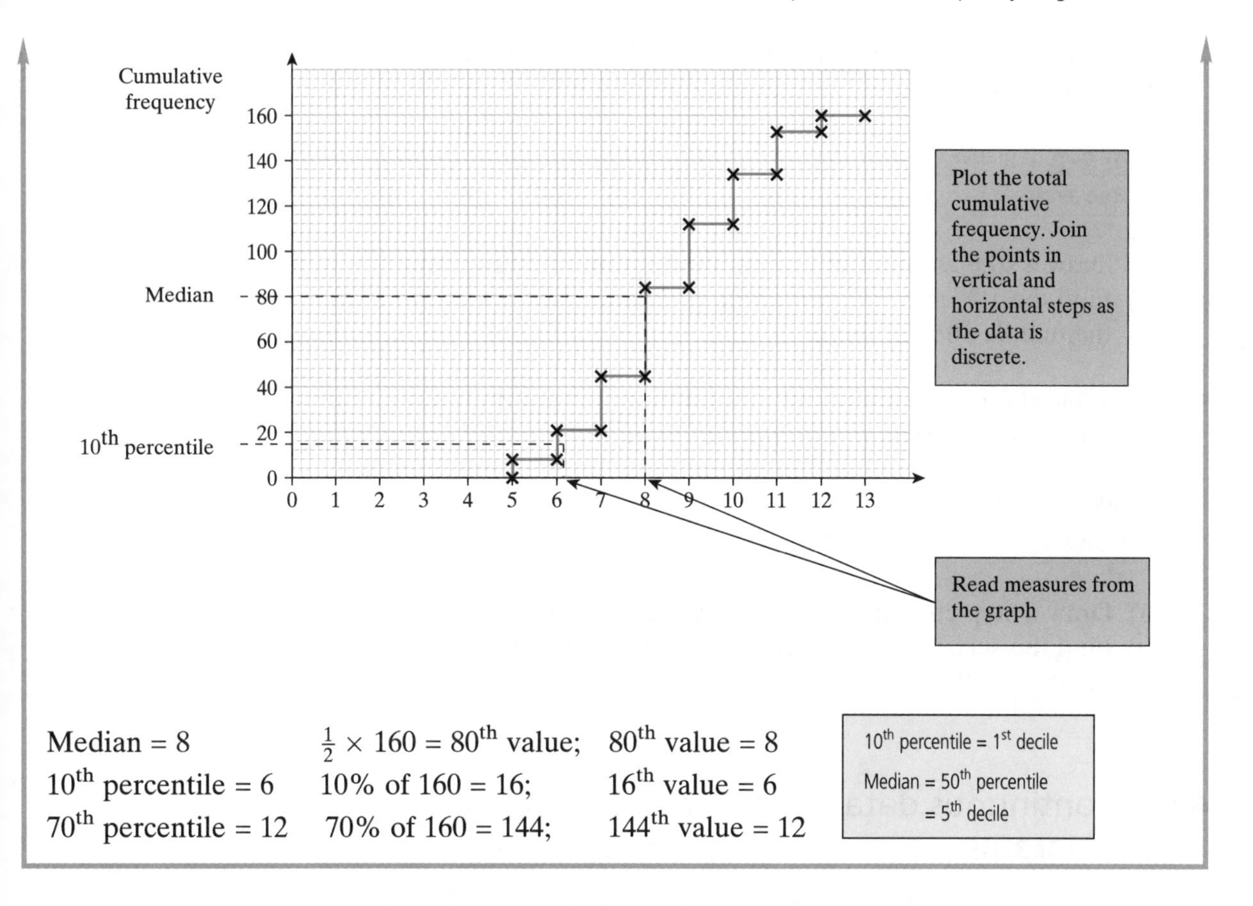

Median = 8 $\quad \frac{1}{2} \times 160 = 80^{th}$ value; $\quad 80^{th}$ value = 8

10th percentile = 6 $\quad$ 10% of 160 = 16; $\quad 16^{th}$ value = 6

70th percentile = 12 $\quad$ 70% of 160 = 144; $\quad 144^{th}$ value = 12

10th percentile = 1st decile
Median = 50th percentile
= 5th decile

Quartiles divide the data into 4 equal groups
Percentiles divide the data into 100 equal groups.
Percentiles are values at a percentage of the frequency.
Deciles divide the data into 10 equal groups.

An interpercentile or interdecile range is found in the same way as IQR range.
Interpercentile or interdecile range are used to analyse data excluding extreme values.

See page 116 for cumulative frequency graph to represent continuous data

Exercise 4D

1. A survey of the number of DVDs bought in one month is summarised in the table.

Number of DVDs bought	0	1	2	3	4	5	6	7
Frequency	2	12	27	18	8	6	4	3

(a) Draw a step cumulative frequency diagram for these data.
(b) Find the median and interquartile range for these data.

2. The table shows the number of GCSE grades A* to C achieved by students at a school.

Number of grades A*-C	2	3	4	5	6	7	8	9	10	11
Frequency	5	10	23	40	42	50	35	17	12	6

(a) Draw a step cumulative frequency diagram for these data.
(b) Find the 10th and 90th percentile and hence find the range of the middle 80% of the data.

3. The table shows the number of articles that contained reference to mathematics in newspapers across one week.

Number of articles	4	5	6	7	8	9	10	11	12
Frequency	12	15	13	11	8	6	3	0	2

(a) Draw a step cumulative frequency diagram for these data.
(b) Find the second and eighth decile and the interdecile range between these two deciles.

4.5 Continuous data: Cumulative frequency diagrams

Cumulative frequency diagrams display large amounts of continuous data.

Example

A survey of the heights of 120 boys is given in the table.
Draw a cumulative frequency diagram for this data.

Height, h cm	$145 \leqslant h < 150$	$150 \leqslant h < 155$	$155 \leqslant h < 160$	$160 \leqslant h < 165$	$165 \leqslant h < 170$
Frequency	8	27	48	31	6

First draw a cumulative frequency table:

Height, h cm	< 150	< 155	< 160	< 165	< 170
Cumulative frequency	8	8 + 27 = 35	35 + 48 = 83	83 + 31 = 114	114 + 6 = 120

Upper bound of each class

Add frequencies to get cumulative frequency (CF)

Then draw the diagram. Scale the x-axis and plot against cumulative frequency (CF):

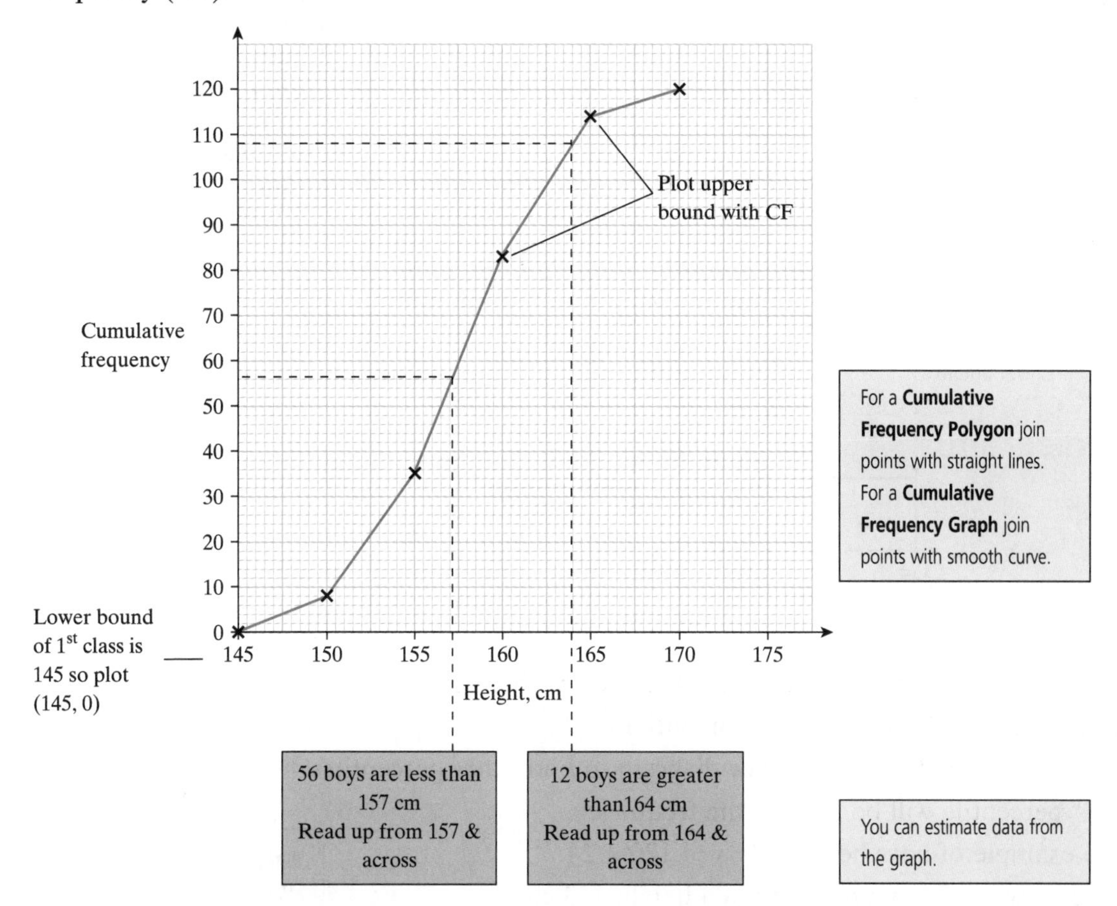

You can use the graph to find estimates of the median and quartiles, and then use these measures to draw a box and whisker plot.

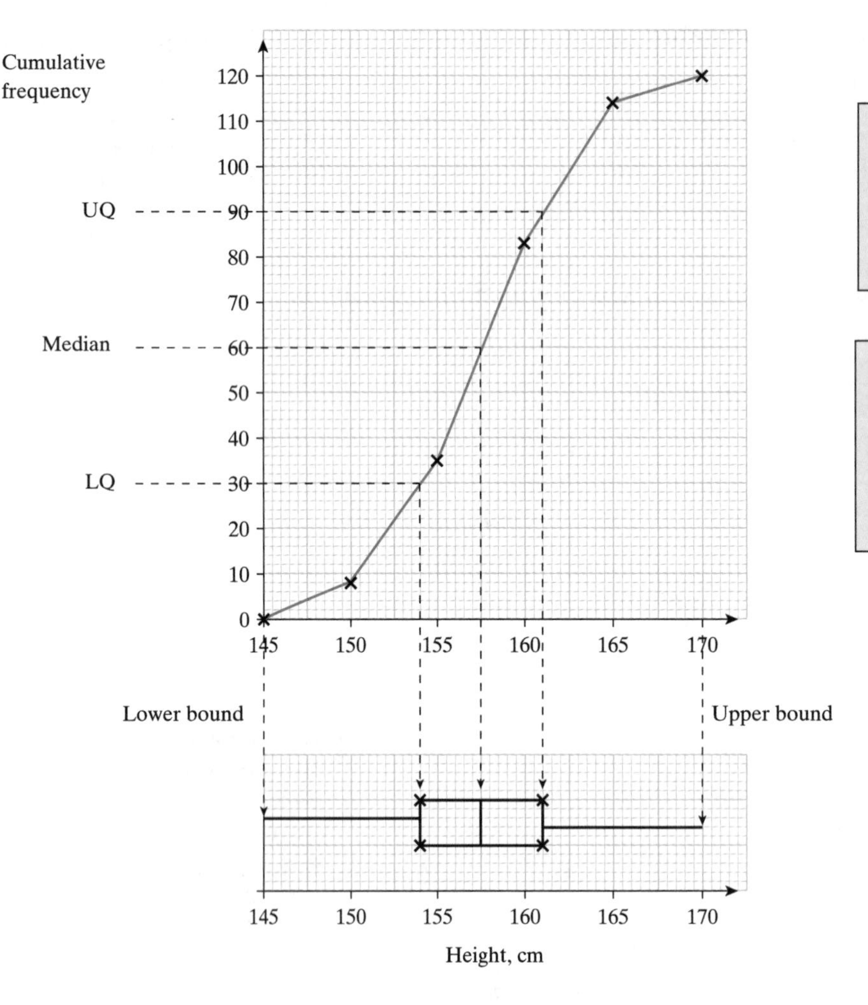

Data set is large so use $\frac{1}{2}$n and not $\frac{1}{2}$(n+1) to find median and quartiles.

Read estimates from the horizontal axis.

Use lower bound of 1st class and upper bound of last class as lowest value and highest value respectively unless actual values are given.

The lower quartile can also be described as the 25th percentile.
The upper quartile is also the 75th percentile.
You can use a cumulative frequency diagram to find other percentiles.
The 20th percentile will be 20% of the frequency.
For the example of boys heights 20% of 120 = 24
Reading across at 24 and down gives a height 153 cm.
This means 20% of the boys have height of 153 cm or less.

Alternatively: 80% of the boys are taller than 153 cm.

Exercise 4E

1. The graph shows the heights of a sample of girls.

   (a) Estimate from the diagram
      (i) the 20th percentile
      (ii) how many girls are less than 156 cm.

   (b) Use the graph to estimate
      (i) median; (ii) IQR

   In the example of the boys survey median = 157.5 cm; IQR = 12.

   (c) Use the data to draw a box and whisker plot.

   (d) Compare the heights of the girls and the boys in these two surveys.

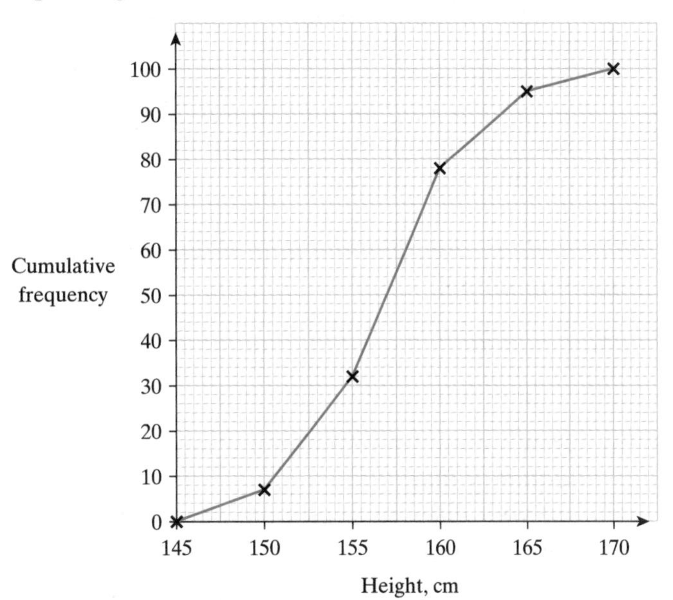

2. The table gives information about the heights of sunflowers growing in a field.

Height, h cm	$60 \leqslant h < 80$	$80 \leqslant h < 100$	$100 \leqslant h < 120$	$120 \leqslant h < 140$	$140 \leqslant h < 160$
Frequency	7	30	52	21	10

   (a) Copy and complete the cumulative frequency table.

Height, h cm	$h < 80$	$h < 100$	$h < 120$	$h < 140$	$h < 160$
Cumulative frequency					

   (b) Draw a cumulative frequency diagram.

   (c) (i) Use your diagram to estimate the median and interquartile range.
      (ii) Draw a box and whisker plot and comment on the skewness.

   (d) Estimate the number of sunflowers less than 90 cm.

   (e) Estimate the number of sunflowers greater than 130 cm.

   (f) Find an estimate of the (i) 20th percentile; (ii) 80th percentile.

   (g) Find an estimate of the interpercentile range between the 20th and 80th percentiles.

3. The table shows a summary of the data from a survey of the time taken for a group of students to complete a sudoku puzzle.

Time, t minutes	$0 \leqslant t < 10$	$10 \leqslant t < 20$	$20 \leqslant t < 30$	$30 \leqslant t < 40$	$40 \leqslant t < 50$	$50 \leqslant t < 60$
Frequency	4	11	29	37	27	12

(a) Draw a cumulative frequency table and hence a cumulative frequency diagram.
(b) Use your diagram to estimate the median and interquartile range.
(c) The same students were also timed completing a crossword puzzle. The median for this was 28 minutes and IQR 11 minutes. Write two comparisons between the times taken to complete the two puzzles.

4. The table summarises the time taken for sample of students to travel to school.

Time, t minutes	$0 \leqslant t < 10$	$10 \leqslant t < 20$	$20 \leqslant t < 30$	$30 \leqslant t < 40$	$40 \leqslant t < 50$	$50 \leqslant t < 60$
Frequency	9	27	42	30	20	12

(a) Draw a cumulative frequency table and hence a cumulative frequency diagram.
(b) Use your diagram to estimate the median and interquartile range.
(c) Find an estimate of the (i) 10th percentile; (ii) 90th percentile.
(d) Find an estimate of the interpercentile range between the 10th and 90th percentiles.

Activity

You can draw cumulative frequency diagrams using a suitable IT package, such as Autograph.
With the data from the questions above, the database in this book or your own data use IT to draw cumulative frequency graphs and from these graphs draw box and whisker plots (also using the IT package). Explore how the skewness of the data is reflected in the steepness of the cumulative frequency graph.

4.6 Continuous data: Grouped frequency diagrams

A grouped frequency diagram will display continuous data that has been grouped in equal class intervals.

The table shows the times taken, to the nearest minute, to complete a Sudoku puzzle.

Time, t minutes	$0 < t \leqslant 5$	$5 < t \leqslant 10$	$10 < t \leqslant 15$	$15 < t \leqslant 20$	$20 < t \leqslant 25$
Frequency	4	11	6	5	2

A grouped frequency graph is like a bar chart, but with the horizontal axis scaled and with no gaps between the bars as the data is continuous.
Modal class: $5 < t \leqslant 10$;
the highest bar.
Data shown by this graph has positive skew.

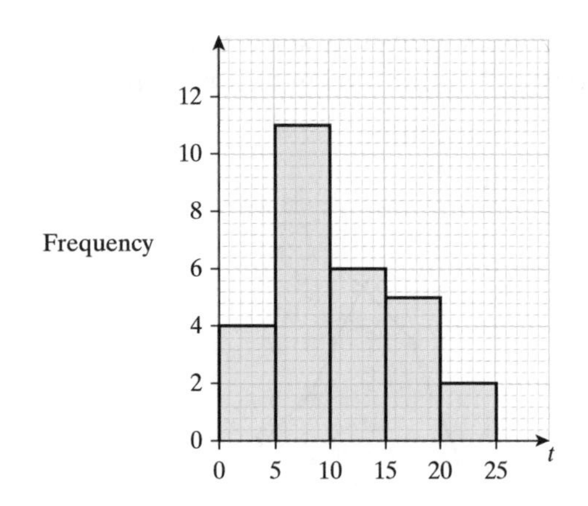

Instead of drawing bars to represent each class interval, plot the midpoint of the interval with the frequency, then join the points with straight lines.
This graph is called a **Frequency Polygon**.

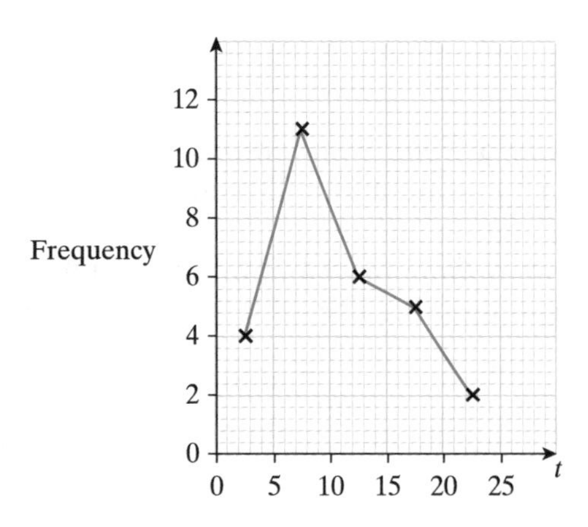

Exercise 4F

1. The tables show the ages of the first 100 people to visit a garden centre on a weekday and a Saturday.

Weekday

Age, a, years	Frequency
$0 < a \leqslant 20$	14
$20 < a \leqslant 40$	28
$40 < a \leqslant 60$	34
$60 < a \leqslant 80$	24

Saturday

Age, a, years	Frequency
$0 < a \leqslant 20$	22
$20 < a \leqslant 40$	48
$40 < a \leqslant 60$	17
$60 < a \leqslant 80$	13

(a) Draw frequency polygons for these data.
(b) Work out for each data set the:
(i) class which contains the modal age (ii) maximum possible range.
(c) Use your answers to (b) and make comparisons, with reasons, between the ages of people visiting the garden centre.

2. The frequency polygons show the number of miles Jayne travelled each day in her car during two months.

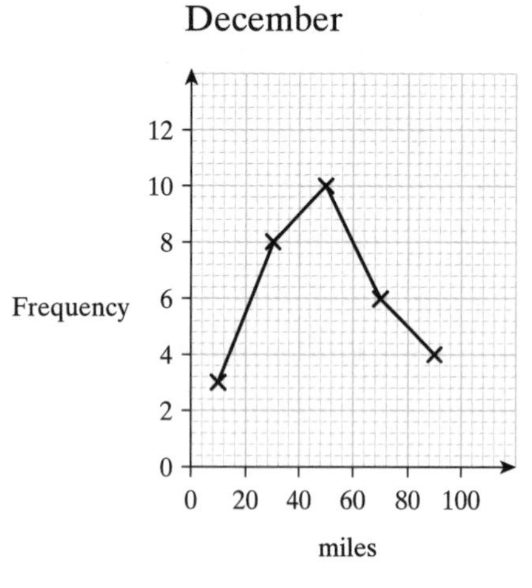

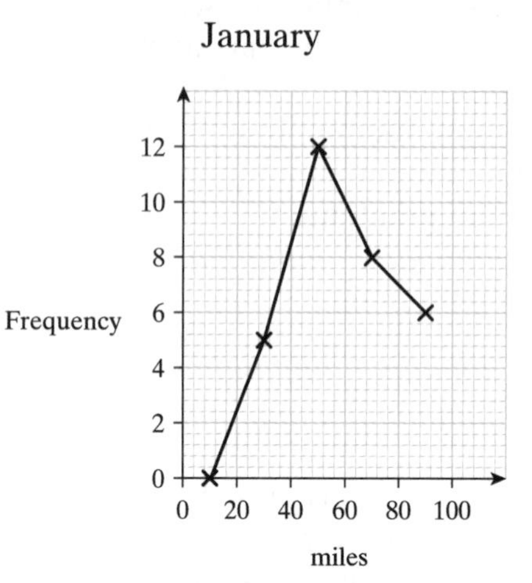

Make comparisons, with reasons, between the number of miles travelled by Jayne during December and January.

3. Clark kept a daily record of the time in minutes he used his phone during two months. The table summarises the data for July.

Time m, minutes	Frequency
$0 < m \leqslant 5$	6
$5 < m \leqslant 10$	11
$10 < m \leqslant 15$	10
$15 < m \leqslant 20$	4

(a) Draw a frequency polygon for these data.
(b) The frequency polygon below represents the data Clark collected for August.

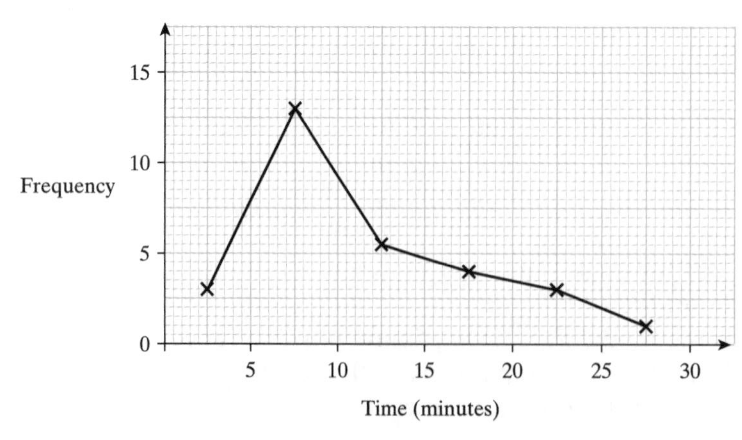

Write down one similarity and one difference for Clark's phone use during July and August.

4. Two different companies, Duracomp and Powerblast, claim that their batteries are the best ones to buy. The tables show the times that samples of batteries from these two companies lasted.

Duracomp	
Time, *t* hours	**Frequency**
$0 < t \leqslant 5$	8
$5 < t \leqslant 10$	6
$10 < t \leqslant 15$	7
$15 < t \leqslant 20$	5
$20 < t \leqslant 25$	0
$25 < t \leqslant 30$	4

Powerblast	
Time, *t* hours	**Frequency**
$0 < t \leqslant 5$	3
$5 < t \leqslant 10$	9
$10 < t \leqslant 15$	7
$15 < t \leqslant 20$	8
$20 < t \leqslant 25$	2
$25 < t \leqslant 30$	1

(a) Draw frequency polygons to represent these data.
(b) By finding appropriate measures, comment on the claims made by these two companies, giving reasons for your comments. Decide which of the two companies you would recommend buying from.

4.7 Continuous data: Histograms

A histogram displays continuous data given in unequal classes.

Example

The table gives the times taken, in seconds, for a group of nine year olds to complete a simple jigsaw puzzle.
Draw a histogram to display the data.

Time *t*, minutes	Frequency
$40 \leqslant t < 60$	6
$55 \leqslant t < 65$	9
$65 \leqslant t < 70$	15
$70 \leqslant t < 80$	23
$80 \leqslant t < 90$	12
$90 \leqslant t < 120$	12

Two classes have the same frequency, 12, but the width of class $90 \leqslant t < 120$ is three times bigger than class $80 \leqslant t < 90$. It would be misleading for both bars to be the same height. Class $70 \leqslant t < 80$ has the highest frequency, but this may not be the modal class as its width is bigger than other class widths.

A histogram represents frequency by the area of the bars.
Area of each bar (class width $\times$ bar height) is proportional to the frequency.

The bar height in a histogram is called the **Frequency Density**:

$$\text{Frequency density} = \frac{\text{frequency}}{\text{class width}}$$

Add columns to the table to work out the frequency density.

Time t, seconds	Frequency	Class width	Freq ÷ CW	Frequency density
$40 \leqslant t < 55$	6	15	6 ÷ 15	0.4
$55 \leqslant t < 65$	9	10	9 ÷ 10	0.9
$65 \leqslant t < 70$	15	5	15 ÷ 5	3
$70 \leqslant t < 80$	23	10	23 ÷ 10	2.3
$80 \leqslant t < 90$	12	10	12 ÷ 10	1.2
$90 \leqslant t < 120$	12	30	12 ÷ 30	0.4

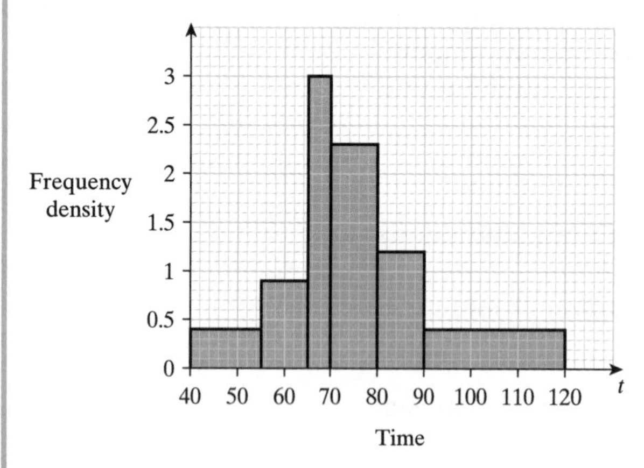

The area of each bar is equal to the frequency it represents.
The modal class is $65 \leqslant t < 70$.
It has the highest bar.
A histogram drawn for data with equal class widths has the same shape as a grouped frequency diagram.

The general shape of the distribution is seen by joining the midpoints of the tops of the bars in a histogram.
The narrower the bars the clearer the shape becomes.

Symmetrical distribution
This describes a distribution which is more or less symmetrical.

Real-life examples include …
- the lengths of leaves on a particular tree
- the heights of a random sample of people.

Positive skew
This describes a distribution with most of the data at the lower values.

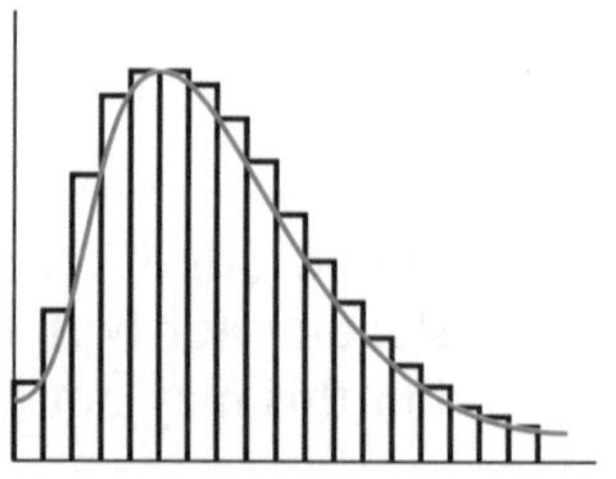

Real-life examples include …
- the age at which a sample of people first learned to read
- the heights of jockeys in a horse race.

Negative skew
This describes a distribution with most of the data at the higher values.

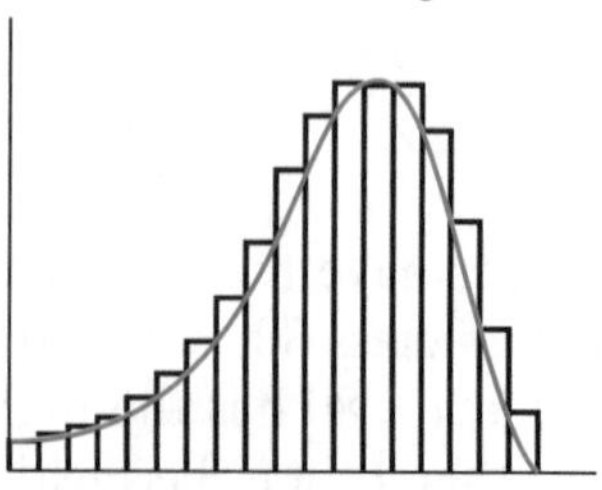

Real-life examples include …
- the age at which a sample of people had false teeth fitted
- the heights of players in a basketball team.

Exercise 4G

1. The table gives information about the reaction times of a sample of students.

Time, t, seconds	$1 \leqslant t < 3$	$3 \leqslant t < 4$	$4 \leqslant t < 5$	$5 \leqslant t < 6$	$6 \leqslant t < 9$
Class width					

Frequency	12	17	19	11	18
Frequency density					

(a) Copy and complete the table to calculate frequency density.
(b) Use your answers to draw a histogram to represent the data.
(c) Write down the modal class.
(d) Comment on the skewness shown by your graph.

2. The table gives information about time people spend walking their dog each day.

Time, t, minutes	$10 \leqslant t < 20$	$20 \leqslant t < 40$	$40 \leqslant t < 60$	$60 \leqslant t < 90$	$90 \leqslant t < 120$
Class width					
Frequency	8	16	28	39	9
Frequency density					

(a) Copy and complete the table to calculate frequency density.
(b) Use your answers to draw a histogram to represent the data.
(c) Write down the modal class.
(d) Comment on the skewness shown by your graph.

3. The incomplete table and histogram give some information about the weight, in grams, of a sample of pears.

Weight, g grams	Frequency
$120 \leqslant g < 140$	10
$140 \leqslant g < 150$	8
$150 \leqslant g < 155$	
$155 \leqslant g < 160$	
$160 \leqslant g < 165$	
$165 \leqslant g < 175$	16
$175 \leqslant g < 185$	12
$185 \leqslant g < 200$	6

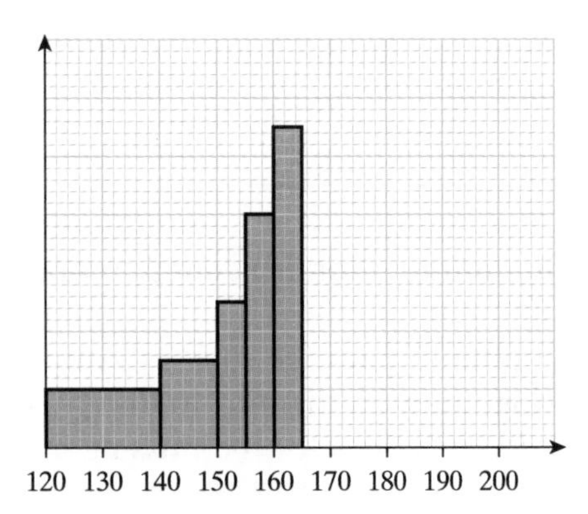

(a) Use the information in the histogram to copy and complete the table.
(b) Copy and complete the histogram.
(c) Write down the modal class.
(d) Comment on the skewness shown by your graph.

4. The incomplete table and histogram give some information about the time, in hours, a sample of light bulbs lasted.

Time, h, hours	Frequency
$0 \leqslant h < 1$	1
$1 \leqslant h < 4$	6
$4 \leqslant h < 8$	
$8 \leqslant h < 10$	
$10 \leqslant h < 12$	10
$12 \leqslant h < 13$	7
$13 \leqslant h < 15$	7
$15 \leqslant h < 20$	6

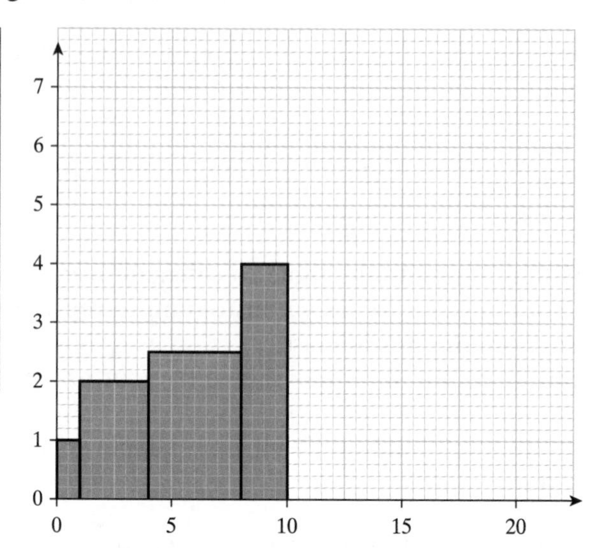

(a) Use the information in the histogram to copy and complete the table.
(b) Copy and complete the histogram.
(c) Write down the modal class.
(d) Comment on the skewness shown by your graph.

5. The table shows the percentage of unemployed of all economically active people in the UK in 2005.

Age	% Unemployed
16–19	38.8
20–24	19.3
25–34	9.4
35–49	6.6
50+	5.4

(a) What further information is needed to draw a histogram for these data?
(b) Using a suitable IT package such as Autograph, or by hand-drawing, draw histograms to display these data using different suitable values for the missing information.

4.8 Population pyramids

A population pyramid has the same shape as a back-to-back stem and leaf diagram with the stem showing age ranges and horizontal bars for the percentage or frequency in each age range.

This population pyramid shows the distribution of ages in Angola in 2005.

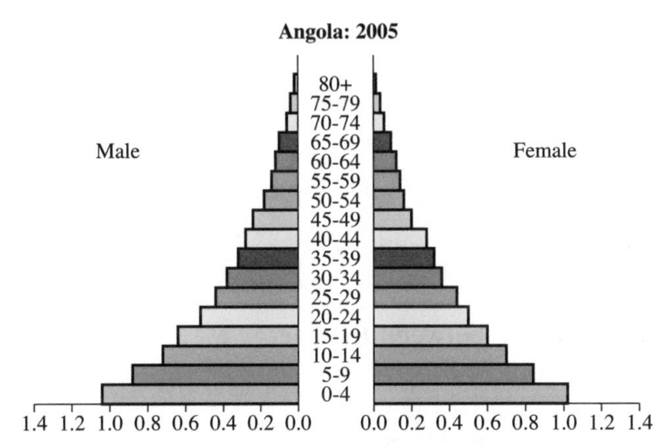

Source: U.S. Census Bureau, International Data Base.

Population is given either as raw data or as a percentage.
The age ranges have equal class widths.
The last age range does not always have an upper limit.

Population pyramids are usually drawn to show age distribution for a country or a region.

A population pyramid is used to compare distributions and inform future planning.

Activity

The last age range in the population pyramid for the population of Angola in 2005 is open-ended. What measures could you find from this graph?
What measures are you unable to find from the graph?
How could you calculate an estimate of the mean ages for males and females?

Exercise 4H

1. The table gives the percentage of population of Austria in 2002.

	Percentage of population	
Age	Male	Female
0–9	11.1	10.0
10–19	12.4	11.1
20–29	12.7	11.9
30–39	17.8	16.4
40–49	15.5	14.2
50–59	12.2	11.6
60–69	9.9	10.3
70–79	6.2	8.9
80+	2.3	5.5

(a) Draw a population pyramid for this data.
(b) Write down one similarity and one difference between the age distribution of men and women in Austria in 2002.

2. The table gives the percentage of population of Bangladesh in 2002.

	Percentage of population	
Age	Male	Female
0–9	22.8	22.6
10–19	25.6	25.8
20–29	18.3	18.8
30–39	12.5	13.0
40–49	9.3	9.3
50–59	6.1	5.5
60–69	3.4	3.1
70–79	1.6	1.4
80+	0.5	0.4

(a) Draw a population pyramid for this data.
(b) Write down three questions that could be answered by studying this graph.

3. Compare the distribution of the populations of Austria and Bangladesh in 2002 using your graphs from questions 1 and 2.

4. The population pyramids show the percentage distribution of ages in Brazil and Kenya in 2006.

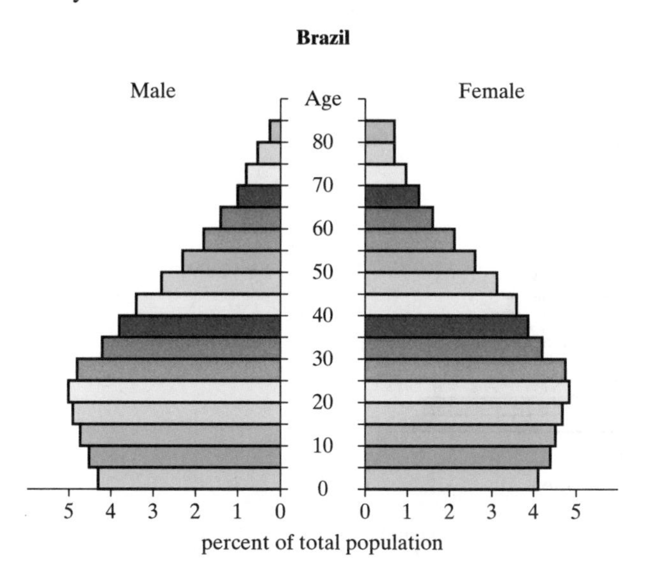

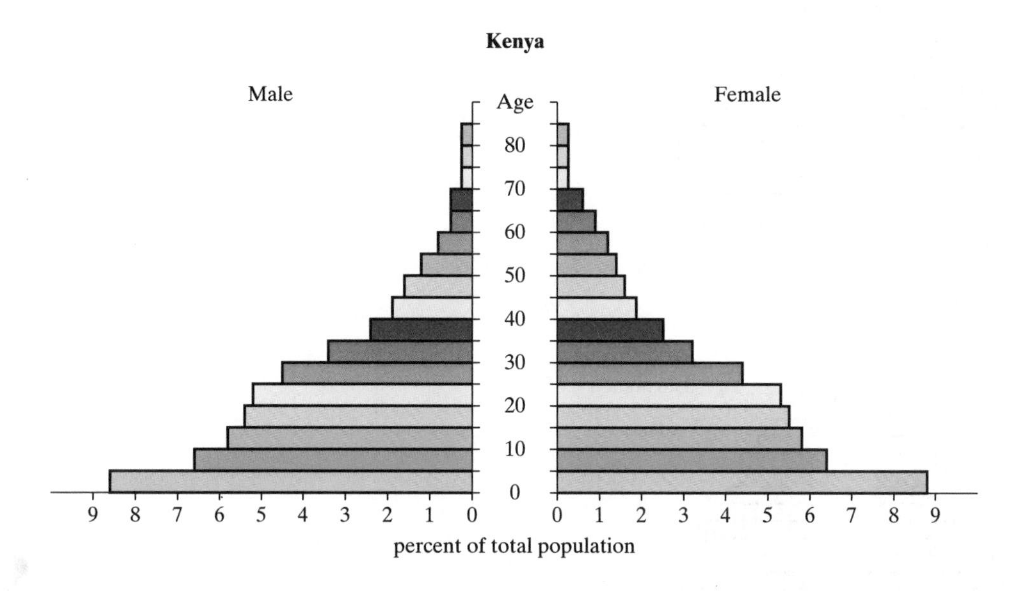

Write down one difference and one similarity shown by these graphs.

5. These population pyramids show the population structure by percentage of the population for the United Kingdom in 1891, 1951 and 2001.

Population structure of the UK

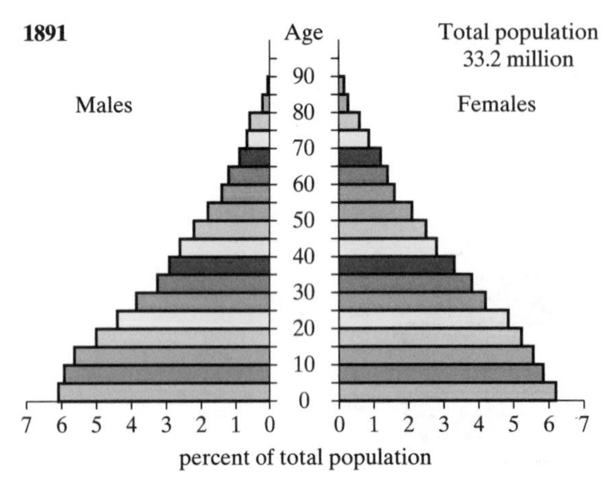

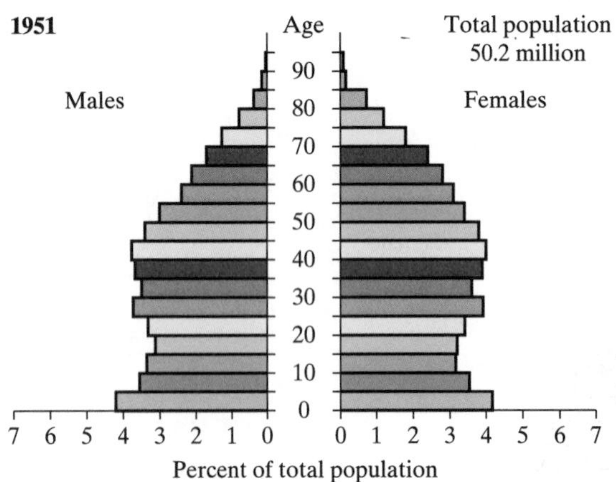

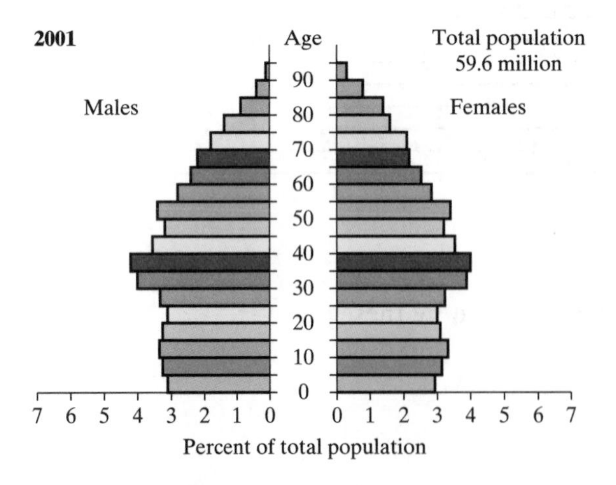

Write about the changes in population in the United Kingdom between 1891, 1951 and 2001 that is shown by these graphs.

4.9 Choropleth maps

A choropleth map is a thematic map widely used by geographers. In a choropleth map areas are shaded to show differences. For example in population density, income from tourism, land use such as forest cover and food produced, and many other variables. The shading ranges from light to dark in proportion to the density of the variable.

Example

The map shows employment in tourism in 2000. What proportion of the workforce work in tourism in London?

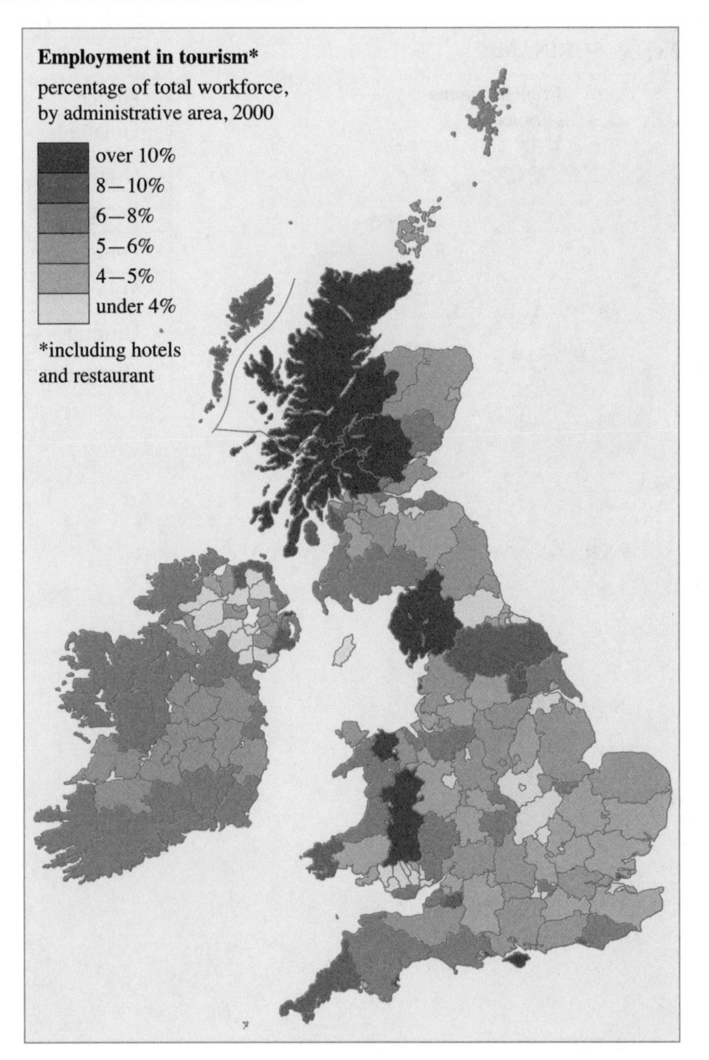

The darker shaded areas show that a greater percentage of the workforce have employment in tourism.
The map shows a greater percentage of the workforce work in tourism in Scotland and Cumbria. In London 5–6% of the workforce work in tourism.

Example

The table shows the population density per km in South America in 2006.
Use the table to colour a choropleth map.

Population density/km^2	0–9	10–19	20–29	30–39	40–49
Shading					

Country	Population density/km^2
Argentina	14.4
Bolivia	8.2
Brazil	22.0
Chile	21.3
Colombia	38.3
Ecuador	47.5
French Guiana	2.2
Guyana	3.7
Paraguay	16.0
Peru	22.0
Suriname	3.1
Uruguay	19.2
Venezuela	28.2

To complete the key choose one colour, shade the lowest population density lightly and the highest population density the darkest, with the others increasing in between. Use the information in the table to shade the countries in the map to match your key.

> Choropleth maps are a visual way to see variation across a geographic area.
> Variation within areas are hidden: the smaller the area the more accurate the map.
> The map can sometimes give an impression of sudden change at a boundary.

Exercise 4I

1. The map shows ethnic minority groups as a percentage of population in different areas of the United Kingdom.

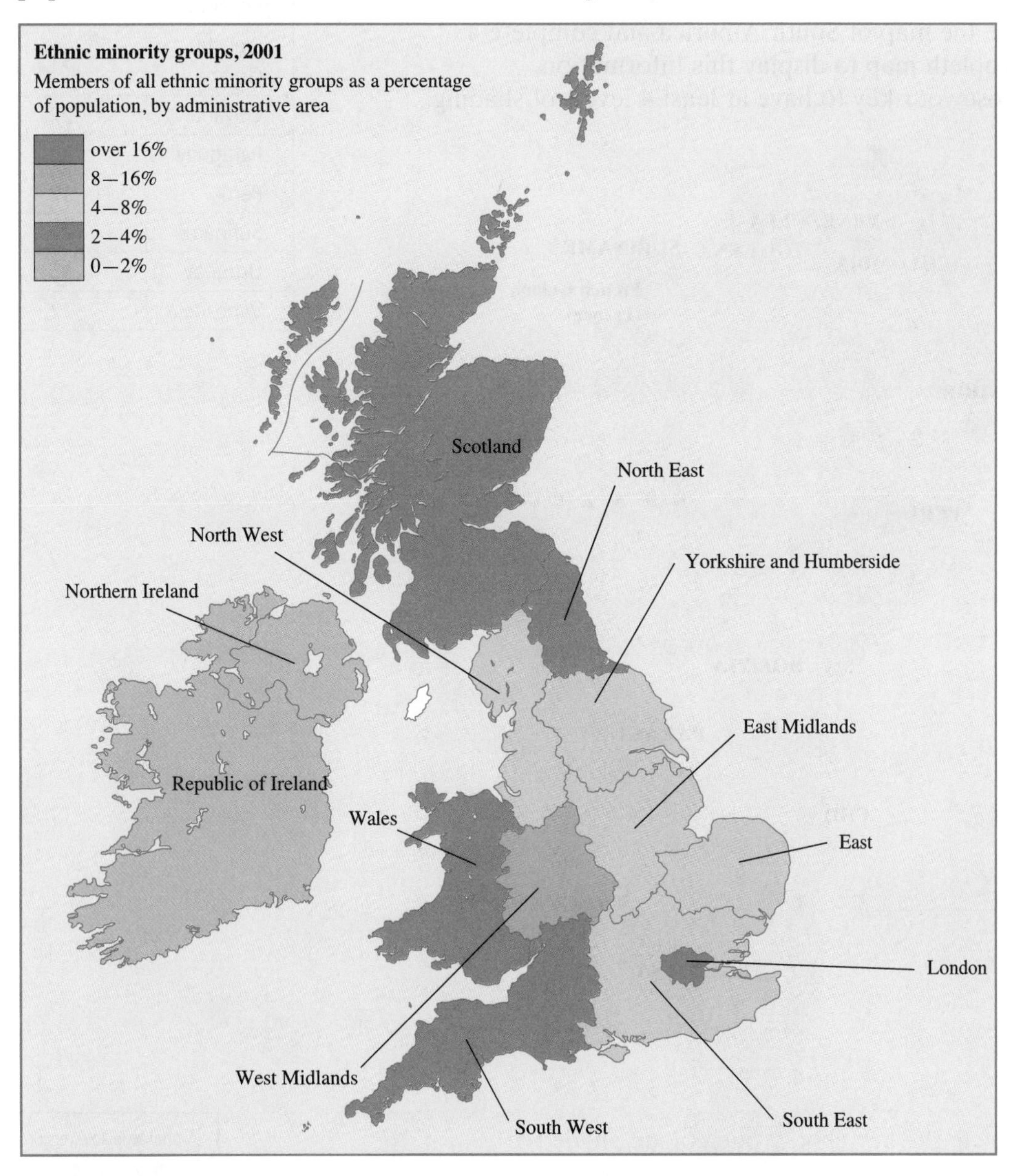

(a) In which area is the percentage of ethnic minority groups the greatest?
(b) What percentage of the population is in an ethnic minority in Northern Ireland?

2. The table shows the number of births per 1000 of the population in 2004 in South America.

Country	Births /1000 of population
Argentina	18
Bolivia	31
Brazil	21
Chile	16
Colombia	20
Ecuador	27
French Guiana	31
Guyana	22
Paraguay	22
Peru	19
Suriname	21
Uruguay	15
Venezuela	22

Trace the map of South America and complete a choropleth map to display this information. Choose your key to have at least 4 levels of shading.

A photocopiable version of this map can be found at the back of the book.

3. The table shows the population density per km^2 for some European countries in 2006.

Country	Population density/km^2
Albania	124.1
Bosnia	88.2
Bulgaria	66.7
Croatia	78.9
Hungary	107.5
Macedonia	80.8
Moldova	126.5
Romania	93.7
Serbia	114.8
Slovakia	110.2
Slovenia	100.0

A photocopiable version of this map can be found at the back of the book.

Trace the map of Europe and complete a choropleth map to display this information.
Choose your key to have at least 4 levels of shading.

Summary of key points

- Qualitative data is represented by pictograms, all types of bar charts and pie charts.
- Discrete data is represented by bar charts, pie charts, stem and leaf diagrams and cumulative step polygons.
- Continuous data is represented by stem and leaf diagrams, cumulative frequency diagrams, frequency polygons and histograms.
- You can move from one representation to another, such as cumulative frequency to box and whisker plot.
- The shape of a distribution shows skewness
- Population pyramids allow comparisons of a population, often by gender.
- Choropleth maps show proportions across an area by the density of shading.

Links to the Real World

In the world of statistics, graphs display the relationship between variables or show the spread of a given variable or phenomenon. They summarize and communicate information.

Graphs are effective visual tools because they present information quickly and easily. Information can often be better understood when presented in graphical form than by a table because a graph can reveal trends in the data and allow easy comparisons between data sets. For this reason graphs are commonly used by print and electronic media in every field of commerce and industry.

Choropleth maps are used to show differences across and between countries for many diverse variables such as coronary heart disease and education provision. They are frequently seen at election time showing actual voting patterns across the country and how voting patterns have changed since the previous election.

Revision Exercise 4

1. The pictogram shows the number of loaves of sliced bread sold during one week at the baker's shop.
The section on thin sliced loaves has been left blank.

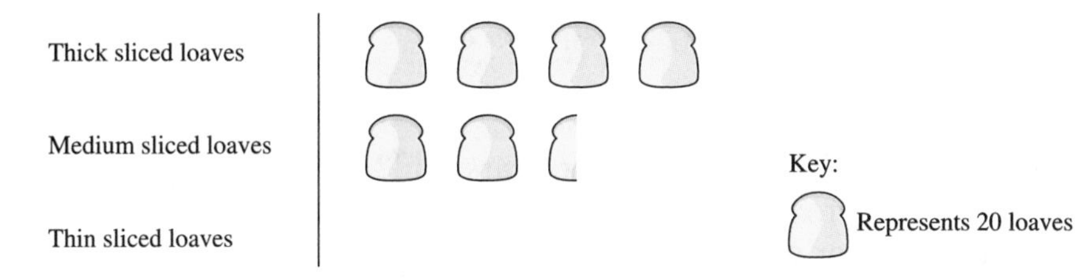

(a) How many thick sliced loaves were sold?
(b) How many medium sliced loaves were sold?
(c) The baker sold 60 thin sliced loaves.
Draw the pictogram for thin sliced loaves.
(d) Work out the total number of loaves sold. [AQA]

2. Fifteen teams took part in a quiz.
Their scores are as follows:

81	64	75	70	68
78	74	69	76	72
62	82	53	75	69

(a) Draw an ordered stem and leaf diagram to illustrate these data.
(b) Find the median and quartiles of the scores.
(c) Draw a box and whisker plot to illustrate these data. [AQA]

3. The time, in minutes, to the first goal in 140 football league matches is given in the table below. At least one goal was scored in each match.

(a) Draw a histogram to represent the data.
(b) Describe the skewness of the data.
(c) Which measures of location and dispersion would be preferred for this data?
Give reasons for your choice. [AQA]

Time, t	Number of matches
$0 < t \leqslant 10$	24
$10 < t \leqslant 20$	33
$20 < t \leqslant 25$	22
$25 < t \leqslant 35$	23
$35 < t \leqslant 45$	10
$45 < t \leqslant 60$	6
$60 < t \leqslant 75$	13
$75 < t \leqslant 90$	9

4. The pictogram shows the numbers of cars sold by a garage in 2002.

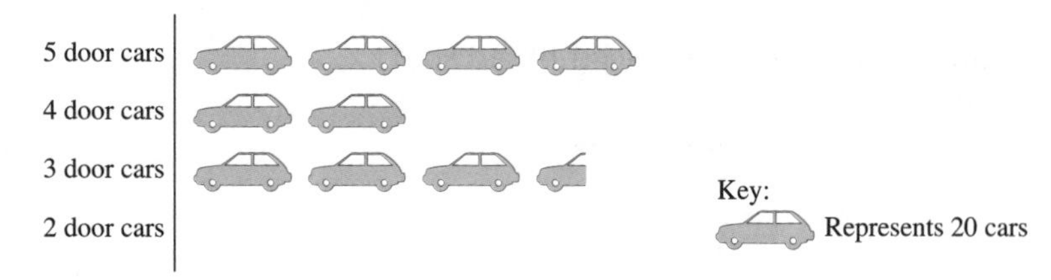

(a) How many 5 door cars were sold?
(b) What was the total number of 3 door and 4 door cars sold?
(c) The garage sold fifteen 2 door cars.
Draw the pictogram for 2 door cars.
(d) A pictogram was drawn to show the sale in 2003. The same key was used. The total number of cars sold was shown by 17 complete symbols and a half symbol. Find the total number of cars sold in 2003. [AQA]

5. An electrical store keeps a record of the number of toasters, kettles and irons sold each year.
The numbers for 2001 and 2002 are shown in the multiple bar chart.

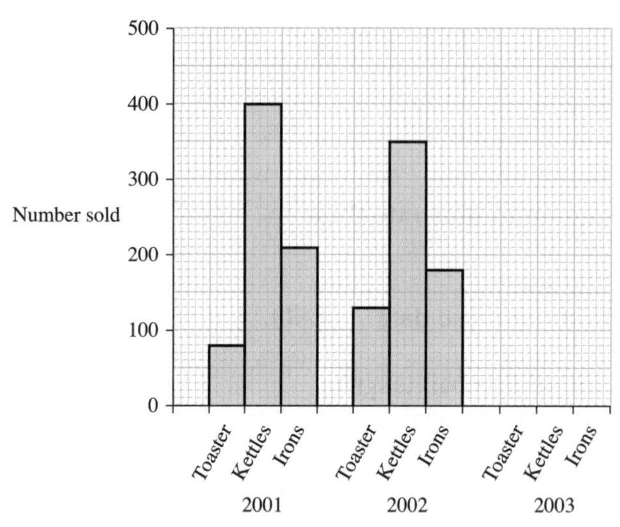

(a) The numbers sold in 2003 were

Toasters	150
Kettles	500
Irons	110

Copy the axes and draw the multiple bar chart for 2003.
(b) (i) How many toasters were sold in 2001?
(ii) How many **more** kettles were sold in 2003 than in 2002?
(c) Describe **two** changes in the pattern of sales from 2001 to 2003. [AQA]

6. A survey of 50 boys and 50 girls recorded the time they spent using the school computers last week.
The time spent, t (hours) by each of the **boys** is given in the following table.

Time spent, t (hours)	Frequency
$1 \leqslant t < 2$	1
$2 \leqslant t < 3$	4
$3 \leqslant t < 4$	5
$4 \leqslant t < 5$	9
$5 \leqslant t < 6$	12
$6 \leqslant t < 7$	16
$7 \leqslant t < 8$	3

The frequency polygon below shows the times for the 50 **girls**.

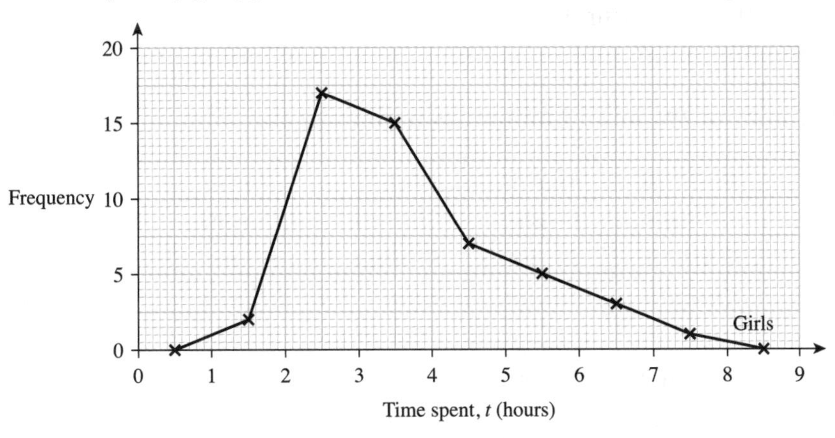

(a) Draw a frequency polygon for the **boys**' times on a copy of the same graph.
(b) What is the modal class for the **boys**' times?
(c) Write down
 (i) the number of **boys** who spent less than 4 hours last week using the school computers,
 (ii) the number of **girls** who spent less than 4 hours last week using the school computers.
(d) Describe the skewness of the **girls**' distribution. [AQA]

7. The number of pupils in each unit area of a playground is shown below.

2	3	4	8	9	7	8	4
3	4	8	10	12	14	10	7
3	7	9	8	13	15	12	8
0	1	4	7	8	10	6	3
0	0	3	2	4	2	1	0

(a) Copy and complete the choropleth map using the given key.

Number of pupils	
0–5	
6–10	(dotted)
11–15	(black)

(b) There is a teacher in the playground.
Where do you think the teacher is? [AQA]

8. The length of reign of each of the last 19 monarchs is given in the table.

George VI	16 years	George IV	10 years	James II	3 years
Edward VIII	0 years	George III	60 years	Charles II	25 years
George V	26 years	George II	33 years	Charles I	24 years
Edward VII	9 years	George I	13 years	James I	22 years
Victoria	64 years	Anne	12 years	Elizabeth I	45 years
William IV	7 years	William III	14 years	Mary	5 years
				Edward VI	6 years

(a) Represent the data in an ordered stem and leaf diagram.
(b) Find the median and quartiles of the length of reign of these 19 monarchs.
(c) Write down the name of any monarch whose length of reign is an outlier.
You **must** show calculations to support your answer.
(d) The box and whisker plot shows the length of reign of the last 19 popes.

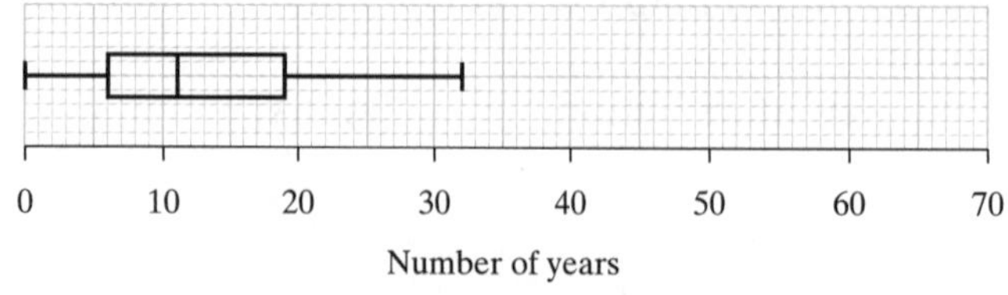

Draw a box and whisker plot for the length of reign of the last 19 monarchs on a copy of the same diagram.
(e) Compare the length of reign of monarchs and popes. [AQA]

9. The pie chart shows the number of people attending a league football match.

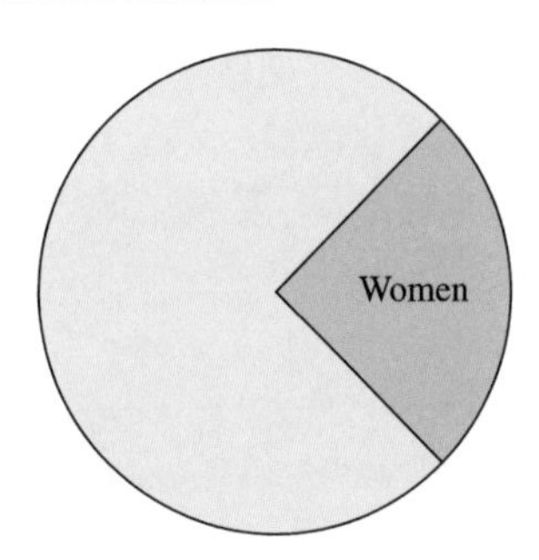

The total number of people attending the match was 15110.
The sector representing the number of women attending the match is labelled.
The angle of this sector is 78.6 degrees.

(a) Calculate the number of women attending the match.
(b) The number of men at the match was 8275 and the remainder were children.
Copy and complete the pie chart.
(c) The radius of the pie chart is 4 cm.
The radius of a comparative pie chart for an international football match is 8.2 cm.
Calculate the number attending the international football match. [AQA]

10. The frequency table gives the length, in mm, of 150 earthworms.
The earthworms range from 80 to 195mm in length.

Length, l (mm)	Frequency
$l < 100$	6
$100 \leqslant l < 120$	16
$120 \leqslant l < 130$	27
$130 \leqslant l < 135$	20
$135 \leqslant l < 140$	17
$140 \leqslant l < 150$	32
$150 \leqslant l < 160$	16
$160 \leqslant l < 180$	12
$180 \leqslant l$	4

(a) Draw a cumulative frequency polygon for these data.
(b) Find an estimate of the interpercentile range between the 10th and 90th percentiles using the graph you have drawn.
(c) Write one advantage of using the interpercentile range that you found in part (b) instead of the full range? [AQA]

11. The choropleth map (shading map) shown population changes in ten districts of a large city between 1991 and 2001.

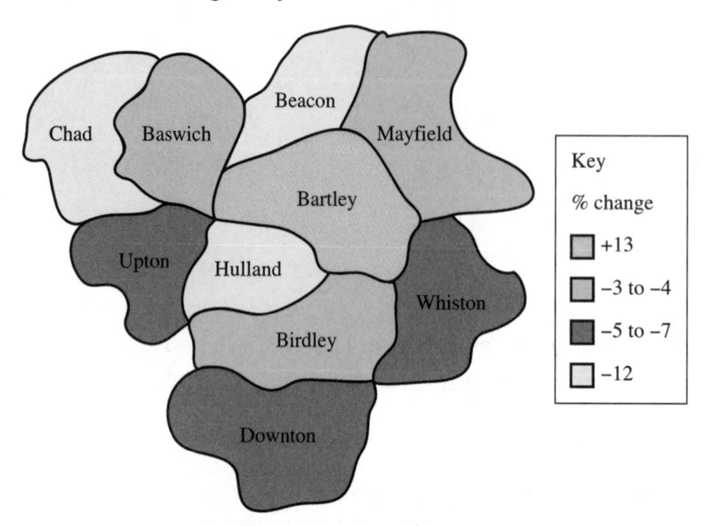

(a) In which district has there been the largest population change?
(b) How many districts show a decrease in population of 5% or more? [AQA]

12. As part of a school project, Paul carried out 2 surveys of the ages of passengers using his local train service.
The surveys were undertaken at 10 am and 5 pm on a Tuesday.
There were 100 passengers in each survey.

The results for the 10 am survey were as follows.

Age, x (years)	Frequency	Cumulative frequency
$0 \leqslant x < 10$	14	14
$10 \leqslant x < 20$	41	
$20 \leqslant x < 30$	13	
$30 \leqslant x < 40$	19	
$40 \leqslant x < 50$	9	
$50 \leqslant x < 60$	4	

(a) Complete the cumulative frequency column.
(b) Draw a cumulative frequency polygon for these data.
(c) Use your diagram to estimate
(i) the median
(ii) the lower quartile
(iii) the upper quartile.
(d) The youngest passenger was 3 years old.
The oldest passenger was 57 years old.
Find the range.

(e) Paul drew a box and whisker plot for the 5 pm survey.

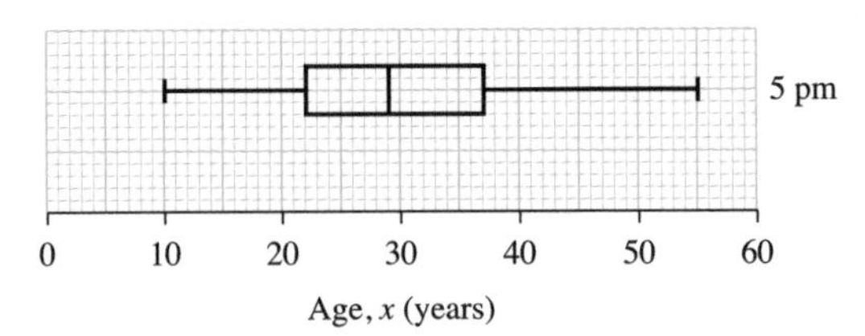

(i) Draw a box and whisker plot for the 10 am survey on a similar grid.

(ii) Write down **two** differences between the ages of passengers in the two surveys. [AQA]

13. 120 boys were given a memory test.
They were presented with 20 random words and given a short time to memorise them. They then had to write down as many words as they could remember.
The table gives the number of boys that recalled the given number of words.

Number of words recalled	Number of boys
8	3
9	0
10	8
11	18
12	22
13	27
14	18
15	18
16	6

(a) Draw a cumulative frequency step polygon for these data.

(b) Find the median, the second and eighth deciles and calculate the interdecile range between these two deciles.

(c) 120 girls were also given the same memory test. Their results are summarized as

Median	12
Second decile	10
Eighth decile	16

Compare the memory test results of the boys and girls. [AQA]

14. The weights, w (grams), of 125 grapefruit are summarized in the table.

Weight, w (grams)	Frequency
$160 \leqslant w < 180$	8
$180 \leqslant w < 190$	15
$190 \leqslant w < 200$	30
$200 \leqslant w < 210$	35
$210 \leqslant w < 220$	X
$220 \leqslant w < 240$	Y
$240 \leqslant w < 260$	Z

Part of a histogram is drawn to represent this data.

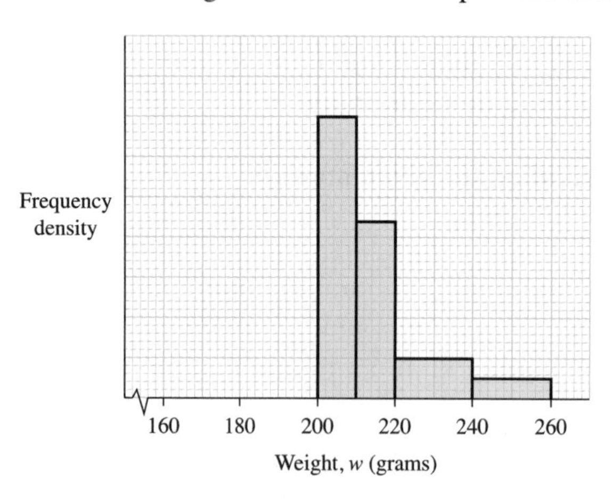

(a) Write a scale for the frequency density axis.
(b) Calculate the value of
  (i) X (ii) Y (iii) Z
(c) Copy and complete the histogram.
(d) Calculate an estimate of the median weight. [AQA]

15. Gareth owns several games that need batteries.
He can buy batteries from two companies, Powerus or Longlast.

Gareth wants to find out how long the batteries last from the two companies.
The frequency polygon shows how long the Powerus batteries lasted.

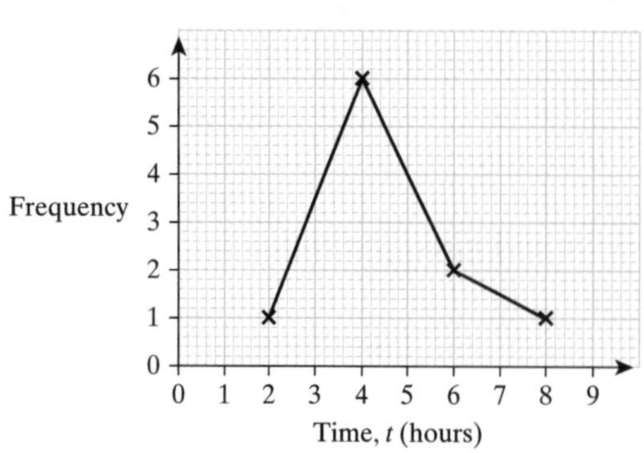

The table shows how long the Longlast batteries lasted.

Time, t (hours)	$1 \leqslant t < 3$	$3 \leqslant t < 5$	$5 \leqslant t < 7$	$7 \leqslant t < 9$
Frequency	1	3	5	1

(a) On a copy of the axes draw a frequency polygon to represent these data.
(b) Use these results to decide which batteries Gareth should use. Given a reason for your answer. [AQA]

16. The population pyramids show the distribution of the population of Angola by age and gender for 2000 and a prediction for 2050.

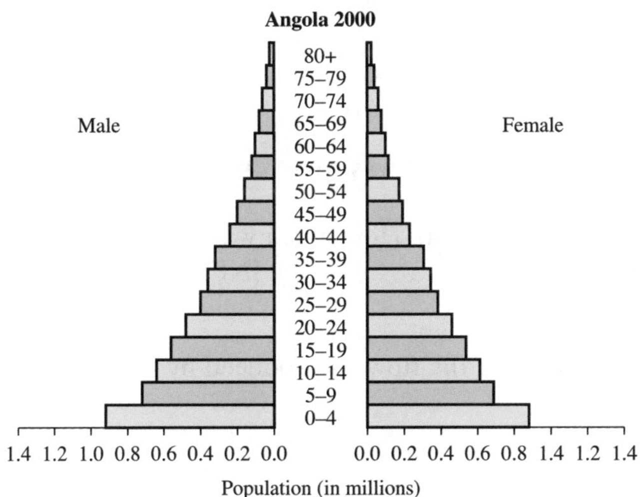

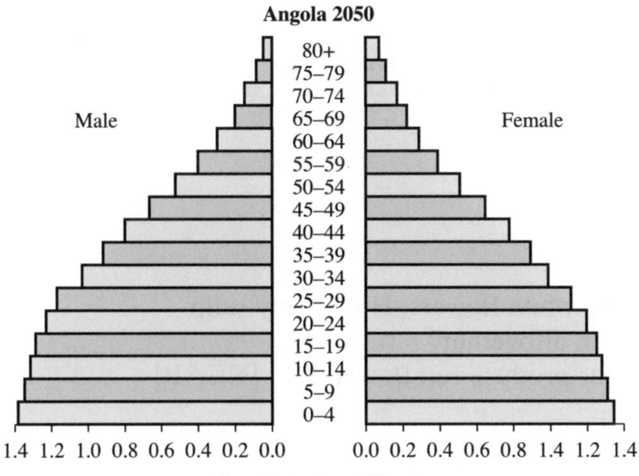

(a) Give one difference between the population for 2000 and the prediction for 2050.
(b) In the 2050 prediction which male age group will have approximately half of the number in the 30–34 male age group?
(c) Estimate the difference between the female population aged 10–14 for 2000 and the predicted value for 2050. [AQA]

17. The diagram below shows how a large company spent its advertising budget in 1996.

Advertising Budget for 1996

Newspapers 55%
Television
Direct mail 10%
Others 8%
0 20 40 60 80 100%

NOT DRAWN TO SCALE

(a) What percentage of the advertising budget was spent on television advertising?
(b) The total advertising budget was £400 000. How much was spent on newspaper advertising? [NEAB]

18. The pie chart below shows the colours of the flowers produced by the tulip bulbs planted in a garden.

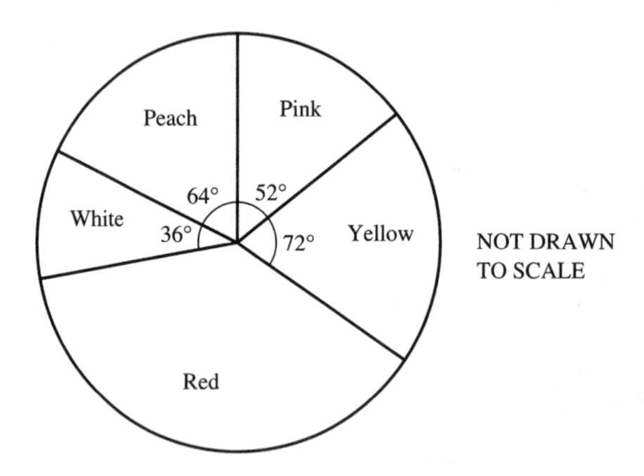

(a) There are 9 bulbs producing white flowers. How many tulip bulbs are there in the garden altogether?
(b) How many of the tulip bulbs produce red flowers? [NEAB]

19. The diagrams below show the percentage of the whole population of the United Kingdom by age and sex for the years 1901 and 1991.

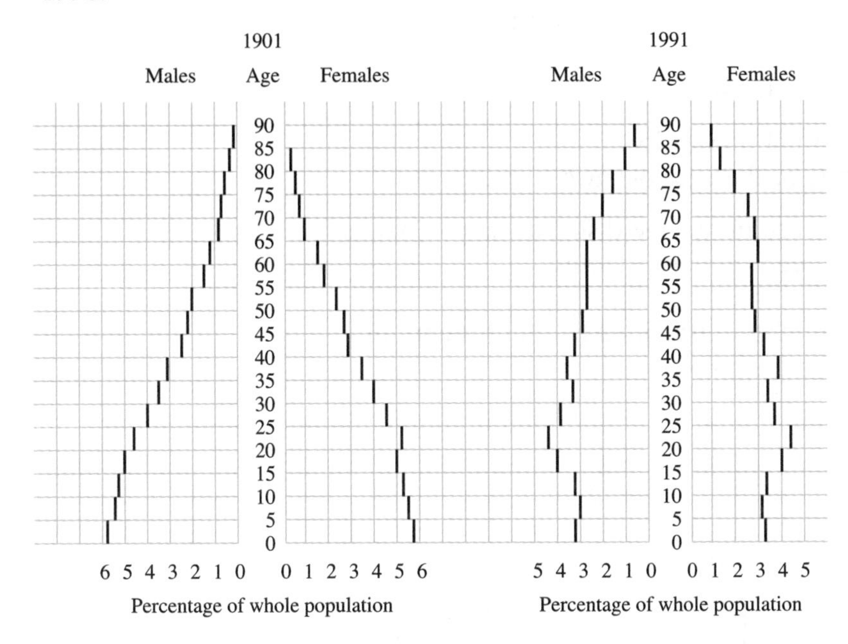

Source: Adapted from *Annual Abstract of Statistics 1992.*

(a) (i) In 1901, what percentage of the population was male and under 15 years?

(ii) In 1991, what percentage of the population was female and in the age group 20 to 40 years?

(b) (i) Comment on the differences in the age structure of the population between 1901 and 1991.

(ii) Give a reason for these differences.

(c) Compare the percentages of males and females aged 60–90 years in 1991. [NEAB]

20. The population pyramid shows the ages, in years, of 6000 people in town X.

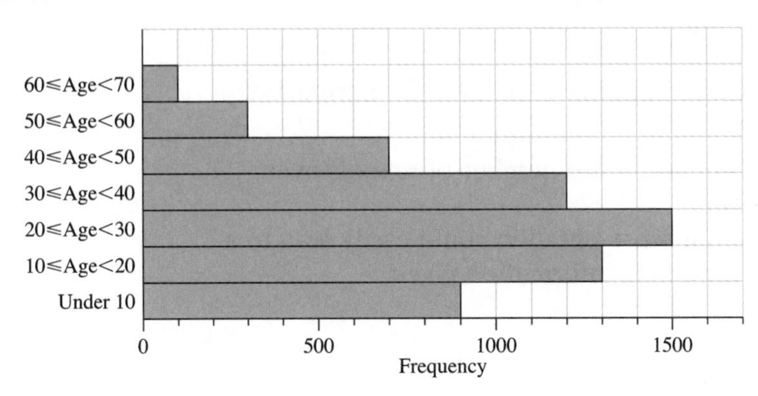

(a) How many people are between 20 and 40 years of age?
(b) List the frequencies for each age interval.
(c) Draw a cumulative frequency curve for age.
(d) Use your cumulative frequency curve to find
  (i) the median age,
  (ii) the interquartile range.

Town **Y** has a similar total population.
The interquartile range of the ages of town **Y** is 30.

(e) Explain **one** difference in the age distribution you would expect to find between these two towns. [SEG]

21. Information about the schools provided by the Ministry of Defence is shown in the diagram.

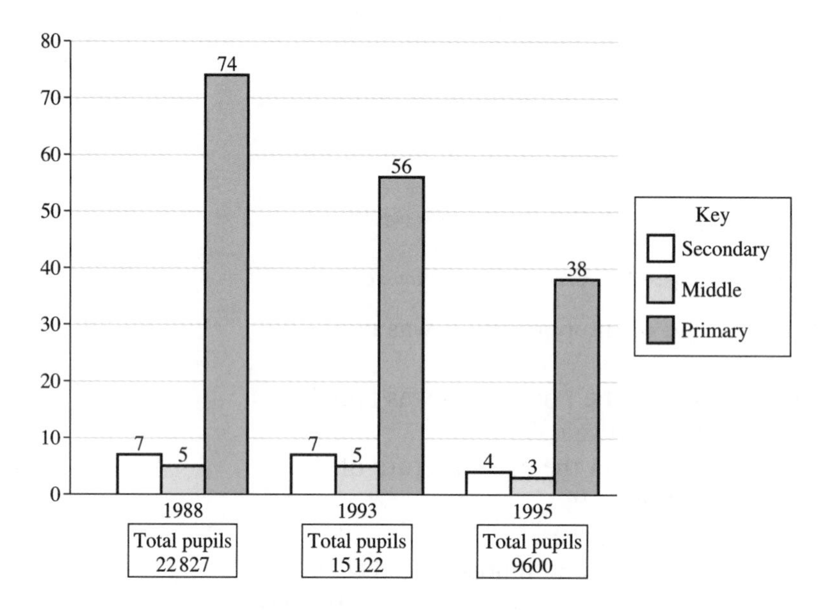

(a) How many schools did the Ministry of Defence provide in 1988?
(b) Calculate, to the nearest whole number, the average number of pupils per school for the year 1995.

The rate of decline in the number of schools over the period 1988 to 1993 was 3.6 schools per year.

(c) Calculate the rate of decline in the number of schools over the period 1993 to 1995.
(d) Explain how the pictorial representation could easily lead to a misinterpretation of the actual information given.

22. Each month 240 people do some work for charity. The pie chart represents the time, t, spent by these people on their charity work.

$6 < t \leqslant 8$
$0 < t \leqslant 2$
120
60
$4 < t \leqslant 6$
$2 < t \leqslant 4$

(a) (i) Copy and complete the frequency table for these data.

	Time, t (hours)	Frequency
	$0 < t \leqslant 2$	
	$2 < t \leqslant 4$	
	$4 < t \leqslant 6$	
	$6 < t \leqslant 8$	

(ii) Draw a bar graph to represent this information.

This graph shows the time spent on charity work by a different sample of 240 people.

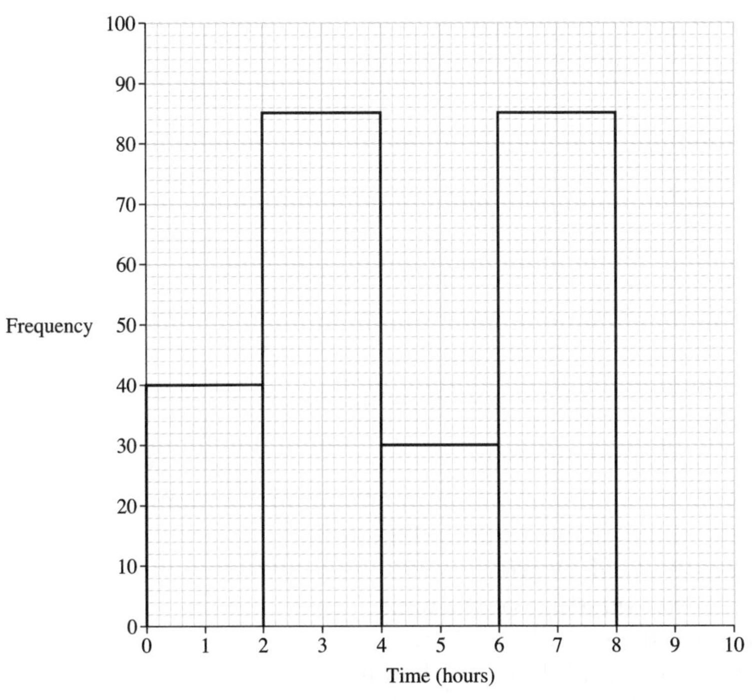

(b) Make **one** comment on the difference between the time spent on charity work by these two groups of people. [SEG]

23. A sample of 27 commuters were asked to record the number of times they travelled to work by rail over a six-month period.

The numbers recorded were as follows.

48	40	59	54	71	60	42
35	42	63	61	54	69	81
36	47	50	46	73	71	64
28	35	45	63	75	56	

(a) Construct a stem and leaf diagram of this information, ensuring that the figures on the leaves are in order of size.
(b) Use your diagram to find
  (i) the median,
  (ii) the interquartile range. [NEAB]

24. This diagram shows the cumulative distribution of times, in minutes, of the lengths of a sample of 100 telephone calls made from a City office.

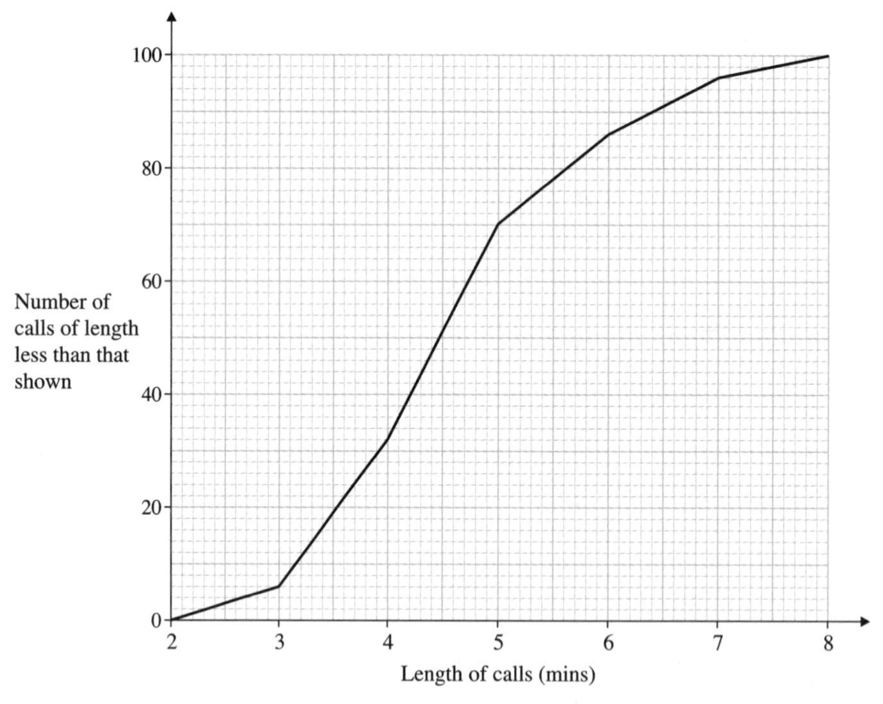

Use the diagram to:
(a) Find the number of calls of less than 6 minutes length.
(b) Estimate the median length of calls made.
(c) Estimate the upper and lower quartiles of the data.
(d) Estimate the time exceeded by 60% of the calls.
(e) Find the probability that any two of these one hundred calls chosen at random each exceeded 5 minutes in length. [NEAB]

25. The table shows the marks achieved in a Mathematics test for 23 candidates.

43	51	65	73	84	55	39	44
23	78	43	49	27	44	36	56
54	48	56	55	67	67	55	

(a) Represent these data in a stem and leaf diagram.
(b) Use your stem and leaf diagram to obtain values for
  (i) the median,
  (ii) the lower and the upper quartiles.
(c) Represent these data on a box and whisker diagram.

The same candidates took an English test.
The table below shows a summary of their results.

Lowest mark	32
Lower quartile	49
Median mark	56
Upper quartile	63
Highest mark	71

(d) Make **two** comments comparing the Mathematics and English test results. [SEG]

26. The bills for a household in January 1999 are shown below.

Gas	Electricity	Council tax	Telephone
£101	£72	£95	£60

The total of the four bills was £328.

(a) Draw a pie chart to illustrate these data.

The bills for January 2000 are shown below.

Gas	Electricity	Council tax	Telephone
£108	£75	£102	£72

The diameter of the pie chart for the year 1999 is 9.6 cm.

(b) Calculate the diameter of the comparative pie chart for the year 2000.

27. The cumulative frequency curve represents the times taken to run 1500 metres by each of the 240 members of the athletics club, Weston Harriers.

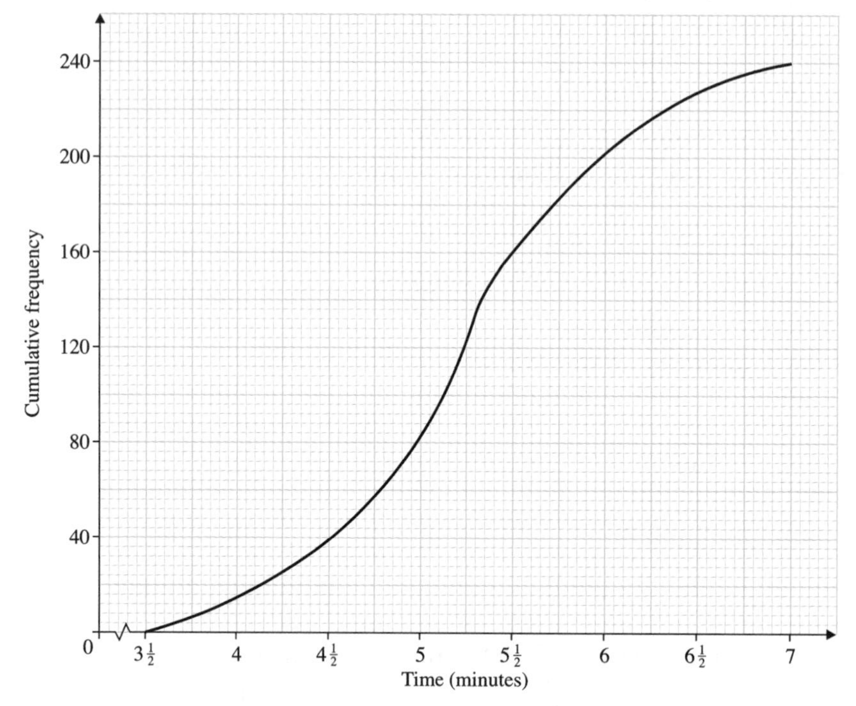

(a) From the graph, find
  (i) the median time,
  (ii) the upper quartile and the lower quartile.

(b) Draw a box and whisker diagram to illustrate the data.

(c) Use your box and whisker diagram to make **one** comment about the shape of a histogram for these data.

A rival athletics club, Eastham Runners, also has 240 members. The time taken by each member to run 1500 metres is recorded and these data are shown in the following box and whisker diagram.

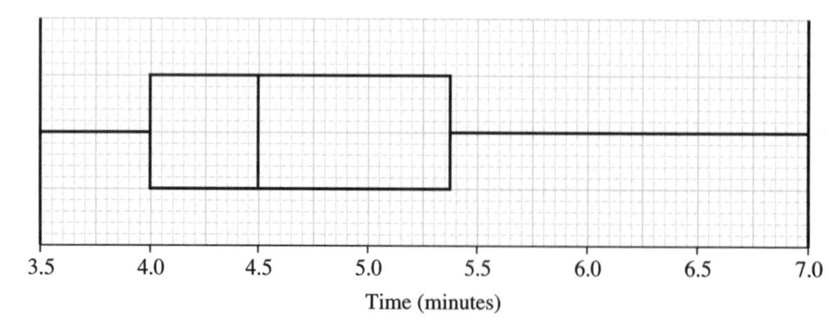

(d) Use this diagram to make **one** comment about the data for Eastham Runners as compared with that for Weston Harriers. [SEG]

28. The diagram represents the response times to the ringing of the telephone in an office.

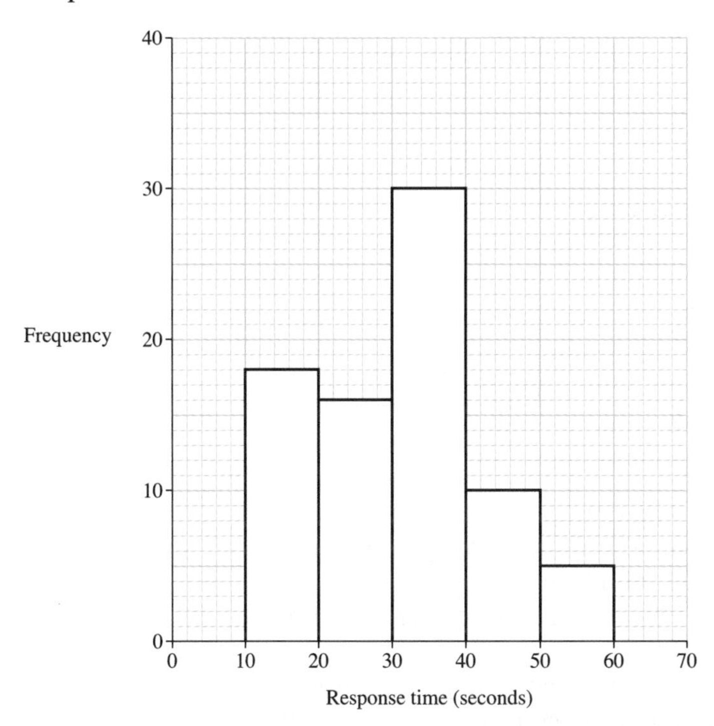

(a) Use the diagram to construct the cumulative frequency table for these response times.
(b) Draw a cumulative frequency polygon.
(c) Obtain an estimate for the interquartile range of these response times.

Six months later a similar survey of response times gave an interquartile range of 10 seconds.

(d) What does this new value suggest about the change in the distribution of response times at this office? [SEG]

29. The prices paid for houses sold in a town in 1988 are shown in the table below.

House price	£30 000–	£50 000–	£60 000–	£70 000–	£100 000–	£120 000–£150 000
Number sold	2	9	14	51	8	6

(a) Construct a histogram for these data.
(b) By taking the midpoints of each class interval: 40 000, 55 000, 65 000, . . . etc, calculate an estimate of the mean and the standard deviation of the prices paid for houses in this town in 1988.

The histogram below shows the number of houses sold in the same town in 1991.

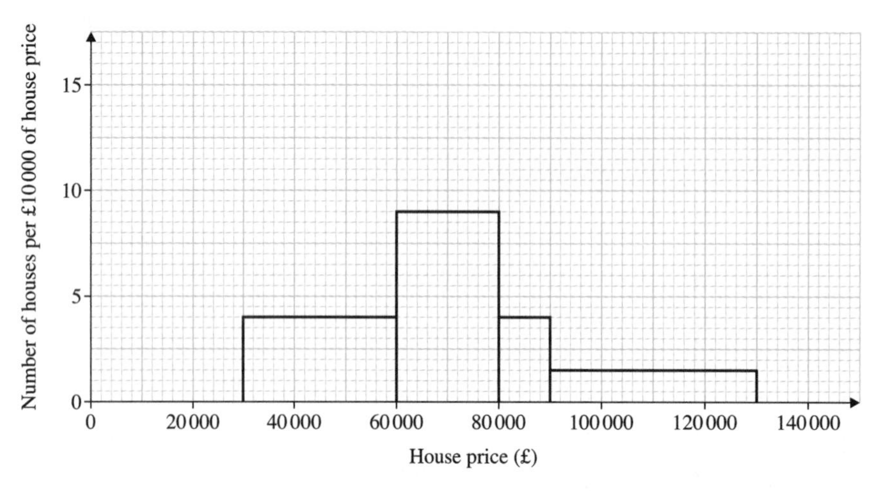

(c) How many houses were sold in 1991?

(d) The mean and standard deviation of the prices paid for houses in 1991 were £70 000 and £21 200 respectively.

(i) In which year, 1988 or 1991, did the greater variation in sale prices occur?

(ii) Calculate the difference in the mean sale price of houses in 1988 and in 1991 as a percentage of the 1988 mean sale price.

(e) Give one reason why houses may not be cheaper in 1991 than in 1988. [SEG]

30. In an attempt to devise an aptitude test for applicants seeking work on a factory's assembly line, it was proposed to use a simple construction puzzle. The times taken to complete the task by a random sample of 90 employees were observed with the following results.

Times to complete the puzzle (seconds) x	Number of employees	Cumulative frequency
$10 \leqslant x < 20$	5	5
$20 \leqslant x < 30$	11	
$30 \leqslant x < 40$	16	
$40 \leqslant x < 45$	19	
$45 \leqslant x < 50$	14	
$50 \leqslant x < 60$	12	
$60 \leqslant x < 70$	9	
$70 \leqslant x < 80$	4	

(a) Copy and complete the table.

(b) Construct a cumulative frequency polygon for this data.

(c) Identify from this polygon:

(i) the median (Q_2),

(ii) the upper quartile (Q_3),

(iii) the lower quartile (Q_1).

(d) (i) Calculate a value for $(Q_3 - Q_2)$ and for $(Q_2 - Q_1)$.
(ii) What do these show about the shape of the distribution?

(e) It is decided to grade the applicants on the basis of their times taken, as good, average or poor.
The percentages of applicants in these grades are to be approximately 15%, 70% and 15%, respectively.

Estimate, from your cumulative frequency polygon, the grade limits. [NEAB]

31. The table shows the total number of goals scored in 165 hockey matches.

(a) Draw a cumulative **step** polygon for these data.

(b) Use your graph to find:
(i) the second decile,
(ii) the eighth decile.

(c) How many games resulted in a total score **completely** within the middle 60% of the total scores? [SEG]

Number of goals	Number of matches
0	10
1	15
2	21
3	35
4	25
5	20
6	16
7	11
8	12

32. The time taken, in seconds, by 120 students to complete a puzzle is given in the following table.

Time (s)	Frequency
$20 \leqslant t < 30$	38
$30 \leqslant t < 40$	44
$40 \leqslant t < 60$	20
$60 \leqslant t < 80$	14
$80 \leqslant t < 100$	4

(a) Draw a cumulative frequency graph of the data.

(b) Use the cumulative frequency graph to obtain estimates of:
(i) the median,
(ii) the interquartile range.

(c) Calculate an estimate of the mean and standard deviation of the times.

(d) Why, in this case, are the median and interquartile range better measures than the mean and standard deviation? [SEG]

5 Representation of bivariate data

Statistics are no substitute for good judgement
Henry Clay (1777–1852)

The bigger the car, the more petrol it uses but the fewer miles per gallon it will do.

This unit will show you how to

- ✦ Draw and interpret scatter diagrams
- ✦ Draw and use lines of best fit
- ✦ Interpolate and extrapolate data from diagrams
- ✦ Draw scatter diagrams for non-linear data
- ✦ Calculate Spearman's coefficient of rank correlation
- ✦ Interpret Product Moment Correlation Coefficient.

Before you start

You should be able to answer these questions

1 Draw a graph with x-values from 0 to 6 and y-values from 0 to 5.
Plot and join the points (2, 1), (6, 1), (4, 5). What shape is this?

2 Find the mean of 17.1, 34.8, 27.1, 8.9 and 22.5.

3 Find the equations of these straight lines.

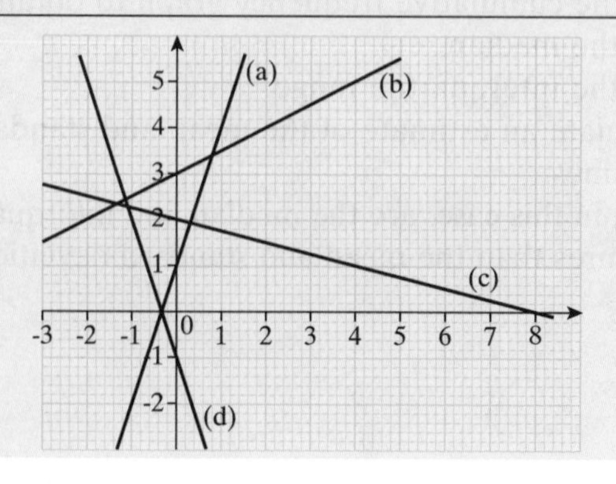

In a survey or experiment you may collect data on more than one variable. For example height, weight, arm span, head circumference, and so on. Bivariate data consists of two items of data collected from every sample and it can be analysed in different ways.

5.1 Scatter diagrams

A **scatter diagram** shows the relationship between two variables.
To draw a scatter diagram you plot points on a graph.

Example

Martin made and sold ice-cream and he wanted to predict how much he needed to make each day.
He believes he sells more when the weather is hotter.
He recorded the maximum temperature and the ice-cream sales every day for eight days.
His results are summarized in the table.

Temperature (°C)	16	15	18	14	21	25	23	24
Sales in £s	75	65	80	60	100	145	130	135

Draw a scatter diagram of this data.
Do you agree with Martin's claim?

Plot the points: (16, 75) (15, 65) (18, 80) (14, 60) (21, 100) (25, 145) (23, 130) (24, 135)

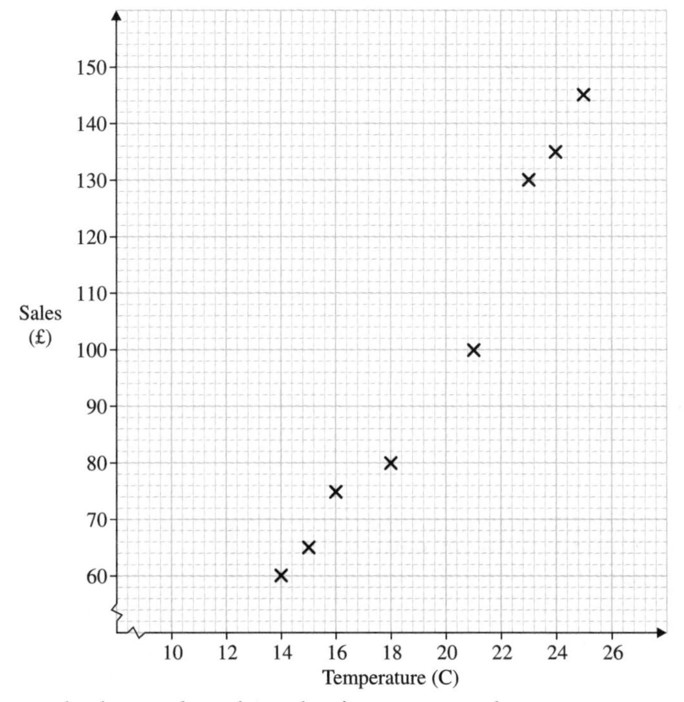

Martin can use the graph to predict sales depending on the temperature.
You can see how to do this in section 5.3.

The graph shows that the sales increase as the temperature increases so, yes, Martin's claim seems correct.

Recognizing correlation

You use a scatter diagram, or scattergraph, to investigate if there is a link, or **correlation**, between two variables.

On a scatter diagram:

If one variable increases as the other variable increases then there is **positive correlation**.

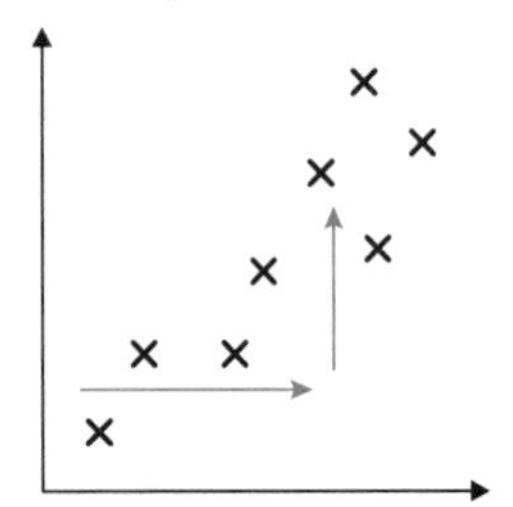

If one variable decreases as the other variable increases then there is **negative correlation**.

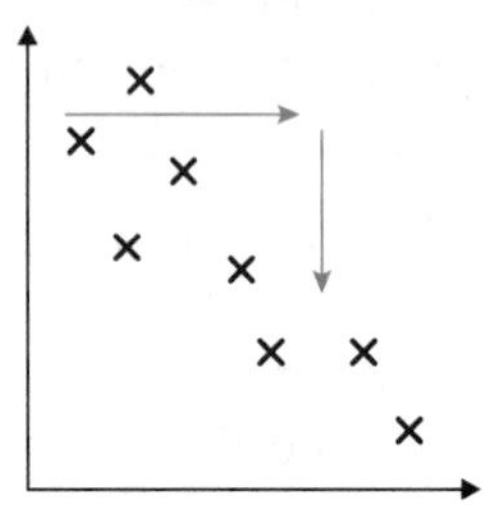

Martin's data showed positive correlation.

There is no correlation when the points are scattered showing no pattern.

For example, Martin asked the age of every child who bought ice-cream.

He plotted his data on a scattergraph:

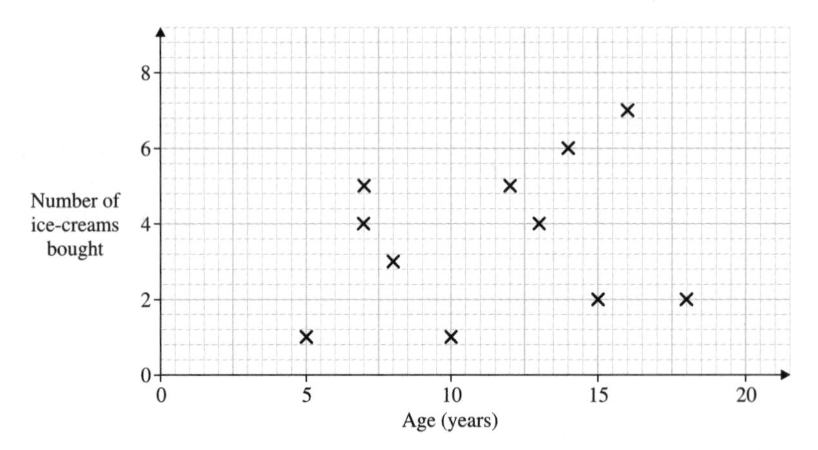

The points are scattered with no pattern. This shows there is no link between the age of a person and the number of ice-creams they buy. There is no correlation.

> On a scatter diagram, if the plotted points do not show any pattern then there is no correlation between the variables.

Exercise 5A

For questions 1–3 choose the most appropriate scatter diagram for the situation: A, B or C.

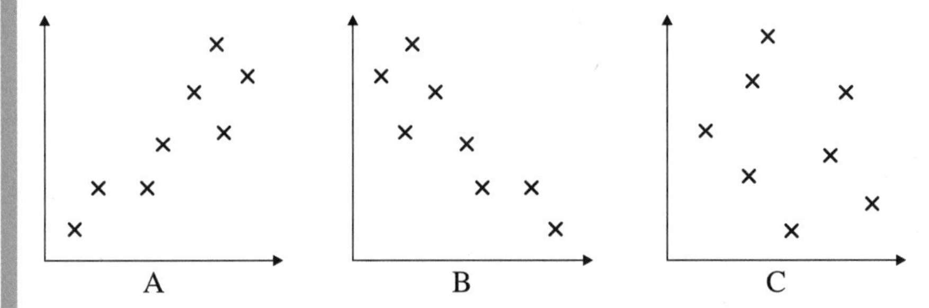

1. As you get older your reaction speed slows down.
2. People who are good at maths are usually good at music.
3. There is no connection between height and hair length of 14-year-old girls.

For questions 4–6, draw a sketch of a suitable scatter diagram, labelling the axes with the appropriate variables.

4. The outside temperature and the amount of gas used for central heating for a house.
5. The weight and age for children aged up to 12 years.
6. The height of a person and the amount they spend on cinema visits each year.

Correlation and causality

Correlation implies a connection between two variables.

For example, people who are good at maths are usually good at music. This is a general trend to which there will often be exceptions.

Causality implies a direct link between two variables. One variable **causes** the change in the other variable.

Scientific experiments often show a causal link between variables.

For example, 'the outside temperature and the amount of gas used for central heating'.

The lower the temperature, the greater the amount of gas used: one variable directly causes the other to change.

Sometimes there is no direct link between two variables, but they are connected by a third variable.

For example, in the last twenty years the number of microwave ovens and the number of television sets have both increased.

One is not directly related to the other, but they are both related to changes in technology.

You can sometimes find correlation when there is no real link. This is known as spurious correlation.

This is a true story...

Data was collected about the number of babies born in different areas and the number of storks nesting on houses in those areas.

When the data was plotted, the scatter diagram showed positive correlation.

But you cannot assume that more storks nesting mean more babies!

> It is possible to find correlation between variables that are unlikely to be connected. This is spurious correlation.

This is more likely if you only collect a small amount of data.

Exercise 5B

For the following pairs of variables, decide whether they are likely to be linked by:

- correlation
- causality
- a third variable.

1. The lengths of a sample of babies and their head circumference.
2. The load attached to a spring and its extended length.
3. The number of deckchairs on a particular beach and the number of ice-cream sales.
4. The height of a sample of students and their shoe size.
5. The volume of traffic and the number of road accidents.

5.2 Lines of best fit

If a scatter diagram seems to show correlation you can often draw a straight line through the points. This is called a line of best fit.

> You can draw a line of best fit on a scatter diagram if the graph shows that there is correlation.

> The line of best fit will pass through the mean average of each data set.

You need to draw a line that best fits the data.

Example

Callum wanted to know how high his power ball would bounce.

He dropped the ball with force from various heights and measured the bounce height.
His results are summarized in the table.

Drop height (cm)	30	40	50	60	70	80	90	100
Bounce height (cm)	27	48	53	62	69	89	102	110

(a) Draw a scatter diagram of this data.
(b) Describe the correlation and draw a line of best fit.

Plot these points: (30, 27) (40, 48) (50, 53) (60, 62) (70, 69) (80, 89) (90, 102) (100, 110)

In an experiment the variable you **control** always goes on the x-axis.
The variable you measure as a **result** always goes on the y-axis.

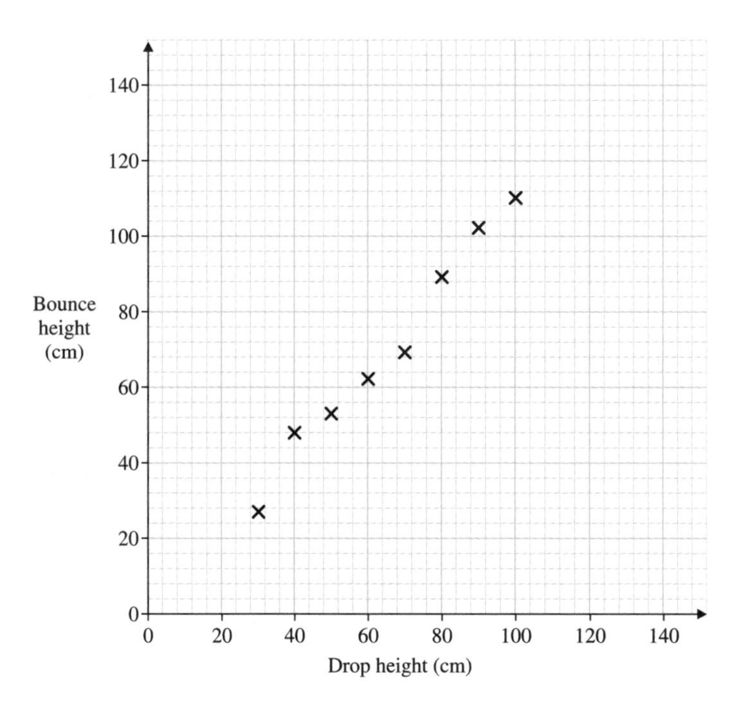

(b) You can see that as the height from which Callum dropped the power ball increased, the bounce height also increased. This means that there is positive correlation between the drop height and the bounce height.

As the points appear to lie close to a straight line, you can draw a line of best fit.

First find the mean of each variable:

Remember: the mean is explained on page 60.

$$\text{Mean drop height} = \frac{30 + 40 + 50 + 60 + 70 + 80 + 90 + 100}{8}$$

$$= \frac{520}{8} = 65\,\text{cm}$$

$$\text{Mean bounce height} = \frac{27 + 48 + 53 + 62 + 69 + 89 + 102 + 110}{8}$$

$$= \frac{560}{8} = 70\,\text{cm}$$

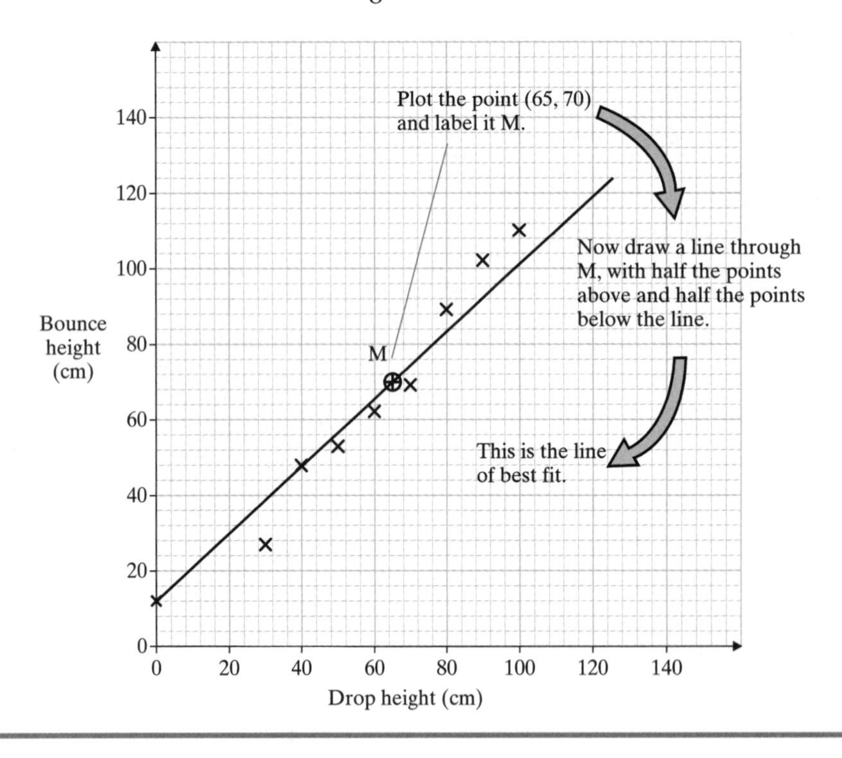

When using IT to draw a scatter graph, take care with drawing a line of best fit. You need to question whether a line of best fit is appropriate for the data before adding it to your diagram.

You can use Autograph to draw scatter diagrams. On a 2-D page go to Object and enter XY data set. Enter your raw data or import data from a spreadsheet and click OK. The data appears as scattered points on the 2-D graph page. To add a line of best fit go to Object and Best fit and Order 1.

Activity

'... They measured my right thumb, and desired no more; for a mathematical computation that twice round my thumb is once round the wrist and so on to the neck and the waist ...' Jonathan Swift, *Gulliver's Travels*

Anthropometry is the study of human measurements. Can there really be a connection between thumb and wrist measurements? How could you check? Where would the study of human measurements be useful?

Exercise 5C

For each of the following questions draw a scatter graph to represent the data.
If appropriate, draw the line of best fit on your graph. Remember to find the mean value first.

1. Carrie conducted an experiment to find out if height and arm span were related. She measured the heights and arm spans in centimetres of eight of her friends.

Height (cm)	136	158	126	131	149	157	143	152
Arm span (cm)	134	146	122	130	147	150	134	145

2. Theo was given a small collection of old pennies. He noted down how old each penny was and how much it weighed.

Age (years)	51	47	54	33	39	46	42	49	36
Weight (grams)	7.2	9.8	6.1	12.0	10.2	8.5	9.7	7.4	11.6

3. Ashish compared the published price of several children's books with the price of the same books in a discount book club catalogue.

Published price	£10.00	£6.00	£11.00	£15.00	£13.00	£5.00	£10.00
Book club price	£7.00	£4.50	£8.50	£11.00	£9.00	£4.00	£8.00

4. The following table summarizes the number of staff absent and the number of thefts each day for two working weeks from a department store.

Absentees	32	19	25	29	11	14	23	12	30	24	16	2
Thefts	16	18	27	8	21	22	5	28	21	17	17	9

The assistant manager has to investigate if there is any connection between the two variables.

Strong or moderate correlation?

In Callum's experiment his results lie on an almost perfectly straight line.

This is **strong positive correlation**.

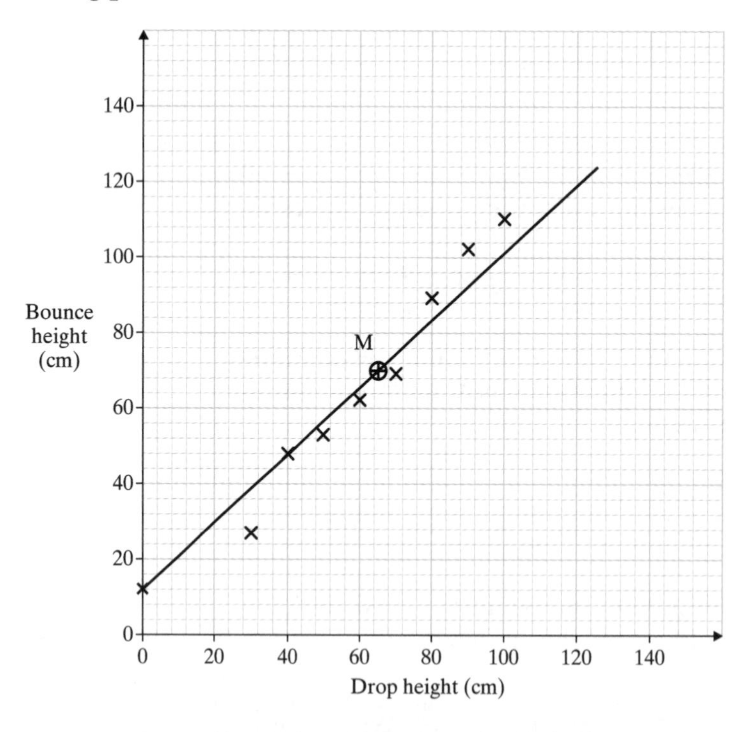

If almost all plotted points lie very close to a line of best fit, then correlation is strong.

If plotted points tend to lie in a line, but not very close to that line, then correlation is moderate.

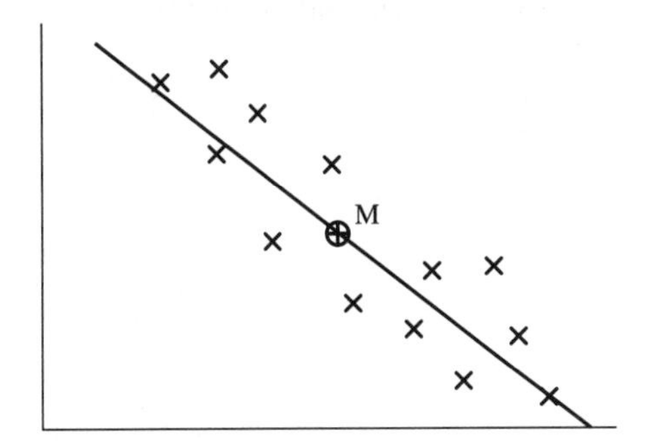

This graph shows moderate negative correlation.

Example

Barry carried out an experiment to find the reaction time of 30 volunteers after they had consumed alcohol. His results are summarized in the scatter graph.

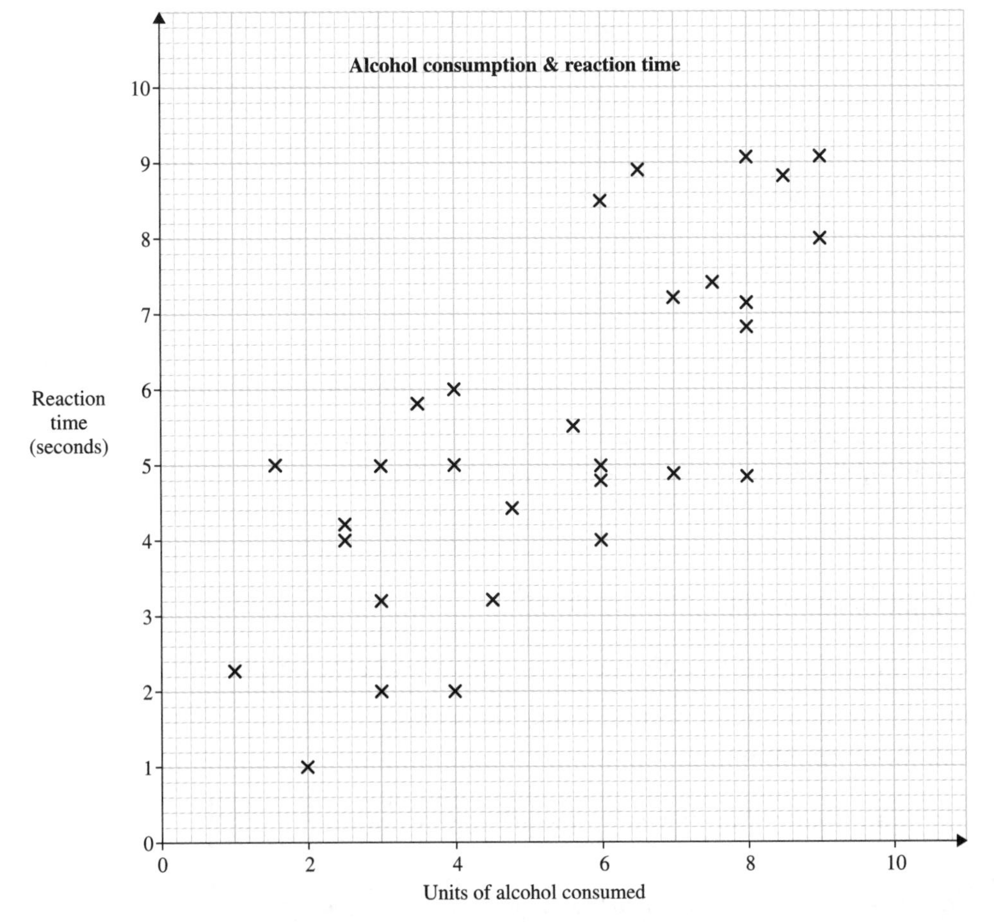

Describe the correlation suggested by the data.

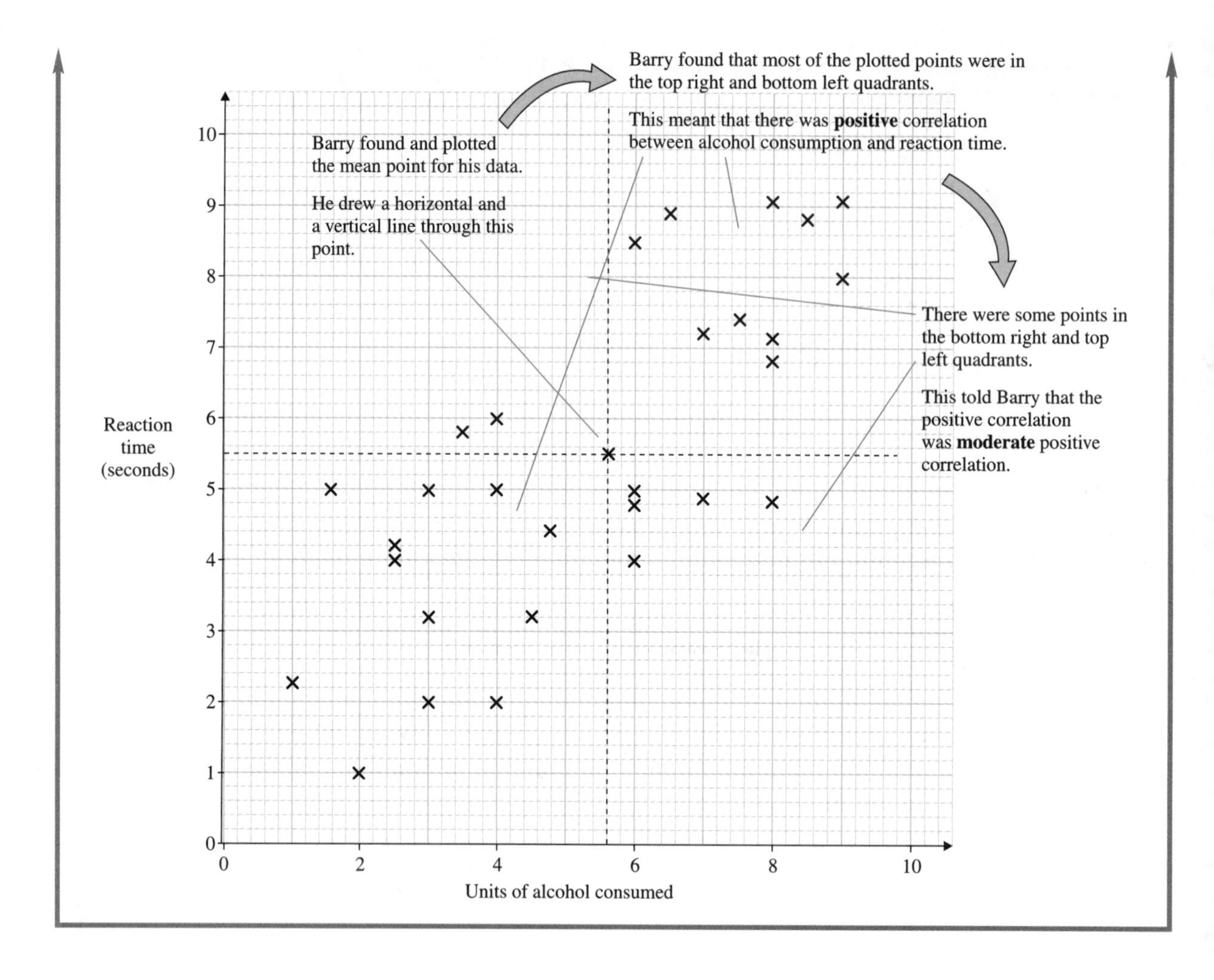

Exercise 5D

For your graphs in Exercise 5C questions 1 to 4, describe the correlation shown.

5.3 Interpolation and extrapolation

You can use a line of best fit to estimate other values from the graph.

Finding estimates from a line of best fit is known as either **interpolation** or **extrapolation**.

Interpolation is an estimate from **within** the range of given x-values.

Extrapolation is an estimate from **outside** the range of given x-values.

Example

Tomris thought that there might be a connection between the life expectancy of mammals and their gestation period.

The scatter graph shows the results of her investigation.

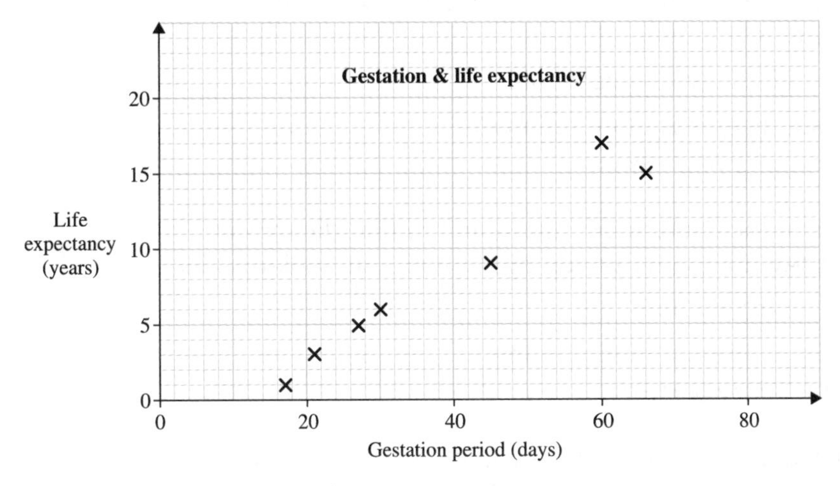

(a) Draw a line of best fit on the graph.

(b) Use the line to estimate the life expectancy of a mammal with a gestation period of:
(i) 50 days, (ii) 75 days.

The graph shows moderate positive correlation so a line of best fit can be drawn.

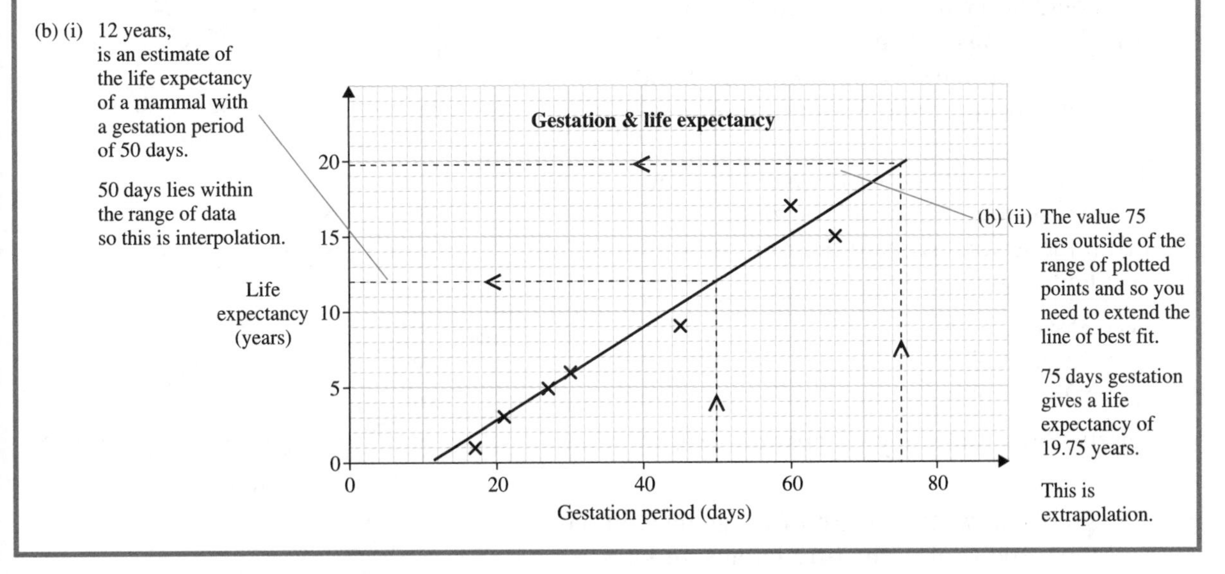

You need to be careful when extrapolating data from a graph because it does not always make sense to extend a line of best fit.

> When extrapolating data always question if the answer is realistic.
> The further you extrapolate, the less reliable your estimate.

Exercise 5E

1. Use your graph from Exercise 5C question 1 to find out the arm span of another of Carrie's friends who is 146 cm tall.

2. Use your graph for Exercise 5C question 2 to find out the weight of a penny that is:

   (a) 44 years old, (b) 60 years old.

   Which of your answers is more reliable?
   Give a reason for your answer.

3. Use your graph for Exercise 5C question 3 to find the expected publisher's price for a book priced by the discount book club as:

   (a) £15.00, (b) £6.50.

   Which of your answers is more reliable?
   Give a reason for your answer.

4. The scatter graph shows the monies gambled on a fruit machine and the amount paid out to eleven different people.

   (a) How much did the unluckiest player lose?
   (b) If you decide to gamble £11, how much could you expect the machine to pay out?
   (c) Tabitha has only got £5. If she gambles it all on the fruit machine, what could she expect to win? Explain your answer.

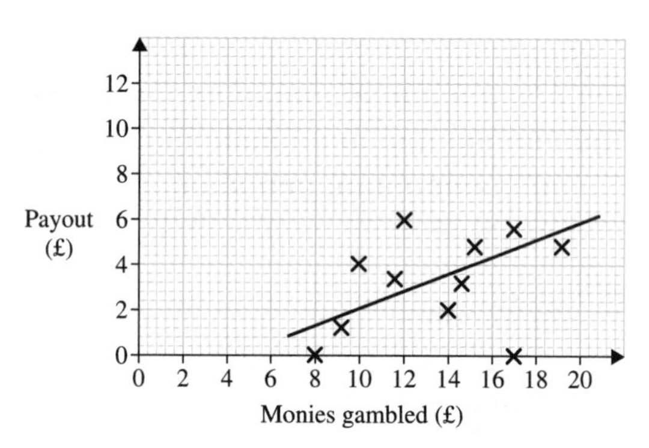

5. The scatter graph shows the ages and the number of road accidents for men.
   From the graph estimate the number of accidents for:

   (i) 35-year-olds,
   (ii) 12-year-olds,
   (iii) 80-year-olds.

   Discuss how realistic your answers are.

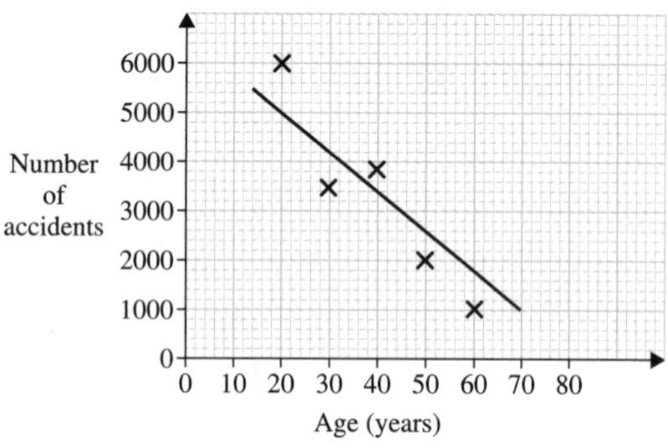

6. The graph shows the length of pregnancy, in days, and the weights of premature babies, in kg.
   Why would it not be sensible to use this graph to estimate the weight of a baby whose mother had been pregnant for 320 days?

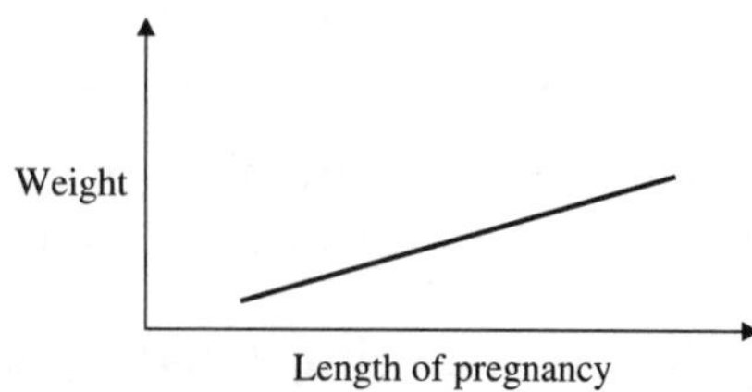

5.4 The equation of a line of best fit

Finding the equation of a line of best fit is exactly the same as finding the equation of any straight line.

You can find the equation by finding:

- the gradient
- where the line crosses the y-axis, the y-intercept.

You can also calculate the equation of a line by equating gradients at two places.

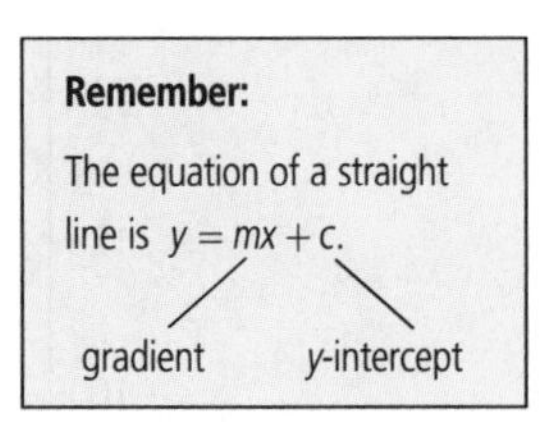

Example

This is Callum's graph from page 162.

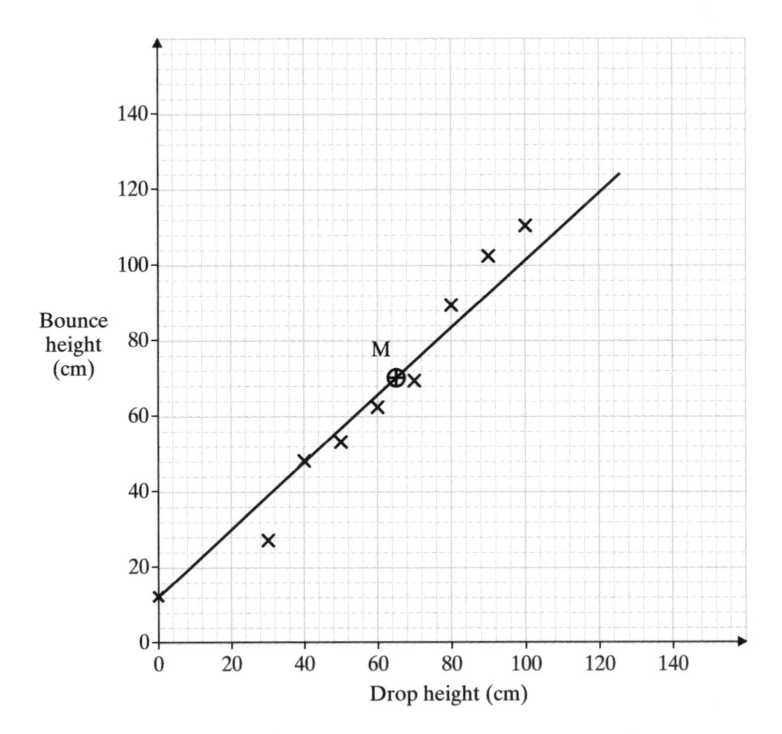

(a) Calculate the equation of the line of best fit.
(b) Use this equation to predict the bounce height (y) for a drop height (x) of 83 cm.
(c) What does the gradient mean in the context of the question?
(d) What does the y-intercept mean in the context of the question? Is it sensible to extend the graph to $x = 0$?

(a) To find the gradient, triangles are constructed on the line of best fit at two different places.

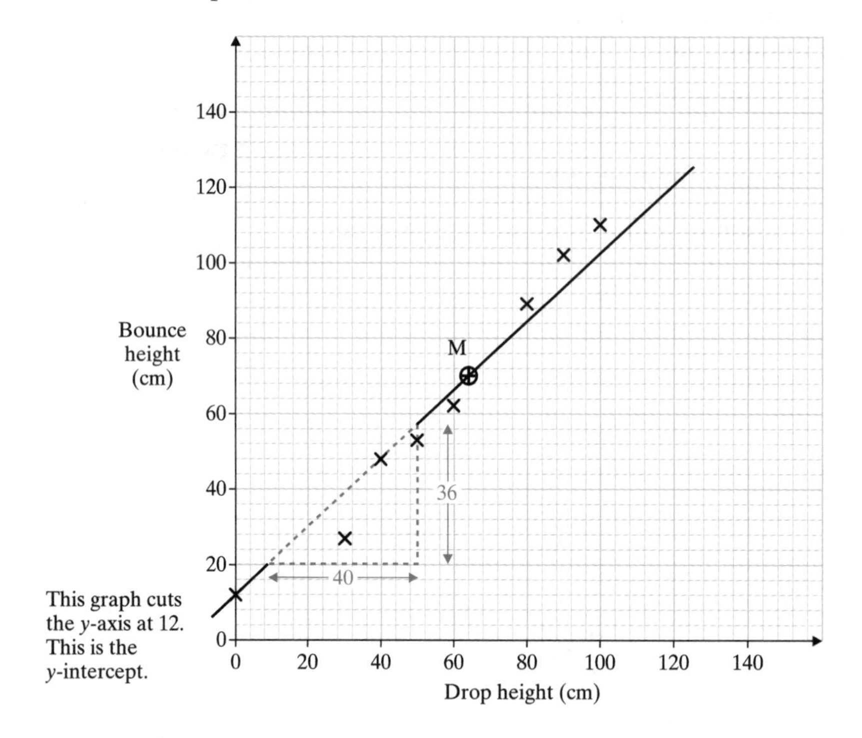

The triangle drawn to show the gradient gives

$$m = \frac{36}{40} = 0.9$$

So the equation of the straight line is

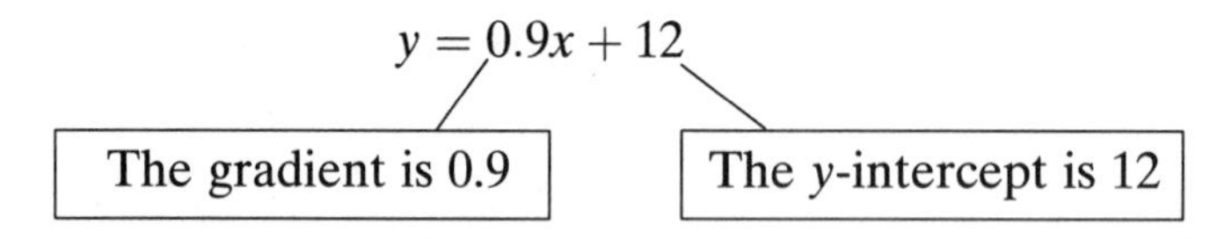

(b) When $x = 83$, $y = (0.9 \times 83) + 12 = 86.7$
So the predicted bounce height is 86.7 cm.

(c) The gradient is 0.9.
This tells you that an increase in drop height of 1 cm will lead to an increase in bounce height of 0.9 cm.

(d) The y-intercept is 12.
This tells you that a drop height of zero will give a bounce height of 12 cm. This is clearly unrealistic, so the line should not be extended to $x = 0$.

Remember: $x = 0$ is an **extrapolated** value outside the range of data.

When you use Autograph to draw a scatter diagram and line of best fit, if you click on the line the equation of the line of best fit will appear below the graph. It is important that you know how to interpret this equation and what the gradient and y-intercept mean. In the exam you may need to find this equation for yourself.

Exercise 5F

1. (a) Calculate the equation of your lines of best fit for:
   (i) Exercise 5C question 1
   (ii) Exercise 5C question 2
   (iii) Exercise 5C question 3.
   (b) For each line
   (i) Explain what the gradient means in the context of the question.
   (ii) Comment on whether the y-intercept gives a realistic value.

2. Calculate the equation of the line of best fit for the graphs in Exercise 5E question 4 and question 5.
   Are these equations appropriate for all values?

Activity

It may not always be sensible to draw a scatter graph with the x-axis starting at zero. For some graphs you would not be able to read the intercept.

An alternative way to find the equation of the line of best fit is to use:

$y - \bar{y} = m(x - \bar{x})$ m is the gradient $\bar{x}$ and $\bar{y}$ the mean values for the data

Use this formula to find the equation of the line of best fit for the example on pages 169–170.

How similar or different is this equation?

Does it matter if the two equations are slightly different?

Non-linear data

You cannot always draw a straight line through plotted points on a scatter graph.

Sometimes the points lie on a curve, and you say that the relationship is **non-linear**.

For straight-line graphs the relationship between the variables is **linear**.

Equations of typical c

$y = \frac{a}{x} + b$, $y = ax^2 +$ … nstants.

Their graphs look like

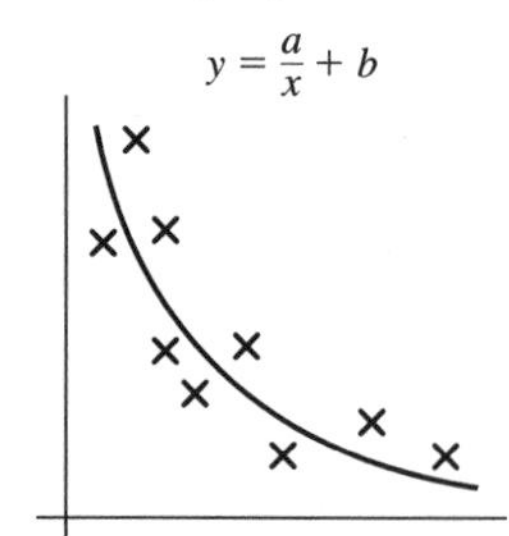

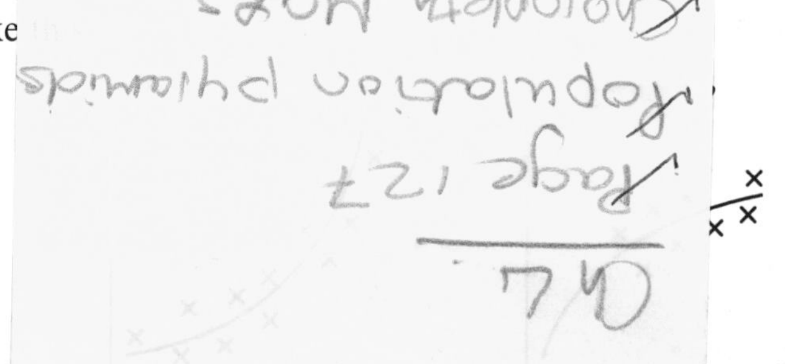

You can change all these curves into straight lines by plotting appropriate graphs. This will help you to find the values of a and b, and then you can find an equation for the graph.

Changing non-linear data to straight lines is called **reducing to linear form**.

If the data resembles $y = \frac{a}{x} + b$, plot y against $\frac{1}{x}$

If the data resembles $y = ax^2 + b$, plot y against x^2

If the data resembles $y = a\sqrt{x} + b$, plot y against $\sqrt{x}$

The gradient of each graph will be a and the y-intercept will be b.

Example

The heating cost (C) of hotels, varies with the number of rooms (N).

Number, N	10	20	50	75	100
Cost, C	245	860	5070	11 300	19 970

The scatter graph looks like a curve of the type $y = ax^2 + b$.

If you are asked to reduce non-linear data to a linear form, a suggested relationship will be given.

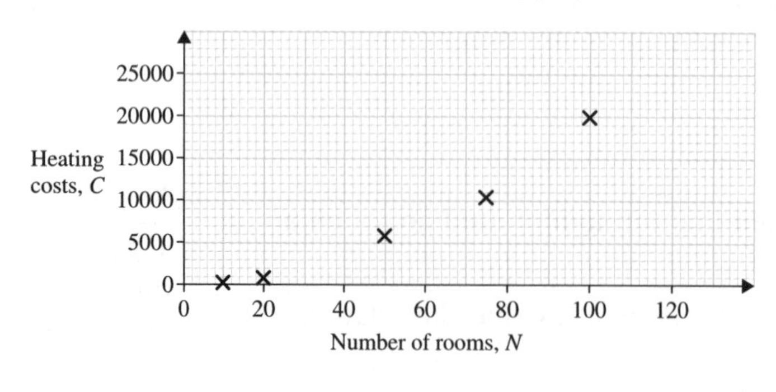

Reduce the data to linear form and draw a new scatter graph.

In this graph C is on the y-axis and N on the x-axis, so $C = aN^2 + b$. To make this data linear, you need to plot C against N^2 (instead of C against N).

N	10	20	50	75	100
N^2	100	400	2500	5625	10 000
C	245	860	5070	11 300	19 970

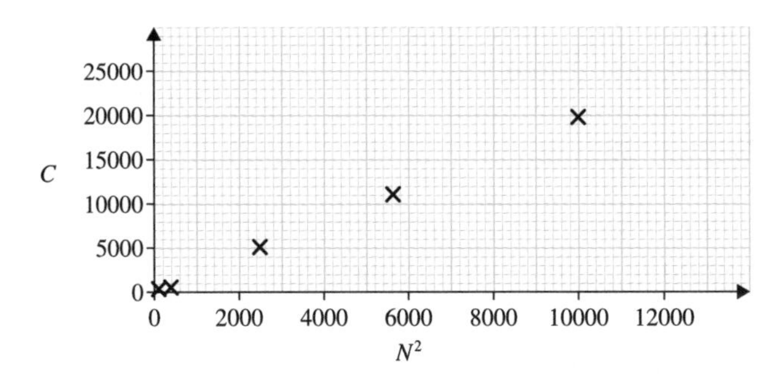

The heating cost graph using N^2 in place of N looks linear.

The data has been reduced to a linear form.

Now follow the method in the example on page 170 to help you find the values of a and b.

Then you can use the equation $C = aN^2 + b$ to make predictions.

Exercise 5G

1. The temperature of a hot drink is measured at one-minute intervals.

Time, s minutes	1	2	3	4	5	6	7	8	9	10
Temperature, T °C	89	46	30	25	20	16	13	11	10	9

It is thought that the temperature, T, of the drink is connected to time, s, by the formula $T = \frac{a}{s}$ where a is a constant.

Draw a scatter graph of T against $\frac{1}{s}$ to check this assumption.

Use your graph to find the value of a.

Using your graph or equation, estimate the temperature of the drink after:

(a) 1.5 minutes, (b) 4.5 minutes, (c) 15 minutes.

2. The head circumference of a baby is believed to be governed by the formula $C = \sqrt{A}$ where A is the baby's age in months. The following data was collected by a mother.

Age A (months)	1	2	4	6	8	9
Head circumference C (cm)	36.4	39.3	42	44	45.4	46

(a) Draw a scatter diagram of C against $\sqrt{A}$ to verify the formula.
(b) Use your graph to predict the baby's head circumference at 12 months.

3. The running costs, C, of a minibus are dependent upon several overheads and the speed, S, at which it is driven.

Speed, S	28	30	35	40	50	55
Running costs, C	20	21	24	30	35	42

The running cost equation is thought to be $C = aS^2 + b$, where a and b are constants.

Draw a scatter graph to verify this equation.
Use your graph to find the values of a and b.

5.5 Measuring the degree of correlation

Correlation describes the relationship between two variables. Inspection of a scatter graph gives an indication of the strength and direction, whether positive or negative, of the linear relationship between the variables.

If both the variables are random samples from normal distributions then a statistic, the **Product Moment Correlation Coefficient**, PMCC, can be calculated to give a numerical estimate of the correlation.

PMCC is a value from –1 to 1.

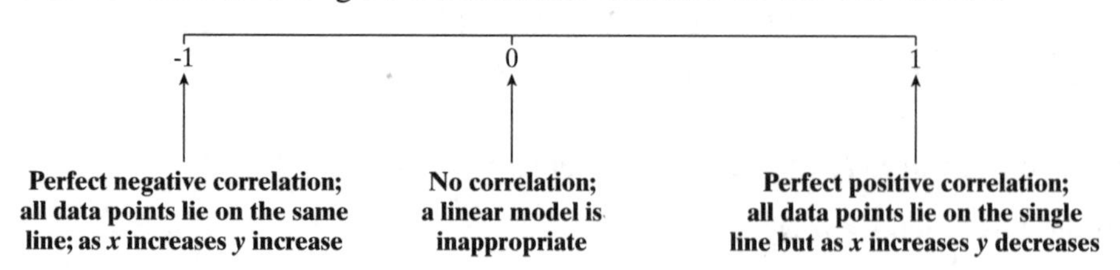

The closer the PMCC is to 1 or –1 the more likely it is that the data is correlated.
A value close to zero implies that there is no linear relationship between the variables.

You are not expected to calculate PMCC.

If you cannot assume that the variables are random samples from a normal distributions or if the data is more subjective, such as the opinions of judges in a competition then **Spearman's Rank Correlation Coefficient** is used to measure the agreement between two data sets.

To calculate **Spearman's Rank Correlation Coefficient**, r_s, each data value is assigned a **rank** depending on its position within its data set and the calculation is based on **differences**, d, between corresponding ranks.

Range of r_s is from −1 to 1 as before.

Spearman's rank correlation coefficient, $r_s = 1 - \frac{6\Sigma d^2}{n(n^2 - 1)}$

where d is the difference between corresponding ranks
and n is the number of pairs of data.

Remember:
Σ means 'sum of'.

The closer r_s is to $^{+}1$, the more agreement there is between the ranks.
The closer r_s is to $^{-}1$, the more disagreement there is.
If r_s is close to zero, the ranks neither agree nor disagree.

Example

Contestants in a gymnastics competition are awarded marks by several judges.

Two of the judges are chosen to see how well their marks correlate.

Their marks are:

Contestant	Abi	Betty	Carly	Debs	Eileen	Fran	Gina	Hannah
Judge Ment	4.5	5.6	3.9	5.2	4.6	5.5	5.9	5.1
Judge Ship	5.3	5.9	4.5	5.6	4.9	6.2	6.7	6.3

Both judges agree the best and worst placed contestant, but you can see that in general Judge Ship is more generous with his marks.

Calculate Spearman's rank correlation coefficient for this data.

✦ First rank the marks in their place order:

Contestant	Abi	Betty	Carly	Debs	Eileen	Fran	Gina	Hannah
Judge Ment	7	2	8	4	6	3	1	5
Judge Ship	6	4	8	5	7	3	1	2

✦ Subtract corresponding ranks to get the differences d:

d	1	2	0	1	1	0	0	3

You only need to find the actual difference, not whether it is positive or negative.

Square the differences, d^2:

d^2	1	4	0	1	1	0	0	9

$\Sigma d^2 = 16$

There are 8 contestants, so $n = 8$.

$$r_s = 1 - \frac{6\Sigma d^2}{n(n^2 - 1)}$$

$$= 1 - \frac{6 \times 16}{8(64 - 1)}$$

$$= 1 - \frac{96}{504}$$

$$= 1 - 0.1905 = 0.8095 \quad \text{or} \quad 0.81 \text{ to 2 d.p.}$$

0.81 is close to 1 so there is a fairly high agreement between the two judges.

r only measures the agreement between **ranks**; it does not give you the correlation between the actual values themselves.

If two data values within a set are equal you can use the method for **tied ranks** outlined in the following example.

Example

Twins Kevin and Perry, whose tastes usually agree, were asked to taste test 10 drinks. They independently awarded marks out of 40 for the drinks.

Drink	A	B	C	D	E	F	G	H	I	J
Kevin	36	10	25	8	12	29	25	33	22	21
Perry	34	27	31	23	13	33	27	27	27	11

Find Spearman's rank correlation coefficient for this data.

For Kevin, C and G have tied ranks at 4th and 5th: the average is 4.5.

For Perry, B, G, H and I have tied ranks at 4th, 5th, 6th and 7th: the average is 5.5.

K rank	1	9	4.5	10	8	3	4.5	2	6	7
P rank	1	5.5	3	8	9	2	5.5	5.5	5.5	10
d	0	3.5	1.5	2	1	1	1	3.5	0.5	3
d^2	0	12.25	2.25	4	1	1	1	12.25	0.25	9

Tied ranks do not always result in 0.5s.

$\Sigma d^2 = 43$

There are 10 drinks so $n = 10$.

$$r_s = 1 - \frac{6 \times 43}{10(100 - 1)}$$

$$= 1 - \frac{258}{990}$$

$$= 1 - 0.261 = 0.739$$

A rank correlation coefficient of 0.739 suggests that there is fairly strong agreement between Kevin and Perry's taste in drinks.

Exercise 5H

1. Which of the numbers $^{-}0.73$, 0.29 and 0.87 indicates the least correlation? Give a reason for your answer.

2. From the numbers 0, 0.78, $^{-}0.39$, 0.12, $^{-}0.81$ and 1.32 choose the most likely correlation coefficient that matches each of the scatter graphs A, B and C.

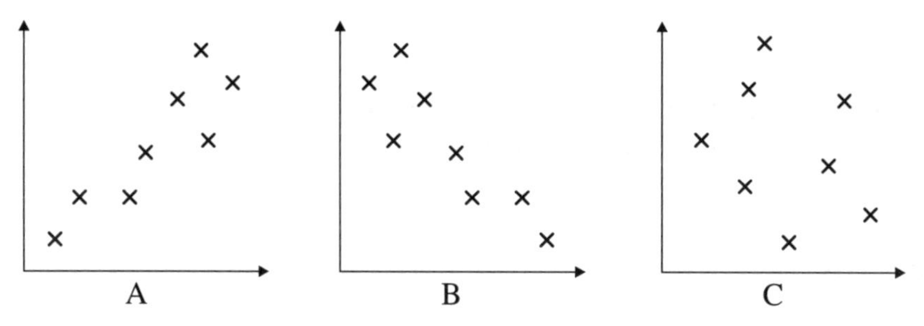

Which one of the numbers cannot be a product moment correlation coefficient?
Give a reason for your answer.

3. The table below gives the marks out of 20 obtained by five students in two tests.

Test 1	2	7	8	9	13
Test 2	4	5	7	10	14

Work out the value of Spearman's rank correlation coefficient between tests 1 and 2. What does this tell you about the students and the tests?

4. Shoshana and Simon ranked seven sports in order of preference.

Sport	Tennis	Squash	Hockey	Football	Badminton	Rugby	Swimming
Shoshana	1	5	4	6	3	7	2
Simon	3	6	4	2	7	5	1

Calculate Spearman's rank correlation coefficient. Comment on your answer.

5. Earl kept a record of how far he travelled, in km, and the petrol used, in litres.

Distance (km)	480	592	656	672	704	720
Petrol (litres)	35	46	44	45	52	52

Calculate Spearman's rank correlation coefficient. Comment on your answer.

6. The following table gives the times taken, in minutes, and the number of errors made in a typing test.

Typist	A	B	C	D	E	F	G	H	I
Time	15	16	10	19	23	15	20	21	15
Errors	7	8	5	6	3	5	4	2	9

Calculate Spearman's rank correlation coefficient. Comment on your answer. Which typist would you employ? Give a reason for your answer.

Summary of key points

- A scatter diagram is used to represent bivariate data.
- Correlation describes the strength of the linear relationship between the variables.
- If the points lie on an approximate straight line then a line of best fit provides a model for the association between the variables.
- Interpolation is when values are estimated within the plotted points.
- Extrapolation is when values are estimated outside the plotted points.
- Product Moment Correlation Coefficient is a numerical measure of the degree of correlation between data drawn from normal distributions.
- Spearman's Rank Correlation Coefficient measures agreement between data sets that have been ranked.

Links to the Real World

Comparing two sets of information between which there may be a connection, such as people's income and their education, or poverty and crime, is one of the most important jobs of statistics. The connection is referred to as correlation. Correlation is the tool used to investigate claims, such as "smoking causes lung cancer" or "living near nuclear power plants leads to health problems", and if any correlation is found then it is possible to determine the strength of the relationship between the two variables.

The key thing to remember when working with correlations is never to assume a correlation means that a change in one variable **causes** a change in another. If sales of mobile phones and training shoes both rise strongly over several years there will be a high correlation between them, but you cannot assume that buying mobile phones causes people to buy training shoes (or vice versa).

In finance, correlation is used to measure how two stocks or bonds move in relation to each other. Where correlation is found the equation of the line of best fit allows statisticians to predict what may happen to one variable in the future as the other changes and thus influence decisions.

Revision Exercise 5

1. As part of her Statistics coursework Sarah draws the following three scatter diagrams.

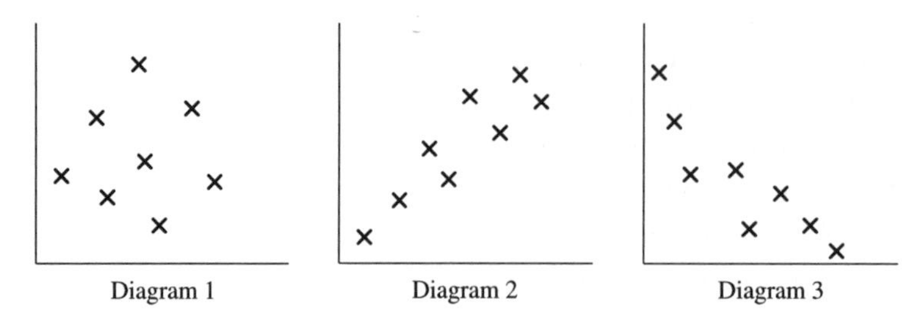

(a) Which diagram shows
   (i) positive correlation
   (ii) no correlation?

(b) One axis for Diagram 3 is labelled 'Age of car'.

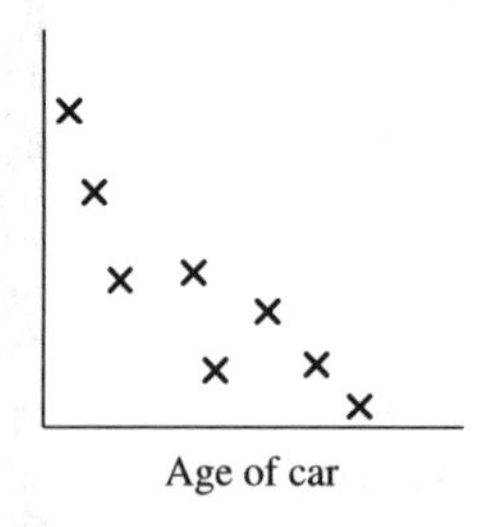

Choose a suitable label for the other axis from the following list.

Engine size   Value of car   Miles travelled   Price of petrol

[AQA]

2. (a) There is a high degree of negative correlation between the amount of heat escaping through the roof of a house and the thickness of the insulating material used in the loft.
   Explain what is meant by this statement.

   (b) There is a high degree of positive correlation between the temperature in New Zealand and the amount of coal sold in the United Kingdom.
   Explain what is meant by this statement.

   (c) In only one of the above cases is there a direct causal relationship between the two variables. In which case is there a direct causal relationship?

   (d) Give an example of your own where there is a high degree of positive correlation between two variables and a direct causal relationship. [NEAB]

3. The scatter diagram shows the area of a forest sector (100 m^2) and the amount of timber felled (tonnes) for a forestry site in Scotland that consists mostly of natural woodland.

(a) The mean forest sector area is 1700 m^2
The mean amount of timber felled is 184 tonnes

Copy the scatter diagram and draw a line of best fit.

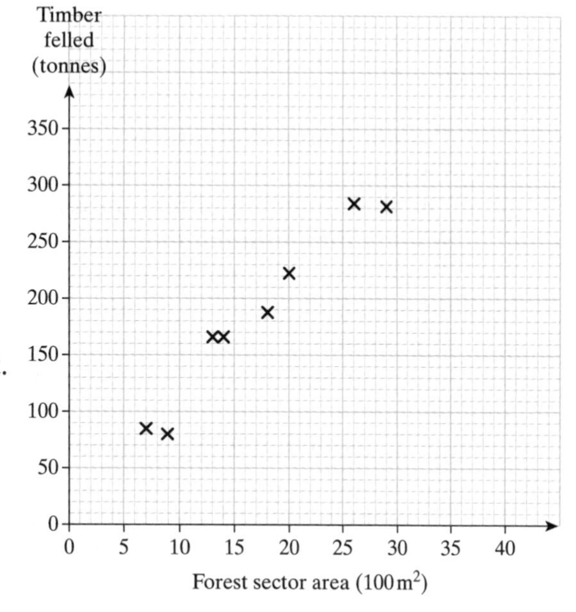

(b) The Forestry commission want to fell timber in two more sectors of the forest. Use your line of best fit to estimate the amount of timber felled from sectors with areas:
(i) 2200 m^2 (ii) 3500 m^2

(c) Which of these estimates is more reliable?
Give a reason for your answer.

(d) What is the expected increase in timber for each extra 100 m^2 of forest?

(e) The equation of the line of best fit for a forestry site of pine trees passes through the points (6, 25) and (20, 250).
Draw this line on the scatter diagram.

(f) Compare the amount of timber felled from the natural woodland and the amount from the pine forest.

(g) The forest sector areas and the amount of timber felled from each forest are given in the table.

Forest sector	A	B	C	D	E	F	G	H
Forest sector area (100 m^2)	7	9	13	14	18	20	26	29
Amount of timber felled (tonnes)	85	82	165	165	188	223	283	281

(i) Calculate the value of Spearman's rank correlation coefficient.
(ii) Interpret the value of Spearman's rank correlation coefficient in the context of the question.

(h) Write the least and greatest amount of timber from forest sector F that will not change the value of Spearman's rank correlation coefficient. [AQA]

4. Kelly asked 8 friends to record the number of text messages they sent and the number of calls they made on their mobile phone during one week.
The results are recorded in the table.

Number of text messages	18	22	24	25	28	32	32	35
Number of calls	36	24	26	20	13	8	10	7

(a) Draw a scatter diagram to represent these data.
(b) Describe the correlation shown by the scatter diagram.
(c) The mean number of text messages sent is 27.
What is the mean number of calls made?
(d) Draw a line of best fit on your diagram.
(e) Susan, another of Kelly's friends, sent 30 text messages during that week.
Use your line of best fit to estimate the number of calls that she made.
(f) Ailsa, another of Kelly's friends, sent 45 text messages during that week.
Give **one** reason why you should not use this line of best fit to estimate the number of calls that Ailsa made. [AQA]

5. An expert from the local antiques club agreed to challenge a number of contestants to correctly rank eight items of Victorian furniture according to their value.

John agreed to take part and his **rankings** along with those of the expert were as follows

Exhibit	A	B	C	D	E	F	G	H
Expert	1	3	6	7	8	2	5	4
John	8	5	2.5	4	1	6	2.5	7

(a) Calculate the value of Spearman's rank correlation coefficient for the two sets of data.
(b) Interpret, in context, your answer to part (a).
(c) A further eight contestants entered the competition.
The values of the correlation coefficients were

0.35 −0.43 0.71 0.05 −3.36 −0.02 0.92 −0.81

(i) Which two of these values show that there is almost no correlation between the individual ranking of that contestant and those of the expert
(ii) Which of these values shows the strongest correlation between the expert and contestant? [AQA]

6. The table shows the number of days of rain and the number of days of sunshine in Stokeham each April for 12 years.

Year	1995	1996	1997	1998	1999	2000	2001	2002	2003	2004	2005	2006
Days of rain	12	10	7	12	9	6	4	7	11	15	12	8
Days of sunshine	6	7	11	8	9	14	15	10	8	4	5	11

(a) The data for the first six years have been plotted on the scatter diagram. Plot the remaining data on a copy of the scatter diagram.

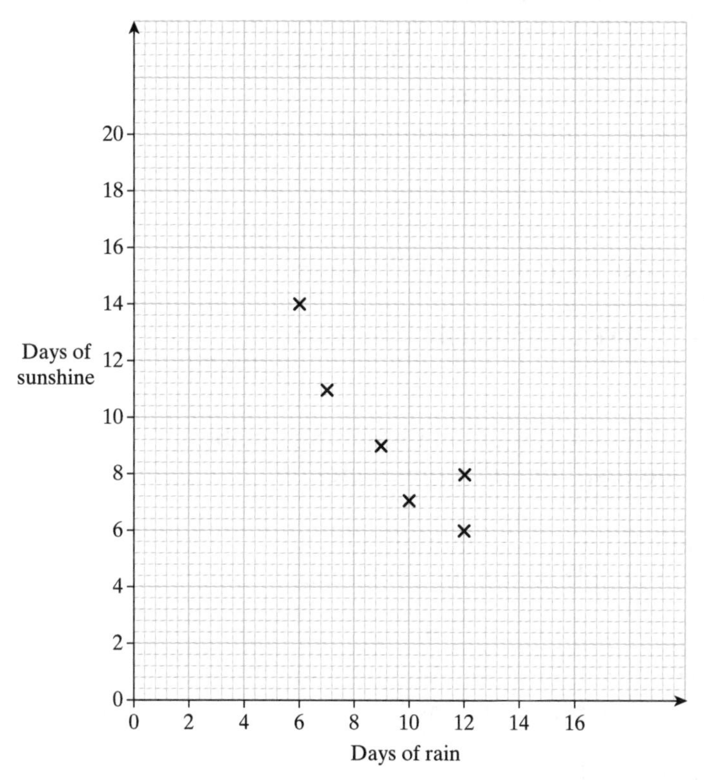

(b) Describe the type of correlation shown.

(c) The mean number of days of rain is 9.4, correct to one decimal place.

(i) Calculate the mean number of days of sunshine.

(ii) Use this information to help draw a line of best fit on your diagram.

(d) Use your line of best fit to estimate the number of days of sunshine in an April which has

(i) 13 days of rain

(ii) 3 days of rain.

(e) Which of your answers in part (d) is more reliable? Give a reason for your answer. [AQA]

7. This table gives the age, in years, and the 'nearest vision distance', in centimetres, of each of ten people. The nearest vision distance is the closest distance at which a person can read.

Person	A	B	C	D	E	F	G	H	I	J	Mean value
Age (years)	20	25	30	35	40	45	50	55	60	65	
Nearest vision distance (cm)	10	21	18	24	28	30	34	40	45	50	30

(a) Draw a scatter diagram of this information.
(b) Calculate the mean age of the 10 people.
(c) (i) Plot the point on the scatter diagram to show the mean age and mean 'nearest vision distance'. Label this point M.
(ii) Draw a straight line to fit your points.
(d) Use your line to estimate the 'nearest vision distance' of a person
(i) aged 15,
(ii) aged 57.
(e) Which of your two estimates do you think is the more reliable? Explain your reasoning.
(f) Which person appears to have an unusually high 'nearest vision distance'? [NEAB]

8. Brunel plc is keen to set up a forecasting system which will enable them to estimate maintenance costs for delivery vehicles of various ages.
The following table summarizes the age in months (x) and maintenance costs £ (y) for a sample of ten such vehicles.

Vehicle	A	B	C	D	E	F	G	H	I	J
Age, months (x)	63	13	34	80	51	14	45	74	24	82
Maintenance cost, £ (y)	141	14	43	170	95	21	72	152	31	171

(a) Draw a scatter diagram of this data.
(b) Find the mean value of the ages (x) and maintenance cost (y)
(c) Use your results from (b) and the fact that the line of best fit for the data passes through the point (20, 24.5) to draw this line on the graph.
(d) Estimate from your line the maintenance cost for a vehicle aged
(i) 85 months, (ii) 5 months, (iii) 60 months.
(e) Order these forecasts in terms of their reliability.
Justify your choice. [NEAB]

9. The scatter diagram shows the weights, in kilograms, and the heights, in centimetres, of seventeen adult males in a rugby club.

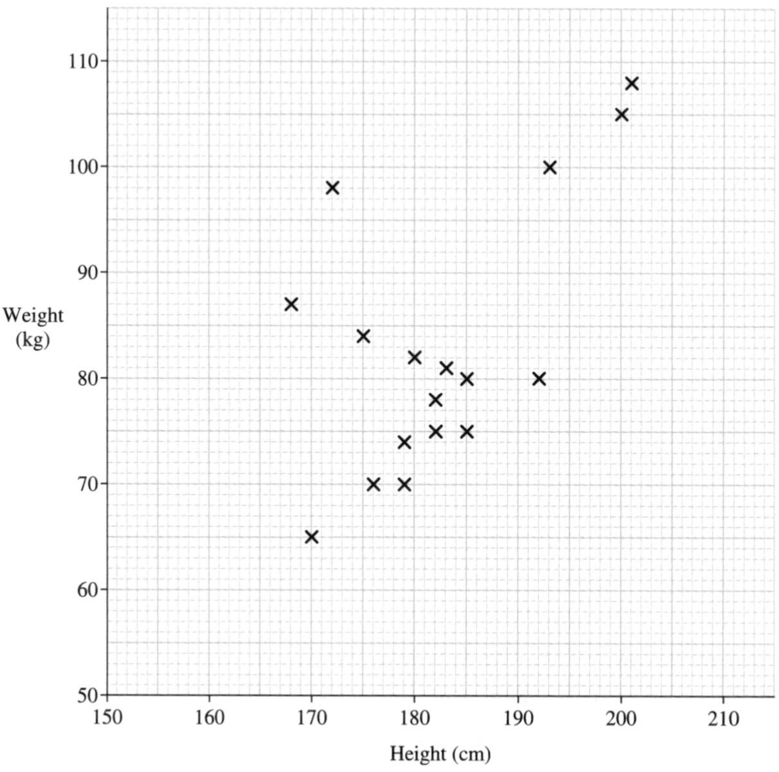

(a) What is the weight of the heaviest player?
(b) What is the height of the shortest player?
(c) One of the players is particularly heavy for his height.
Write down the coordinates of the **X** that represents this player.
(d) What type of correlation does the diagram show?
(e) The team captain uses the diagram below to categorize the players.

		Height	
		Very tall	Not very tall
Weight	Very heavy	3	2
	Not very heavy	1	11

How does the team captain decide if someone is
(i) very heavy, (ii) very tall? [NEAB]

10. The dots on the scatter diagram represent the sale price and the usual price of some cameras sold at the Nixon Camera Company.

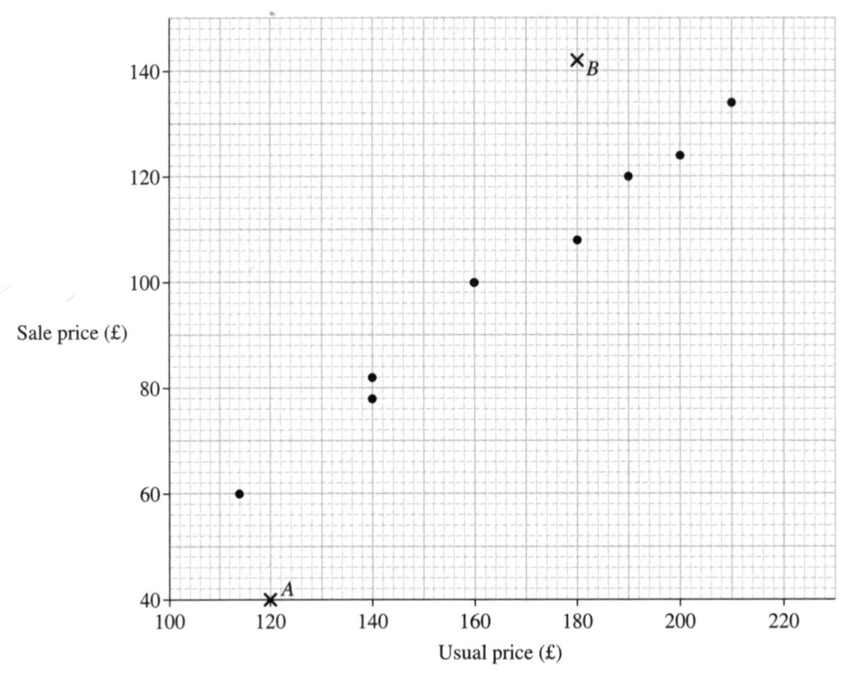

The average price of these cameras before the sale was £167.
The average price of these cameras in the sale was £101.

(a) Copy the scatter diagram and plot the point representing these average prices.
(b) On your scatter diagram, draw the line of best fit.
(c) Use your line to estimate the saving you would make on a camera whose usual price was £150.

The Beetall Camera Company recorded similar information in its sale. The line of best fit for this company was a line joining the points A and B on the scatter diagram.
Dawn has £55 to spend and her sister Julie has £120 to spend. They both want to buy a camera.

(d) (i) Which shop would give Dawn a better deal? Give a reason for your answer.
(ii) Explain why Julie would get a better deal at the other shop. [SEG]

11. Tanya produced these three scatter diagrams in her GCSE projects.

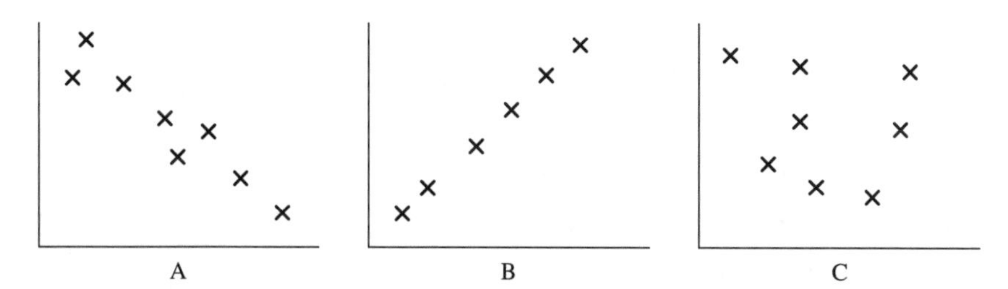

The titles for the diagrams are reproduced on the table below. Copy and complete this table to show which diagram would best suit the titles and indicate the type of correlation shown by each diagram. [SEG]

Title	Diagram letter	Type
Marks scored in a test and the percentage for that test.		
The age of a family car and its value.		
The time to run 200 metres and the number of people in their family.		

12. The graph shows the line of best fit to show the relationship between the straight-line distance (x) and the journey distance (y) of pupils to school.

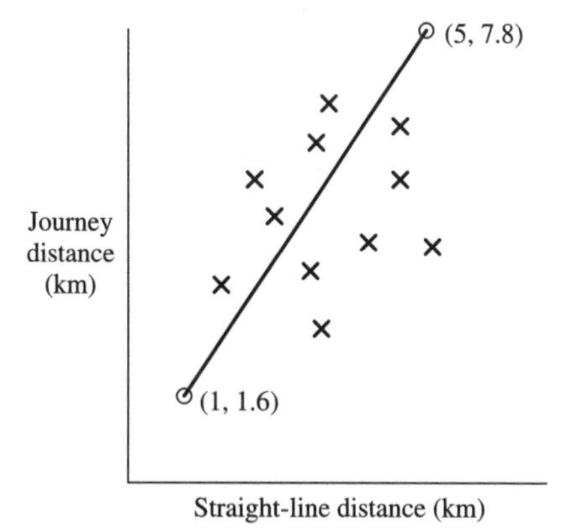

(a) Calculate the equation of the line of best fit.
(b) Explain why the intercept with the y-axis is small.
(c) Interpret the gradient of the line. [SEG]

13. The following data relate to the age and weight of ten randomly chosen children in Bedway Primary School.

Age (years)	7.8	8.1	6.4	5.2	7.0	9.9	8.4	6.0	7.2	10.0
Weight (kg)	29	28	26	20	24	35	30	22	25	36

(a) Draw a scatter diagram to show this information.

The mean age of this group of children is 7.6 years.

(b) Calculate the mean weight of this group.
(c) On the graph, draw the line of best fit.
(d) Use your graph to find the equation of this line of best fit, in the form $y = mx + c$.

Jane is a pupil at Bedway Primary School and her age is 8.0 years.

(e) Use your answer to (d) to estimate Jane's weight.
(f) Give **one** reason why a prediction of the weight of a twelve-year-old from your graph might not be reliable. [SEG]

14. A student carried out an experiment to investigate the effectiveness of a fertilizer.
Five plants of the same height were chosen and a different amount of fertilizer was given to each plant. The student plotted the results of the experiment on a scatter diagram and drew the line of best fit.
(a) Comment on the line of best fit.
(b) Explain why it would be inadvisable to use this line of best fit to predict the growth for a 6-gram dose of fertilizer.

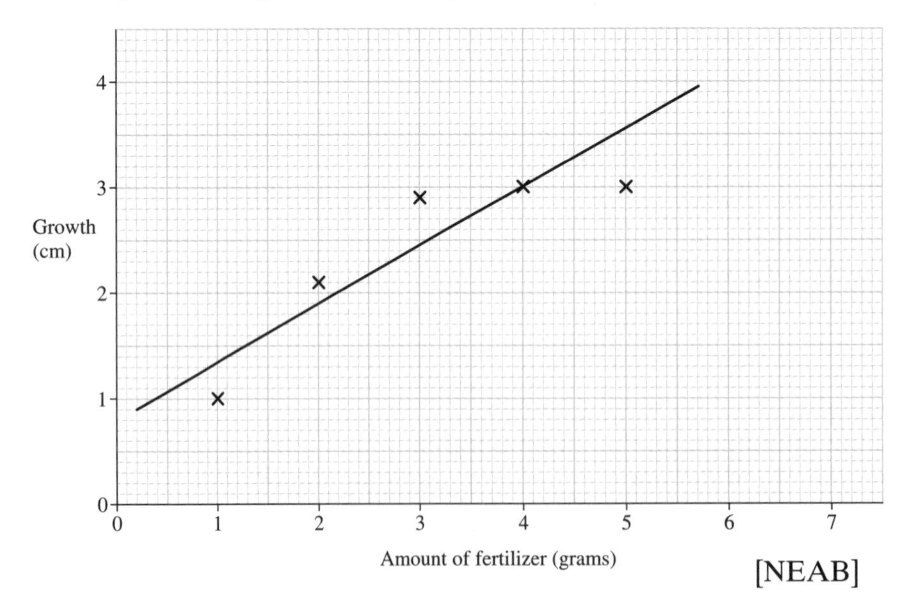

[NEAB]

15. For twelve consecutive months a factory manager recorded the number of items produced by the factory and the total cost of their production.

Number of items (x)	18	36	45	22	69	72	13	33	60	79	10	53
Production cost (£ y)	37	54	63	42	84	91	33	49	79	98	32	70

(a) Draw a scatter diagram for the data.
(b) Find the mean value of x and y.
(c) Use your results from (b), and the fact that the line of best fit for the data passes through the point (70, 88), to draw this line on the graph.
(d) Estimate, from your line, the production cost for
  (i) 65 items, (ii) 84 items.
(e) Which of your forecasts in (d) is the more reliable? Justify your choice.
(f) Find, from your graph, the gradient of the line.
(g) Describe briefly, in the context of the question, what the gradient measures. [NEAB]

16. When two judges ranked ten television programmes, the value of Spearman's rank correlation coefficient was –0.05.
(a) Which of the following scatter diagrams could represent this information?

X Y Z

(b) Give estimates for Spearman's rank correlation coefficient for the other two diagrams. [SEG]

17. Two judges had to rank ten gymnasts in order of ability. The table gives their respective rankings.

Gymnast	A	B	C	D	E	F	G	H	I	J
Judge 1	5	1	10	6	2	7	9	8	3	4
Judge 2	6	4	10	9	1	3	8	5	7	2

(a) Use the table to calculate Spearman's rank correlation coefficient between the judges' rankings.
(b) What does your answer suggest about the judges' level of agreement? [SEG]

18. The table shows the number of points achieved and the number of goals conceded by eight netball teams.

Team	A	B	C	D	E	F	G	H
Points	29	28	27	25	24	22	23	21
Goals conceded	15	12	13	16	19	14	21	17

(a) Calculate Spearman's coefficient of rank correlation between the number of points achieved and the number of goals conceded.

$$\text{Spearman's coefficient} = 1 - \frac{6\sum d^2}{n(n^2 - 1)}$$

Spearman's coefficient of rank correlation between the number of points achieved and the number of goals **scored** is 0.45.

(b) Which is the better relationship to use for predicting the points obtained, the relationship between:
(i) the number of goals conceded and the number of points achieved, or
(ii) the number of goals scored and the number of points achieved?
Explain why you chose this answer. [SEG]

19. In a music festival, each competitor is judged on his performance on two different musical instruments. The judge awards marks out of 100 for each instrument, as follows.

Competitor	A	B	C	D	E	F
1st Instrument	90	75	62	70	75	56
2nd Instrument	95	76	64	76	86	60
Rank 1	1					
Rank 2	1					

(a) Copy the table and complete the ranks.

The rank correlation coefficient for these data was found to be 0.96.

It was later discovered that the marks from one of the judges, for one competitor, had been misread. This competitor should have had 10 more marks on his second instrument.

The mark was changed and on recalculation it was found that the correlation coefficient remained the same at 0.96.

(b) (i) Which competitor's mark was originally incorrect?
(ii) Give a reason for your answer. [SEG]

20. At the Deepdale 'Best of British Pie' competition two judges award marks for nine different pies as follows.

Pie	A	B	C	D	E	F	G	H	I
Judge 1	18	24	23	13	27	19	30	10	20
Judge 2	7	18	9	4	17	8	20	5	10

(a) What do the scores tell you about the two judges?
(b) (i) Calculate Spearman's coefficient of rank correlation between the two judges.
(ii) What does your result suggest about the judges' decisions?
[SEG]

21. The table shows the results of three tests given to seven pupils in a technology class.

Pupil	Test 1 Class position	Test 2 Score out of 60				Test 3 percentage
A	1st	40				*
B	3rd	35				48
C	2nd	34				40
D	7th	25				36
E	5th	29				38
F	6th	20				*
G	4th	42				53

(a) Copy the table and use it to calculate Spearman's coefficient of rank correlation between Test 1 and Test 2.

All seven pupils took Test 3.
The rank order for Test 3 was the same as the rank order for Test 2.
The percentages of pupils **A** and **F** in Test 3 were then lost.

(b) What would be the maximum percentage in Test 3 for pupil **F**?
(c) What would be
(i) the lowest percentage in Test 3 for pupil **A**?
(ii) the highest percentage in Test 3 for pupil **A**?
(d) Without further calculation, state the value of the rank correlation coefficient between Test 2 and Test 3. [SEG]

22. The table shows the percentage of the total lottery ticket sales and the National Lottery grant for each of the ten different regions.

Region	Percentage of total lottery sales	Lottery grants (£m)	Ranks		d	d^2
			Sales	Grants		
London	22.3	125.0				
Midlands	15.7	11.7				
North West	11.7	5.7				
The South	10.4	17.5				
Yorkshire	9.5	5.1				
Scotland	8.8	5.9				
Wales	7.4	4.3				
The East	6.5	12.6				
North East	5.3	2.4				
N. Ireland	2.4	0.5				

(a) Copy the table and complete the ranking columns for each set of data.

The formula for calculating Spearman's rank correlation coefficient is:

$$r_s = 1 - \frac{6\sum d^2}{n(n^2 - 1)}$$

(b) Calculate this rank coefficient for the above data.
(c) Use your value of Spearman's rank correlation coefficient to comment about the way money is distributed.
(d) By what amount could the National Lottery grant for London be reduced without changing the value of Spearman's rank correlation coefficient? [SEG]

23. Attendances at some of the most popular tourist attractions in the UK charging for admission (in millions) are shown below.

Attractions	1981	1991
Madame Tussaud's	2.0	2.2
Alton Towers	1.6	2.0
Tower of London	2.1	1.9
Natural History Museum	3.7	1.6
Chessington World of Adventures	0.5	1.4
Science Museum	3.8	1.4
London Zoo	1.1	1.1

(a) Calculate to 3 decimal places, Spearman's rank correlation coefficient for these data.
(b) The equivalent rank correlation coefficient for 1986 attendances compared with 1991 was +0.724.

By reference to this value and the one obtained in part (a), comment on the differences apparent. [NEAB]

24. In a ski jumping contest each competitor made two jumps. The orders of merit for the fifteen competitors who completed both jumps are shown in the following table:

Ski jumper	A	B	C	D	E	F	G	H	I	J	K	L	M	N	O
First jump	8	10	15	3	9	2	11	1	12	4	5	13	6 =	6 =	14
Second jump	5	15	6	1	12	2	14	3	7 =	10	11	7 =	4	13	7 =

(a) Calculate Spearman's rank correlation coefficient for these data.
(b) What does this tell us about the skiers' performances on the two jumps?
(c) State what you would conclude if from three further sets of rankings, involving the same number of skiers, the following values for Spearman's rank correlation coefficient were obtained.
(i) –0.04 (ii) 0.92 (iii) –1.14 [NEAB]

25. The table below shows the weather recorded on Monday 14 March 1997 in ten Scottish towns.

WEATHER

Last night's reports for 24 hours to 6 pm

	Sunshine hours	Maximum temperature °F	Weather (day)	Rank sunshine hours	Rank temperature		
Aberdeen	2.7	36	snow				
Aviemore	1.8	32	cloudy				
Edinburgh	0.2	33	cloudy				
Eskdalemuir	0.0	34	cloudy				
Glasgow	0.2	39	cloudy				
Kinloss	2.6	37	bright				
Lerwick	3.4	35	snow				
Leuchars	5.7	38	bright				
Tiree	1.2	40	bright pm				
Wick	6.4	37	snow am				

Source: *The Guardian*, 15 March 1997

(a) Rank each town in relation to hours of sunshine and maximum temperature °F.

(b) Using the formula $1 - \dfrac{6\sum d^2}{n(n^2 - 1)}$ calculate Spearman's rank correlation coefficient for these data.

(c) Comment on the correlation shown.

(d) Suppose the equivalent rank correlation coefficients for Saturday 12 March and Sunday 13 March were, respectively, +0.07 and –0.95.

What would these two values suggest about the relationship between daily hours of sunshine and maximum temperature?

(i) Saturday value (ii) Sunday value [NEAB]

6 Analysing data over time—trends and forecasting

> *First get your facts: then you can distort them at your leisure*
> Mark Twain

Charts and graphs can be used to show changes over time.

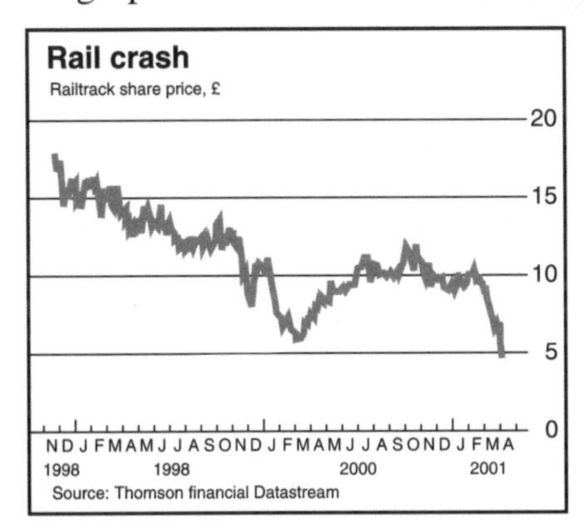

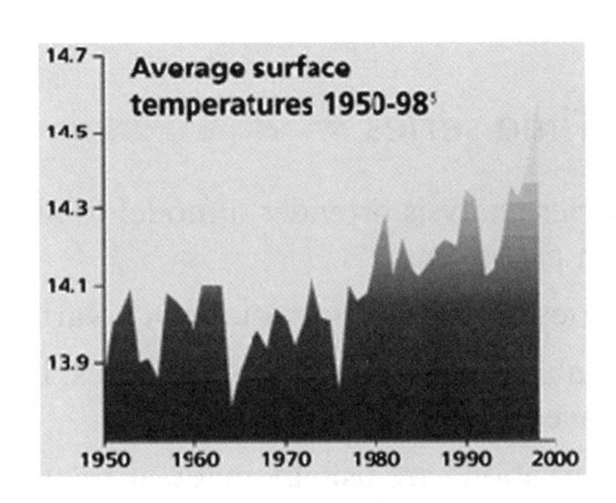

This unit will show you how to

- Draw time series graphs and trend lines
- Calculate moving averages and seasonal variation
- Draw and interpret Z charts
- Find index numbers
- Interpret Output Gap Charts
- Calculate population averages

Before you start

You should be able to answer these questions

1 Find the mean of
(a) 6, 18, 37, 14 and 22 (b) 29, 36, 18, 22, 13 and 14

2 Work out these test results as percentages.
(a) 48 marks from a total of 80 (b) 55 marks from a total of 75

3 Write as ratios
(a) 8 girls to 15 boys (b) 30 red to 13 black pens

4 Draw axes numbered from 0 to 8.
Plot the following points A(3, 4) B(2, 7) C(4, 1) D(6, 5).

Forecasts are based on past behaviour of collected data; the assumption being that past trends will continue for a reasonable length of time.

What counts as reasonable depends on the variable. Salary changes are likely to be seen over a period of years while cost of heating a house changes with each season. However even these costs can show a trend over a longer period of time.

For example, sales of lollies and ice-cream change weekly depending on the weather, there are trends in sales depending on the time of year and over several years a different trend may be observed.

6.1 Time series

Time series analysis provides a model to allow for future planning based on past events.

Time series data are observations of a variable over a period of time.

The variable could be temperature, sales, heating costs, number unemployed, ...

The observations are usually made at regular time intervals.

Drawing graphs & seasonal variation

Time series data is displayed as a series of plotted points on a graph with time on the horizontal axis.

Example

The quarterly heating bills over three years for a household are given in the table.

	Jan.–March	April–June	July–Sept.	Oct.–Dec.
Quarter	1st	2nd	3rd	4th
1996	£80	£54	£47	£75
1997	£88	£68	£53	£82
1998	£97	No bill available	£60	£89

Plot the data on a time series graph.

What does your graph show?

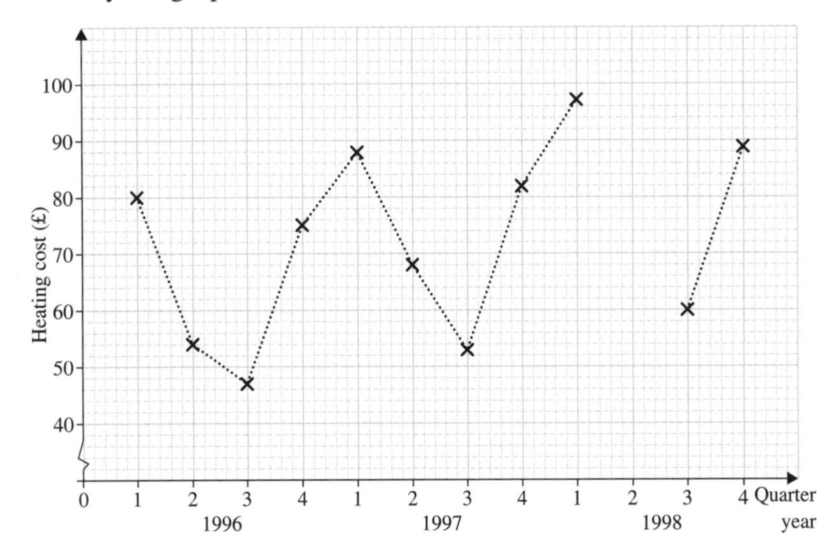

There are no heating bills issued to this household during the intervening months, so joining the points has no real meaning but is often done to help spot trends.

The graph shows that quarterly heating bills fall and rise throughout the year. This pattern is repeated the following year. This is due to seasonal variation and the need for more heating during the winter months.

Seasonal variation is the regular rise and fall over a fixed period of time. It is sometimes called cyclical variation.

If you ignore the seasonal variations you can see the general trend of the data. For example, if you look at the first quarter only you will see that the general trend is that heating costs are rising.

General trend is the underlying long-term trend. It is important in forecasting. It is sometimes called secular variation.

Predicting using trend lines

The general trend can be shown on the graph by drawing a trend line. Look at the general trend of the data and draw a line through the middle of the data.

Here is the trend line for the example on this page.

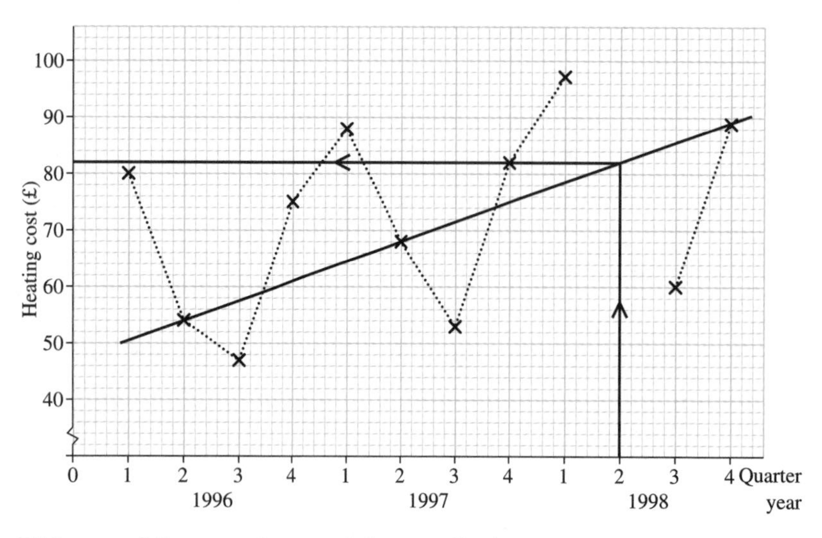

In this example the general trend is increasing. This means that your line should slope upwards. The data peaks and falls with every four points plotted so for each cycle there should be two points above the line and two points below the line.

This trend line can be used for prediction.

For example, you can predict that the second quarter of 1988 had a bill of around £82.

Sometimes a random event will cause an unusually large or small value. For example, the second quarter of 1998 may have been a very cold Spring. This would result in a different heating bill to the one predicted.

Chance events cause random variation.

Exercise 6A

1. The table shows the quarterly electricity bills for a bungalow over three years.

Quarter	1st	2nd	3rd	4th
1987	£70.00	£30.00	£20.00	£69.00
1988	£75.00	£34.50	£28.50	£75.00
1989	£79.00	£41.00	No bill available	£84.00

Plot the data on a time series graph and draw a trend line by eye. Use your trend line to estimate the missing electricity bill.

2. The table shows the half-yearly profits made by a toy shop.

Year	1996	1997	1998	1999	2000
Jan.–June	£21 000	£21 000	£24 500	£26 000	£27 500
July–Dec.	£30 000	£34 000	£35 000	£37 500	£39 000

Plot the data on a time series graph and draw a trend line by eye. Suggest a reason why the profits for the second half of the year should be more than in the first half of the year.

3. The numbers of people absent from work at a small factory were recorded.

	Monday	Tuesday	Wednesday	Thursday	Friday
Week 1	12	3	2	3	6
Week 2	11	3	3	4	7
Week 3	11	4	2	3	6

Plot the data on a time series graph and draw a trend line by eye. Suggest a reason why there should be more absenteeism on Monday and Friday.

4. A cinema manager had been asked to forecast how much profit he might make in the next month. He decided to do this by monitoring the number of people visiting his cinema over the past eight weeks.

Week	1	2	3	4	5	6	7	8
Attendance	9700	9400	10 500	9500	9600	9300	9550	9400

(a) Suggest a reason why attendance in week 3 is higher than the other weeks.
(b) Plot these values on a time series graph.
Draw a trend line by eye. What does the trend line suggest?
(c) Discuss what other factors the cinema manager should consider when forecasting next month's profit.

Moving averages

An efficient and practical way of finding the trend and hence making accurate predictions is to find the moving averages for a set of data.

So long as you choose a whole cycle to average, this should eliminate any seasonal variations.

> Moving averages tend to reduce the amount of variation present in a time series, leaving only the trend.

You use a 4-point moving average when the data is based on four quarters in a year, for example phone bills, gas bills etc.

Example

(a) Calculate moving averages for the data in the example on page 196.
(b) Use these averages to draw a trend line for the data and use it to estimate:
(i) the bill for the second quarter of 1998, (ii) the bill for the first quarter of 1999.

(a) Using a 4-point average, you calculate the average for every four consecutive data points.

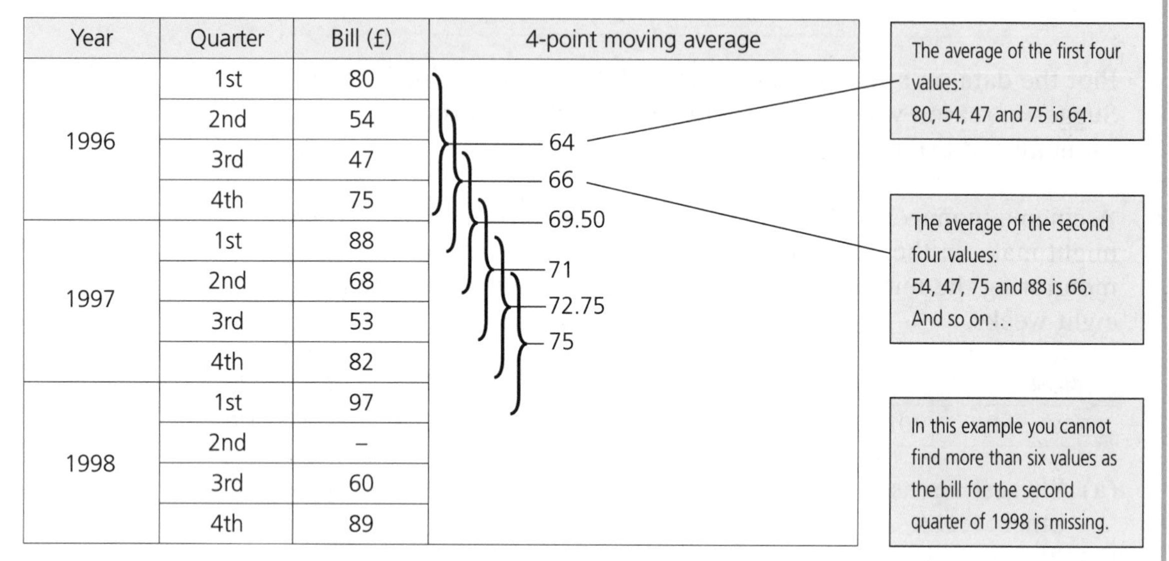

Year	Quarter	Bill (£)	4-point moving average
1996	1st	80	
	2nd	54	64
	3rd	47	66
	4th	75	69.50
1997	1st	88	71
	2nd	68	72.75
	3rd	53	75
	4th	82	
1998	1st	97	
	2nd	–	
	3rd	60	
	4th	89	

The average of the first four values: 80, 54, 47 and 75 is 64.

The average of the second four values: 54, 47, 75 and 88 is 66. And so on…

In this example you cannot find more than six values as the bill for the second quarter of 1998 is missing.

Plot each of the averages at the midpoint of its range.

For example the first moving average, 64, is plotted midway between the second and third quarter of 1996. The second is plotted between the third and fourth quarter of 1996 and so on.

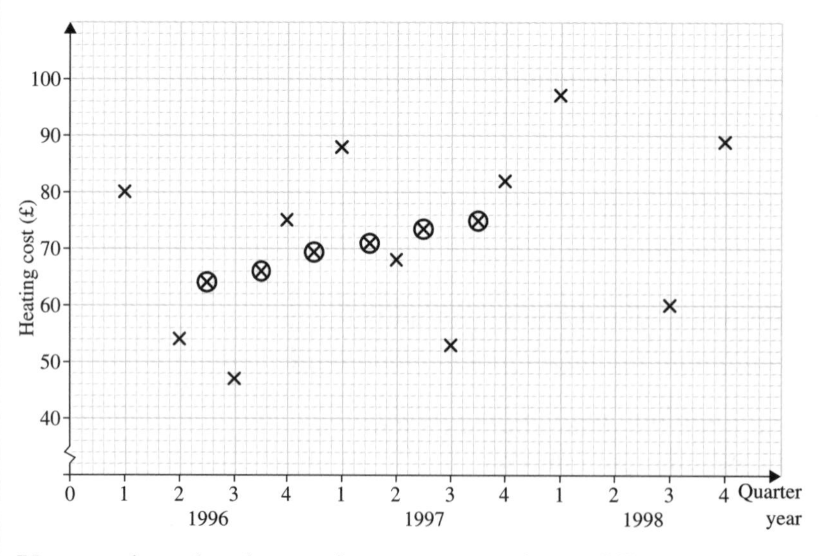

You need to plot the moving averages using a different colour from the time series data or circle them to tell easily which is which.

(b) Draw the best straight line you can through the moving averages. This is a trend line based upon moving averages.

Note how much easier it is to draw the trend line using moving averages.

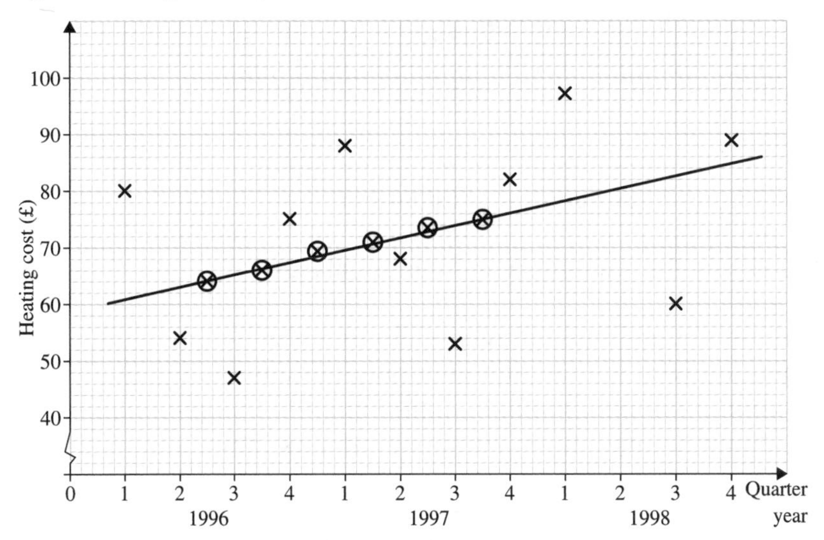

(i) To estimate the bill for the second quarter you need to consider where the moving average would have been and work out what the missing value is. Let the missing value (second quarter 1998) be £y.

The moving average you would calculate would be: $\dfrac{53 + 82 + 97 + y}{4}$

53, 82 and 97 are the bills for the third and fourth quarters in 1997 and the first and second quarters in 1998.

This moving average would have been plotted between the fourth quarter in 1997 and the first quarter in 1998. Reading from the trend line this gives £77. So:

$$\frac{53 + 82 + 97 + y}{4} = 77$$

$$\frac{232 + y}{4} = 77 \qquad 232 + y = 308 \qquad y = 76$$

An estimate for the missing bill is £76.

(ii) To predict a future value you can continue the trend line and extrapolate.
From the trend line the first quarter in 1999 is £88.
The first quarter in 1996 is £20 above the trend line. This is called **Seasonal Effect**.
The seasonal effect for the first quarter of 1997 is £18.50 and for 1998 is £18.

A value from the graph **below** the trend line would be a **negative** number.

The first quarter average seasonal effect is $\dfrac{20 + 18.5 + 18}{3} = 18.83$. This is called Average Seasonal Variation.

The predicted estimated bill for the first quarter in 1999 is £88 + £18.83 = £106.83 (trend line value plus average seasonal variation).

Seasonal effect at a given data point is the difference between the actual value and the value read from the trend line at that point.

Average seasonal variation is the average of the seasonal effects for the same point in each cycle.

Exercise 6B

1. (a) For the data given in Exercise 6A question 1, calculate appropriate moving averages.
   (b) Draw a new graph and plot the data given and the calculated moving averages.
   (c) Draw a trend line and use it to estimate the missing electricity bill.
   (d) Compare and comment on your answer with your previous answer.
   (e) Find the average seasonal variation for the first quarter.
   (f) Predict the value of the electricity bill for the first quarter of 1990.

2. (a) For the data given in Exercise 6A question 2, state why it would be appropriate to calculate 2-point moving averages.
   (b) Calculate 2-point moving averages for these data.
   (c) Draw a new graph and plot the original data and your moving averages.
   (d) Draw a trend line and use it to predict the half-yearly profits for 2001.

3. (a) For the data given in Exercise 6A question 3, calculate appropriate moving averages.
   (b) Draw a new graph and plot the original data and your calculated moving averages.
   (c) Use your moving averages to draw a trend line.
   (d) Use your trend line to predict the number of absentees on the Monday and Tuesday of the following week.

4. A street trader records his sales every four months. They were:

	1996	1997	1998	1999
Jan.–April	£315	£325	£330	£350
May–Aug.	£360	£375	£390	Figures missing
Sept.–Dec.	£410	£440	£465	£500

   (a) Plot the data on a time series graph.
   (b) Calculate appropriate moving averages and plot these on the same graph.
   (c) Use your moving averages to draw a trend line.
   (d) Use your trend line to estimate the missing sales figure for May–August 1999.
   (e) Find the average seasonal variation for January–April.
   (f) Predict the sales figure for the first four months of 2000.

6.2 Z charts

You can review progress of a project or business over different timescales, short term, long term and intermediate term.

- ✦ In the short term: what's happening each week or each month
- ✦ In the long term: a projection of growth or decline without seasonal variation
- ✦ The intermediate term: cumulative effect of how short term achievement is connected to longer term goals

The three ways of exploring the data can be shown in one diagram, a Z-Chart, as three connected graphs.

Example

The table gives the sales, in millions of units, for a company. Data has been collected each month.

	This month	Total since March	Rolling 12 month total
March	5	5	46
April	2	7	45
May	5	12	47
June	10	22	46
July	3	25	48
August	5	30	47
September	7	37	49
October	2	39	50
November	4	43	51
December	2	45	50
January	7	52	58
February	3	55	55

The middle column for the cumulative total is calculated just for the year that is shown.

The final column includes past data from the previous year so figures from two years are needed for the calculation. It is calculated by adding a new month and dropping a month from the previous year.

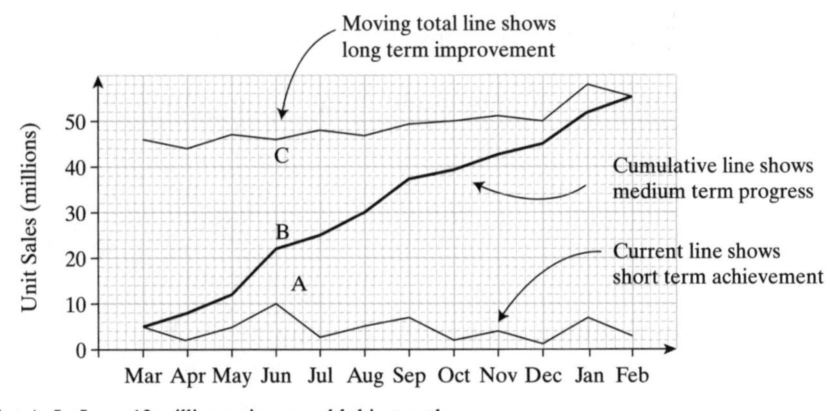

e.g. Point A: In June, 12 million units are sold this month
Point B: 22 million have been sold since March, the start of this financial year
Point C: 46 million have been sold over the last 12 months

The medium term line shows how sales have built throughout the year.
The short term line shows changes month by month.
The long term line for the 12 month rolling total shows an upward trend.

Z-Charts are used to show:

- The original actual data: the short term line
- The long term trend: this is a moving seasonal total and relies on having data across two seasons
- The intermediate effect: the cumulative total for that season or period and connects the short and long term lines.

Exercise 6C

1. The table gives production figures, in thousands of units, for a company.

   Draw a Z-Chart for this data and comment on the trend shown by the graph.

	This month	Total since April	Rolling 12 month total
April	7	7	68
May	8	15	70
June	5	20	71
July	6	26	73
August	12	38	75
September	16	54	74
October	9	63	75
November	3	66	77
December	4	70	82
January	7	77	80
February	6	83	84
March	3	86	86

2. The table shows the number of hits, in tens of thousand, on a website.

	Jan	Feb	March	April	May	June	July	Aug	Sept	Oct	Nov	Dec
This month	10	12	13	11	10	8	9	8	5	6	7	7
Cumulative total	10	22	35	46	56	64	73	81	86	92	99	106
Rolling 12 month total	128	125	120	117	114	116	117	112	115	110	108	106

   Draw a Z-Chart for this data and comment on the trend shown by the graph.

3. The Z-Chart shows the sales, in hundreds, for a cottage industry selling jars of honey.

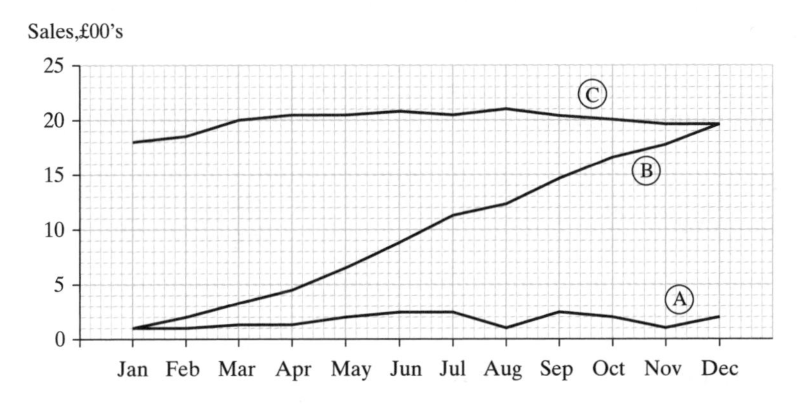

(a) How many jars of honey were sold in (i) July, (ii) November?
(b) How many jars of honey were sold in the first six months of this year?
(c) How many jars of honey were sold in the 12 months until August?

4. The Z-Chart shows the sales, in thousands of units, for a company.

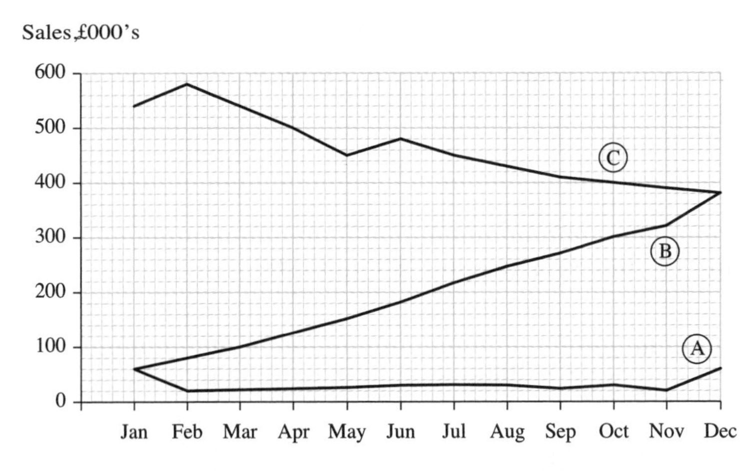

(a) How many units were sold in (i) March, (ii) June?
(b) How many units were sold in the last four months of this year?
(c) How many units were sold in the 12 months until May?
(d) Comment on the trend in sales for this company.

6.3 Index numbers

An index number is a measure that shows average changes in price, quantity or value of an item or group of items over a period of time.

An index number is a percentage which gives the value or size of a quantity relative to a standard number, or base.

The **standard number** is the value from a previous point in time known as the base year.

$$\text{Index number} = \frac{\text{quantity}}{\text{quantity in base year}} \times 100$$

Simple index numbers

A simple example of an index number is a **price relative**.

A price relative shows how the price of goods changes over time. It is calculated as a percentage of its value at a given base year.

$$\text{Price relative} = \frac{\text{price}}{\text{price in base year}} \times 100$$

Example

The table shows the price, to the nearest pound, of a toy as it rose and fell in popularity.

Year	1998	1999	2000
Price	8	15	6

Using 1998 as the base year, find the price relative in 1999 and 2000. Comment on these indices.

$$\text{The price relative for 1999} = \frac{\text{price in 1999}}{\text{price in 1998}} \times 100$$

$$= \frac{15 \times 100}{8} = 187.5$$

This means that the price of the toy in 1999 is 187.5% of its price in 1998. It is 87.5% more expensive.

$$\text{The price relative for 2000} = \frac{\text{price in 2000}}{\text{price in 1998}} \times 100$$

$$= \frac{6 \times 100}{8} = 75 \text{ (the price relative)}$$

This means that the price of the toy in 2000 is 75% of its price in 1998. It is 25% (= 100 – 75) less expensive than it was in 1998.

The value of the index number (price relative) for the chosen base year is always given as 100.

In the example above this could be written as 1998 = 100.

Example

A product's index numbers for three years are:

Year	1995	1996	1997
Index	100	105	126

(a) Which year is taken as the base year?
(b) What do the index numbers tell you about the price of the product?
(c) Find the price of the product in 1997 if its price in 1996 was £630.
(d) If 1996 is to become the new base year, find the new index number for 1997. Comment on this new index number.

(a) 1995 is the base year because its index is 100.
(b) The index numbers suggest that the price of the product is increasing year on year. There was a 5% increase from 1995 to 1996 and an increase of 26% from 1995 to 1997.
(c) In 1997 the price is 126% of the 1995 price: 126% = £?
The price in 1996 is 105% of the 1995 price: 105% = £630

$$\frac{126}{105} = \frac{?}{630} \qquad \frac{126 \times 630}{105} = ? \qquad ? = £756$$

(d) If 1996 is the new base year then its index will be 100.

The index for 1997 relative to 1996 $= \frac{126}{105} \times 100 = 120$

This index number, 120, means that the price increased by 20% from 1996 to 1997.

Exercise 6D

1. The price of a 200 g jar of coffee in 1997 was £3. In 2000 the same jar of coffee cost £3.25. Calculate an index number (price relative) using 1997 as the base year.

2. In 1998 the price of a new small car (basic model) was £7400. The same car would have cost £6950 in 1996. Calculate a price relative using 1996 = 100.

3. In January 2000 unleaded petrol cost 84p/litre. In January 2001 it cost 77p/litre. Calculate a price relative using 2000 as the base year.

4. The price relative for a one-day travel card to London in 2001 is 116.7, using 1998 as the base year. If the price of the travel card in 1998 was £4.20, calculate its price, to the nearest 10p, in 2001.

5. The selling price of a scooter had an index of 132 in 1999 where 1995 = 100. If the selling price of the scooter in 1999 was £99, find its selling price in 1995.

6. A toyshop restocks each year after its summer sale and then always changes the price of its own brand toys. The year the shop opened is used as the base year. The table below gives the index numbers used by the shop for price changes.

Year	1992	1993	1994	1995	1996
Index	100	105	112	120	136

(a) In which year did the shop open?
(b) What do the index numbers tell you about the prices of the shop's own brand toys?
(c) If the shop's own brand tricycle cost £18 in 1992, how much would it cost in 1994?
(d) In 1996 the shop's own brand play-house cost £170. Find its selling price in 1994.
(e) If 1995 is to become the new base year, find the index number for 1996.

7. In 1993 the retail prices of a washing machine and a dishwasher were £180 and £300 respectively. In 1997 equivalent models cost £252 and £390 respectively.

(a) Using 1993 as the base year, calculate index numbers for each item.
(b) Which item had the greatest percentage increase in price?
(c) Which item had the greatest actual increase in price?
(d) Comment on your answers to parts (b) and (c).

6.4 Chain base numbers

To find out how the price of an item has changed over a year, you use the previous year as the base year.

A chain base index number gives the relative value of an item using the previous year as the base year.

A chain base index number tells you the annual percentage change.

Using chain base index numbers:

- The increases and decreases in price are always relative to the previous year.
- The base year changes for each calculation.

Example

The table shows the price changes over four years of a child's toy as it rose and fell in popularity:

Year	1998	1999	2000	2001
Price (£)	8	15	6	3

Find the chain base index number for each year.
What do the chain base index numbers show?

The index number for 1999 $= \frac{15}{8} \times 100 = 187.5$ (Base year is 1998)

The index number for 2000 $= \frac{6}{15} \times 100 = 40$ (Base year is 1999)

The index number for 2001 $= \frac{3}{6} \times 100 = 50$ (Base year is 2000)

This shows that the price of the child's toy increased by 87.5%, then decreased by 60% (= 100 – 40), then decreased by 50% (= 100 – 50).

Exercise 6E

1. The chain base index numbers for successive years for several different items are given below. Describe the price changes for each item during this time.

   (a) 150, 160, 170 (b) 98, 120, 156 (c) 100, 100, 100
   (d) 140, 100, 90 (e) 125, 80, 100

2. The prices of a child's shoes are given in the table.

Year	1990	1991	1992	1993	1994
Price (£)	12	20	25	29	35

   Calculate the annual percentage change (chain base index numbers) for the price of the shoes.

3. The list price of a second-hand car over successive years is as follows:

Year	1993	1994	1995	1996	1997
Price (£)	6000	3600	2500	1800	1450

   Use the chain base method to calculate index numbers for the price of the car. Comment on your results.
   Using 1993 as the base year, calculate an index number for 1996.
   Compare and comment upon your index numbers for 1996 using these two methods.

4. The index numbers for a toyshop's own brand toys are given in the table.

Year	1992	1993	1994	1995	1996
Index	100	105	112	120	136

Recalculate the index numbers using the chain base method to find the annual percentage change in the toy prices.

5. The index numbers in the table show the annual percentage change in price.

Year	1986	1987	1988	1989	1990
Index	100	120	124	124	110

Calculate the index numbers for 1987 to 1990 using 1986 as the base year. Comment on the 1990 price compared with the price in 1986.

Weighted index numbers

Bronze is made using 92% copper and 8% tin.
If the price of either element changes then the cost of producing bronze also changes. The change in cost is affected more by the cost of copper than by the cost of tin.

A price index for bronze needs to reflect the different proportions of copper and tin so you need a weighted index number to help calculate any change in cost.

To calculate a weighted index number you:

- calculate the index number for each element, then
- find the weighted average of those elements.

The index is weighted according to the importance of each element; that is the contribution of each element to the index.

$$\text{Weighted index number} = \frac{\Sigma\,(\text{index number} \times \text{weight})}{\Sigma\,(\text{weights})}$$

Example

The table gives average price per ton for copper and tin for two years.

	1950	1955	Weight
Copper	£178	£351	92
Tin	£746	£740	8

Using 1950 as the base year, find the weighted average for the change in cost. What does the weighted average show?

Copper index number $= \frac{351}{178} \times 100 = 197.191\ldots$

Copper index number × weight $= 197.191\ldots \times 92 = 18\,141.57\ldots$

Tin index number $= \frac{740}{746} \times 100 = 99.1957\ldots$

Tin index number × weight $= 99.1957\ldots \times 8 = 793.5656\ldots$

Total weight $= \Sigma$ weights $= 92 + 8 = 100$.

$$\text{Weighted index number for bronze} = \frac{18\,141.57\ldots + 793.5656\ldots}{100} = \frac{18\,935.1\ldots}{100} = 189.35 \text{ (to 2 d.p.)}$$

This shows that the average price of the raw materials to produce bronze increased by 89.35% (to 2 d.p.) from 1950 to 1955.

Remember: The price relative is the index number. You can see how to calculate it on page 206.

Exercise 6F

The table gives the market price in US dollars per tonne of six metals on the last trading day of the year. All prices have been rounded to the nearest $10.

	Copper	Nickel	Lead	Tin	Zinc
1992	2280	5920	450	5780	1060
1993	1770	5300	470	4760	1000
1994	3040	8870	650	6020	1140
1995	2800	7940	720	6280	1000
1996	2220	6350	700	5790	1050
1997	1720	5990	560	5400	1090

For questions 1–5, find the weighted index for the following alloys.

1. Brass (70% copper, 30% zinc) for 1994 with base year = 1993.
2. Bell metal (78% copper, 22% tin) for 1996 with base year = 1995.
3. Soft solder (60% tin, 40% lead) for 1995 with base year = 1994.
4. Gun metal (85% copper, 10% zinc, 5% tin) for 1993 with base year = 1992.
5. Statuary bronze (90% copper, 5% tin, 4% zinc, 1% lead) for 1996 with base year = 1993.

6. A company produces gilding metal (15% zinc, 85% copper) and Dutch metal (20% zinc, 80% copper). Calculate which of these two metal's costs changed the most from 1996 to 1997.

7. Calculate a chain base index for British 'silver' coins (75% copper, 25% nickel) from 1992 to 1997. Comment on the cost of producing British silver coins during this time.

8. £1 coins consist of 70% copper, 24.5% zinc and 5.5% nickel. Calculate a chain base index for £1 coins from 1992 to 1996.

Retail Price Index (RPI)

The **retail price index** is a form of weighted index which is used to monitor changes and make comparisons. However it only shows change in the cost of living of an 'average' person or family.

A bakery would be interested in the weighted index for the ingredients of bread, pastries and so on for cost analysis.

The retail price index is a weighted mean of the price relatives of goods and services.

Weightings are chosen to reflect the spending habits of an 'average' household.

In 1914 the RPI was based on what the government thought of as essential expenditure of working class families and assigned weights of food 60%, housing 16%, clothing 12%, heat & light 8% and miscellaneous 4%.

These weights became out of date with the rising standard of living. These categories needed revising with changes in lifestyle, for example entertainment, use of cars, holidays and so on.

Since the Second World War the index has been calculated on what households *actually* bought. In 1962 it was decided to revise the weightings annually, based on the actual expenditure of the previous three

Activity

Conduct a survey of expenditure for your class or a group of friends.

Decide how you will classify spending habits.

Find average prices for goods (magazines, CDs etc) bought now and over the past three years. You could use the internet to help you.

Calculate a retail price index for your group.

Discuss what implications this could have for pocket money increases, Saturday job pay rises and so on.

General Index of Consumer Price (CPI)

The consumer price index (CPI) is a measure of the average price of consumer goods and services bought by households. The percentage change in the CPI is a measure of inflation. The CPI can be used to adjust for the effects of inflation in determining new annual pay scales, pensions and regulated prices of services. It forms the basis for the Government's inflation target which the Bank of England's Monetary Policy Committee is required to achieve.

Gross Domestic Product (GDP)

One measure of the national income and output for a country's economy is the gross domestic product (GDP). GDP is the amount of money raised in a country, excluding foreign earnings and investment. It is the total market value of all the goods and services produced in a year and is used as an indicator of the measure of wealth of a country.

6.5 Output gap charts

Output gap is a measure of the wealth of a country. It is used by economists to assess the degree of recession or growth in the economy.

Output gap is the difference between the potential amount of money that a country could achieve when it is most efficient and the actual amount of money earned in a country. Money is earned through the value of goods and services produced by a country in a year. Foreign earning or investment is not included.

A positive output gap means actual output is greater than potential output; the economy is growing and this could mean an increase of inflation.

A negative output gap means potential output is less than actual output; the economy is in recession.

Example

The chart shows the output gap of percentage production capacity from 1992 to 2007. Comment on the trend shown.

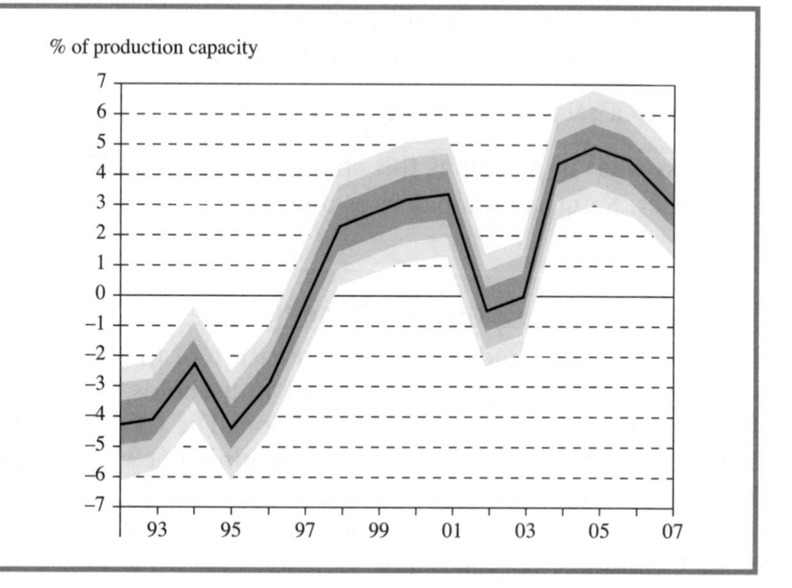

The output gap generally increased until 2001 when it fell then rose. It was strongly positive in 2006 and appears to be turning negative. There is no indication that actual and potential output are close to balance.

Exercise 6G

Comment on the changes in the economy of each country as shown by these output gap charts.

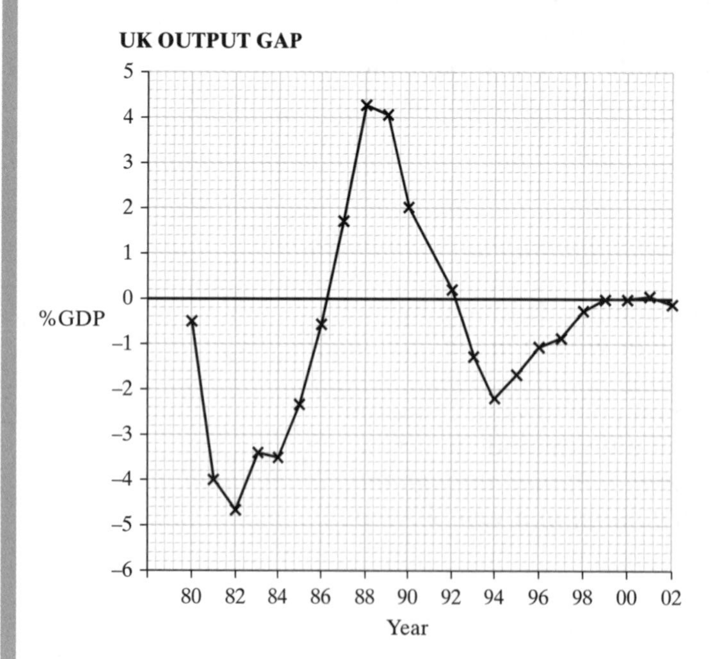

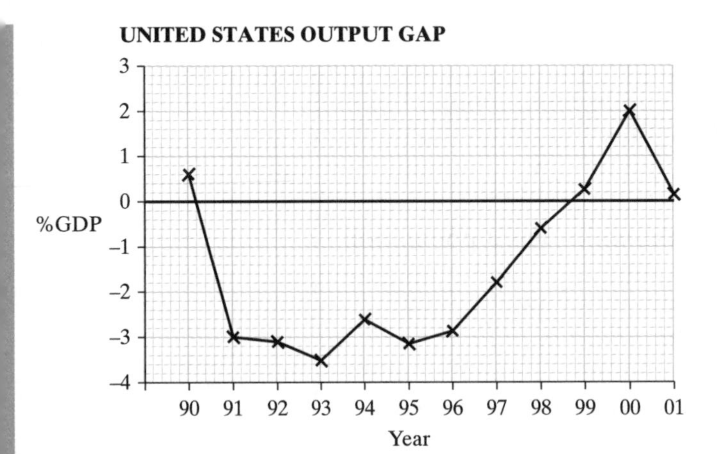

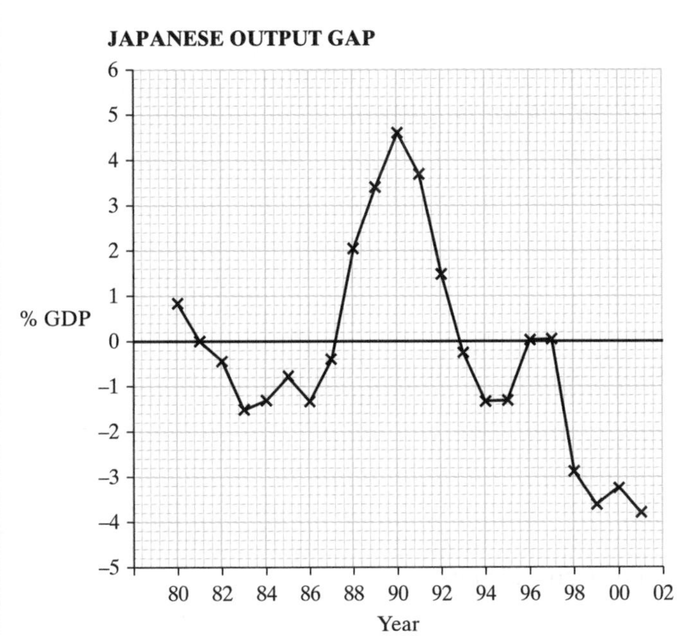

6.6 Population averages

The accurate recording and analysis of statistics, such as the number of births, deaths, marriages, crimes and accidents, are important for government departments to plan for the needs of housing, roads, education, health and so on.

These statistics are expressed as a number per thousand of the population. The actual total population is changing all the time as babies are born and people die, so the figure used can only be an estimate.

> Total population is the population at a specified time in the middle of the year.

> Population averages are given per 1000 of the population.

Crude rates

$$\text{Crude (birth/death/...) rate} = \frac{\text{number of (births/deaths/...)}}{\text{total population}} \times 1000$$

Example

There are 384 deaths in the town of Antville, which has a population of 16 000. Find the crude death rate.

$$\text{Crude death rate} = \frac{384}{16\,000} \times 1000 = 24$$

This means that there are 24 deaths per thousand of the population of Antville.

Example

This table gives the population and number of deaths for Brighthove.

Age group	Population	Number of deaths
0–14	3000	27
15–44	4000	33
45–64	4000	42
65+	1000	45
Totals	12 000	147

Find the crude death rate for Brighthove.

$$\text{Crude death rate} = \frac{147 \times 1000}{12\,000} = 12.25$$

This means that there are 12.25 deaths per thousand of the population of Brighthove.

Exercise 6H

1. There were 4350 house crimes reported in Dodge City. If Dodge City had 20 000 households, calculate its crude house crime rate.

2. Last year in Dangerville, which had a population of 18 900, there were 2835 road traffic accidents. These resulted in 567 deaths.
   (a) Calculate the crude (road traffic) accident rate in Dangerville.
   (b) Calculate the crude (road traffic accident) death rate in Dangerville.

3. The crude birth rate in Cupston, which had a population of 8000 women of child-bearing age, was 62. How many births were there in Cupston?

4. The crude unemployment rate in a small village with a population of 2500 was 42.5. How many of the villagers were unemployed?

5. The table shows the number of births, age of mother and female population for a town.

Age (years)	Female population	Number of births
Under 18	16 000	322
18–44	45 000	1247
45 & over	34 000	31

Using this information, calculate a crude birth rate for the town. Why is this crude birth rate a distortion of the true crude birth rate for the town?

Standardised rates

The death rate in an area with a large number of elderly people is likely to be higher than in an area where the population is younger.

To make comparisons of population averages between different areas of a country, or between different countries, you need to consider the age distribution of each area.

Standardised rates take account of the age distribution.

Standardised rates are a weighted mean of crude rates. The weights are standard population data, the percentage of a population for different age groups.

Example

The table shows the crude and standardised death rates for two areas, Area A and Area B.

	Area A	Area B
Crude death rate	24	12.5
Standardised death rate	19.8	17.3

(a) Make two comments on the rates for these two areas.
(b) Which area do you think has a greater population of elderly people? Give a reason for your answer.

(a) The crude rates for Area A is almost double that of Area B making it appear a very unhealthy place to live.
The standardised rates are more similar suggesting that there is much less difference in death rates between the two towns.
(b) Area A has a greater percentage of elderly people as the standardised death rate is lower in Area A than the crude death rate.

Exercise 6I

1. Joan is researching the health of two villages. The table shows the crude and standardised death rates for Antville and Brighthove.

	Antville	Brighthove
Crude death rate	17.8	26.2
Standardised death rate	19.9	19.3

(a) Make two comments on the crude and standardised rates for these two places.
(b) In which village would you prefer to live? Give a reason for your answer.

2. The table shows the crude and standardised birth rates for two places Clawtown and Dannington.

	Clawtown	Dannington
Crude birth rate	16.3	11.5
Standardised birth rate	14.8	14.2

(a) Make two comments on the crude and standardised rates for these two places.
(b) Which place do you think has a greater population of people in the 20–40 age group? Give a reason for your answer.

3. Mark is moving to a town. He is choosing between Earlsham and Frissom. The table shows the crude and standardised unemployment rates for the two towns.

	Earlsham	Frissom
Crude unemployment rate	28.9	14.7
Standardised unemployment rate	17.9	16.9

Compare the crude and standardised unemployment rates for these two towns and comment on your answer.

4. The table shows the crude and standardised accident rates for two cities.

	Grocaster	Henbury
Crude accident rate	22.1	13.7
Standardised accident rate	18.7	17.6

Compare the crude and standardised accident rates for these two cities and comment on your answer.

Summary of key points

- Trend lines on time series graphs show the general trend without seasonal variation.
- Index numbers show the rate of change over a period of time.
- Output gap charts show whether the economy is in recession or growth.
- Crude rates are used by governments when planning future provision of housing, health services and so on.
- Standardised rates are used to compare, for example, birth and death rates between different areas.

Links to the Real World

'Time is money' is especially true in the business world and in finance. Analysis of time series information attempts to understand the complexity of general economic factors over the long term by looking at the cyclical nature of business rather than short-term changes. This allows better management and more strategic financial decisions to be made. Time series forecasting is used to forecast the opening value of a share price based on past performance.

Index numbers produced by the Office for National Statistics are used principally in the field of economics. The Retail Price Index (RPI) has been measured continuously since 1947 and with the Consumer Price Index (CPI) it is used by government to set levels of pensions and benefits. Other sectors use these indices to set maintenance payments, house rents and in wage bargaining. Gross Domestic Product (GDP) is a measure of the wealth of a country.

Crude and standardised rates are used by government, in particular the health department, to monitor change and compare rates of mortality, incidence of disease and so on. For example the use of standardised rates allows a direct comparison to be made of the impact of a disease on mortality in different areas with different population profiles. Crude rates do not take account of the age structure within a population, but are useful when planning for improved provision of services in different areas.

Revision Exercise 6

1. On the 1st of January 2002 the population of Longtown was 12 027. The population of a neighbouring town, Greenfield, was 11 860. The following table gives the numbers of births and deaths for each town during 2002.

	Longtown	Greenfield
Births	129	214
Deaths	241	95

(a) Show that the crude birth rate for Longtown is 10.7
(b) Calculate the crude death rate for Longtown.
(c) The crude birth rate for Greenfield for 2002 is 18.0
The crude death rate for Greenfield for 2002 is 8.0
Which of the two towns has an increasing population?
Give a reason for your answer. [AQA]

2. (a) The table gives the population distribution by age in town Q and the number of deaths for each age group.

Age group	Population in thousands	Number of deaths
0 to under 17	25	463
17 to under 30	22	201
30 to under 45	23	257
45 to under 65	18	329
65 and over	14	589

Calculate the crude death rate for town Q.
(b) Why are standardized death rates better measures than crude death rates? [AQA]

3. The table shows the cost indices for renting a shop, using 1997 as the base year.

Year	1997	1998	1999	2000	2001	2002
Cost Index	100	115	96	118	110	113

(a) In which years did the rent fall?
(b) The annual rent was £6900 in 1998.
(i) Calculate the annual rent in 1997.
(ii) Calculate the Annual rent in 2002.
(c) In which year was the annual rent the highest?
(d) Calculate the percentage increase in the annual rent between 2001 and 2002. [AQA]

4. The number of weddings, in thousands, for 14 consecutive quarters are given in the table Some of the four-point moving averages have been calculated.

Year	Quarter	Number of weddings (thousands)	Four-point moving average (1 d.p.)
1996	1	41.0	
1996	2	91.4	79.4
1996	3	129.4	79.0
1996	4	55.8	77.9
1997	1	39.3	77.8
1997	2	87.1	77.6
1997	3	128.9	77.2
1997	4	54.9	76.8
1998	1	37.7	75.9
1998	2	85.6	76.2
1998	3	125.5	
1998	4	56.0	
1999	1	36.9	
1999	2	83.2	

(a) Calculate the value of the next **two** four-point moving averages.

(b) The original data is plotted on the grid.
Plot all the four-point moving averages on a copy of the same grid.

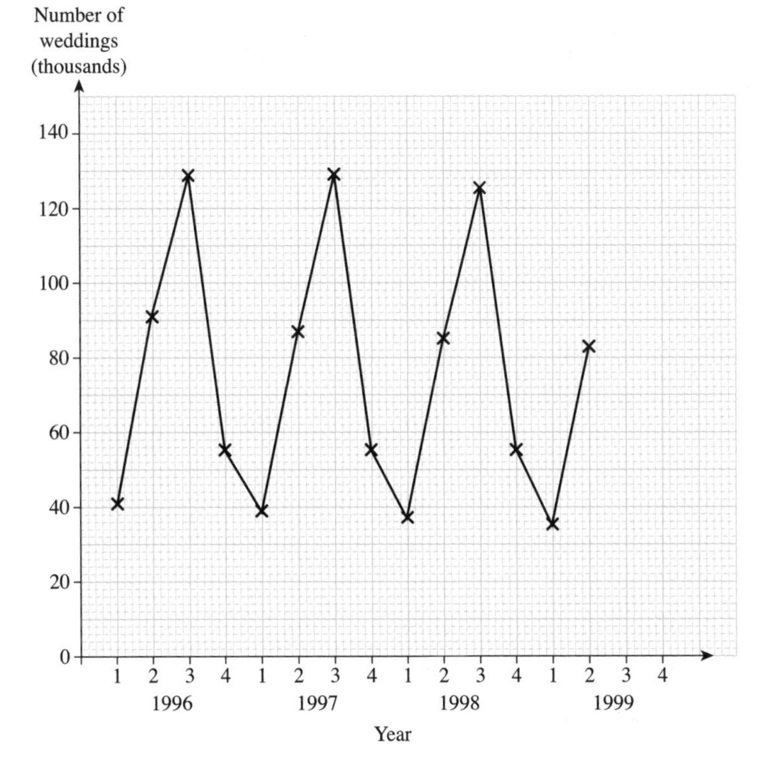

(c) The seasonal variations for quarter 3 are 52 000, 52 000 and 49 000. Use this information together with a trend line to obtain an estimate for the number of weddings in quarter 3 of 1999. [AQA]

5. A local newspaper investigates unemployment in the town of Stokeham.
The table gives unemployment data for Stokeham.

Age group	Population in thousands	Number unemployed	Standard population
16–24	16	1020	25%
25–44	28	1540	30%
45–54	32	1206	30%
55–64	14	680	15%

(a) Calculate the crude unemployment rate for Stokeham.
The standardized unemployment rate for Stokeham is 51.
(b) What is the advantage in using the standardized rate rather than the crude unemployment rate in this case?
(c) The nearby town of Bloomfield has a standardized unemployment rate of 71.4 per thousand.
Michelle is moving into one of these towns.
In which town would she stand a better chance of finding employment?
Give a reason for your answer. [AQA]

6. The table shows the number of visits to America by UK residents each quarter from 2002 to 2004.

Year	Quarter	Visits (tens of thousands)
2002	Q1	88
	Q2	100
	Q3	118
	Q4	114
2003	Q1	98
	Q2	106
	Q3	124
	Q4	118
2004	Q1	102
	Q2	116
	Q3	134
	Q4	126

Source: *Adapted from Social Trends 2005*

(a) The data for 2002 have been plotted on the time series graph. Copy and complete the graph.

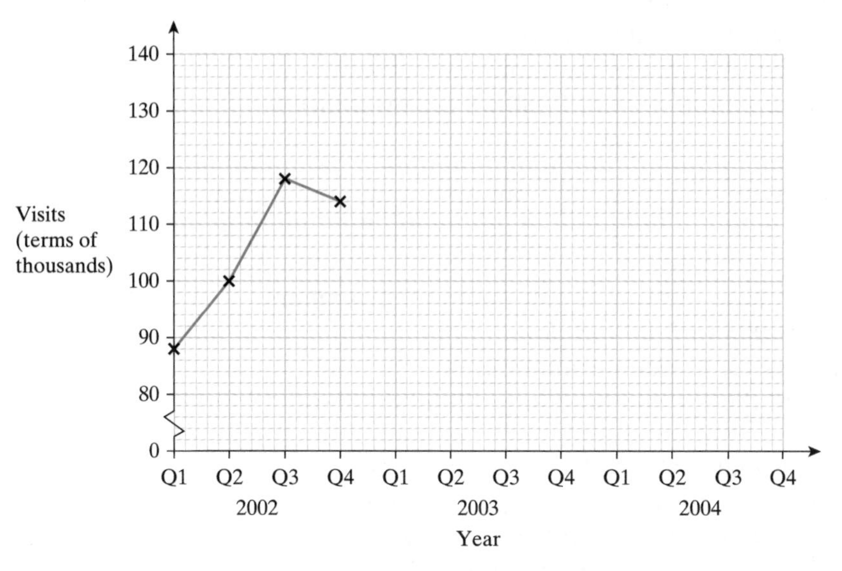

(b) Describe two different patterns in the data. [AQA]

7. The table shows the breakdown of the Retail Price Index at July 2004.

	Group	Weight	Index (1987 = 100)
1	Food	111	152.9
2	Catering	49	231.8
3	Leisure goods	46	99.1
4	Leisure services	70	251.3
5	Housing	209	263.8
6	Fuel and light	28	139.4
7	Household goods	71	145.3
8	Household services	59	180.4
9	Clothing and footwear	51	99.0
10	Personal goods and services	42	200.0
11	Motoring expenditure	146	184.5
12	Fares and other travel costs	21	215.6
13	Alcoholic drink	68	204.3
14	Tobacco	29	313.7

(Based on the Retail Price Index, Monthly Digest of Statistics, July 2004)

The 'All groups' index for July 2004 is 198.4

(a) (i) Calculate an 'All groups' index, **excluding** expenditure on both Alcoholic drink and Tobacco.
Give your answer to one decimal place.
(ii) Explain why the 'All groups' index has decreased.

(b) The table shows the annual cost of Rashid's car insurance for the past five years.

Year	2002	2003	2004	2005	2006
Annual cost (£)	500	546	670	640	625

(i) Use the chain base method to calculate index numbers for the years 2003 to 2006 inclusive.
Give your answers to one decimal place.
(ii) Describe what these chain base index numbers show. [AQA]

8. Fabro plc uses four raw materials, A, B, C and D, in the manufacture of a product. The ratio, by weight, of the four raw materials, A, B, C and D, needed to produce each item is 2 : 4 : 12 : 1, respectively. One kilogram of material D is used in the manufacture of one item. The costs of these raw materials in the years 1995–97 were as follows.

Cost per kilo (£)

Raw material	1995	1996	1997
A	2.50	2.50	3.00
B	1.00	1.20	1.50
C	4.00	4.50	4.50
D	5.00	5.00	6.00

(a) Show that the total raw material cost for **one** item in 1995 was £62.00.

(b) Calculate the raw material cost of producing **one** equivalent item in 1997.

(c) Use the results obtained in parts (a) and (b) to calculate, to one decimal place, a raw material cost index for 1997 using 1995 as base.

(d) An index of Fabro's labour costs is as follows.

Year	1995	1996	1997
Labour cost index	120	130	160

Calculate the percentage increase in these costs from 1995 to 1997.

(e) Compare the change in labour costs between 1995 and 1997 with the change in raw material costs. [NEAB]

9. The table shows the indices for bicycle insurance costs.
The base year for these indices is 1994.

Year	1994	1995	1996
Index	100	105	108

(a) What does the index number of 105 for 1995 tell you about insurance costs?

The cost of insuring a particular type of bicycle in 1995 was £31.50.

(b) (i) How much was the insurance in 1996?
(ii) What was the actual increase in cost for this insurance from 1994 to 1996?

In 1997 the insurance cost for this bicycle was £34.80.

(c) Calculate the index number for 1997. [SEG]

10. The price of a CD system was £480 in 1994 and £540 in 1995.

(a) Calculate the price index number for 1995 using 1994 as the base year.

The price index number for 1996 using 1994 as the base year was calculated to be 125.

(b) Calculate the price of the CD system in 1996.
(c) What was the percentage change in price of the CD system between 1994 and 1996?
(d) What was the percentage increase for the CD system during 1996? [SEG]

11. In January 1989 the cost per litre of petrol was 41.2 pence.
In January 1994 the cost per litre had increased to 51.5 pence.

(a) With 1989 as the base year, express the cost of petrol in January 1994 as an index number.
(b) With 1994 as the base year, the index number for the cost of petrol in January 1996 was 120.
Find the cost per litre of petrol in January 1996.
(c) Explain the meaning of the index number 120. [NEAB]

12. The table below shows the price of a mountain bike and a racing bike in 1988 and 1990.

	Price (£) 1988	Price (£) 1990	Price index (1990 relative to 1988)
Mountain bike	400	300	X
Racing bike	200	300	Y

(a) (i) Find the value of X, the price index of a mountain bike.
(ii) Find the value of Y, the price index of a racing bike.
(b) In 1995 the price index (relative to 1988) of a mountain bike was 100. What can you say about the 1995 price of a mountain bike?

13. The Managing Director of Crunch is keen to assess the impact that retail prices may have on sales. He therefore obtains, in summarized form, the following information from the Monthly Digest of Statistics.

Item group	Single Item Index 1995	Single Item Index 1998	Weights
Food	250	291	208
Alcoholic drink	305	310	77
Tobacco	358	364	38
Housing	308	320	149
Fuel and light	391	402	67

(a) (i) Show that the total weighted index of retail prices for 1995 is 299.
(ii) Work out the equivalent weighted index of retail prices for 1998.
(iii) Hence calculate the all item (aggregate) weighted index of retail prices for 1998 using 1995 as a base year.
(b) If the Food Group were excluded from the calculations in (a) (iii), what effect would this have had on the resultant index? Without further calculations justify your answer. [NEAB]

14.

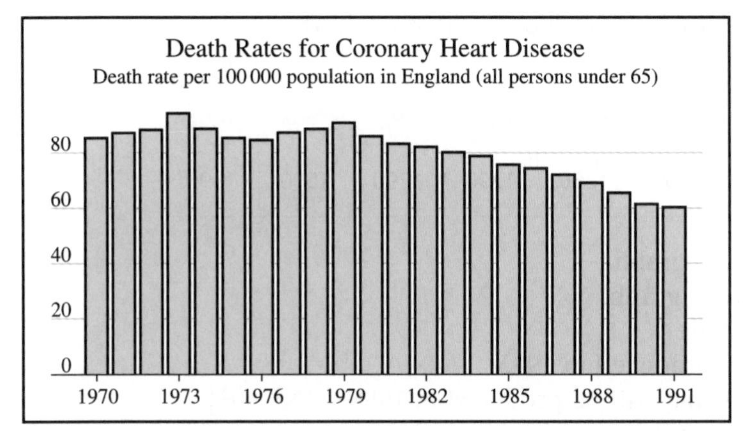

Source: The Guardian, 16 November 1993

The bar chart shows how the death rates for coronary heart disease have changed over the period 1970 to 1991.

(a) In which year was the highest death rate recorded?

The death rate for 1983 was 80.

In 1983 Burntwood, with a population of 85 000, recorded 71 deaths from heart disease.

(b) By suitable calculations show whether the 71 deaths recorded is higher or lower than the number you would expect from the Burntwood area.

The diagram shows a downward trend in death rates.

(c) Indicate a likely reason for this downward trend. [SEG]

15. The population of Alphaville was 7500 at the beginning of 1996.

(a) The crude birth rate per thousand for 1996 was exactly 3.2. How many births were there in 1996?

(b) The crude death rate per thousand (correct to 1 decimal place) for 1996 was 2.5.
How many deaths were there in 1996?

(c) What was the population of Alphaville at the end of 1996? (Assume that no one left or moved into the town.) [NEAB]

16. The table shows the number of cars produced in Britain, in the years shown, from 1984 to 1996.

Year	1984	1986	1988	1990	1992	1994	1996
Production of cars (thousands)	900	1000	1250	1290	1290	1500	1690

(a) Plot this information on a graph.
(b) Draw a trend line on your graph.
(c) Use your graph to estimate
   (i) the number of cars produced in 1985,
   (ii) the number of cars that will be produced in 1998. [NEAB]

17. The table below shows the number of licences issued for televisions from 1986 to 1993.

Year (X)	1986	1987	1988	1989	1990	1991	1992	1993
Number in millions (Y)	19.6	20.3	21.2	21.6	22.0	22.4	22.8	23.1

(a) Plot the time series on a graph.
(b) Draw the trend line by eye.
(c) Use your trend line to estimate the number of licences issued in 1994.
(d) State, with a reason, whether your answer to part (c) is likely to be too high or too low. [NEAB]

18. A school canteen manager notes the quarterly turnover as follows.

	Jan–Mar	Apr–June	July–Sept	Oct–Dec
1992	£7500	£5500	£2000	£8200
1993	£6700	£4300	£1600	£8200
1994	£5100	£3900	£1200	£7500

(a) Which year has the biggest turnover?
(b) Give a reason why the third quarter turnover is the lowest in each year.
(c) Plot the data on a graph.
(d) Draw the trend line by eye.
(e) What does the trend line tell you about the canteen's turnover? [SEG]

19. Leena wanted to estimate how much her next electricity bill might be.
She found her last 11 bills.
The table shows, in £, her last 11 quarterly bills.

	Spring	Summer	Autumn	Winter
1992	95	60	110	155
1993	108	66	120	170
1994	110	80	135	

(a) Plot these data on a graph.
(b) Calculate the 4-point moving average for these data.
(c) Plot the moving averages on the graph and draw the trend line.
(d) Use your trend line to predict the bill for Winter 1994. [SEG]

20. The following data give the quarterly sales, in £10 000's, of gardening equipment at the Green Fingers Garden Centre over a period of four years.

	Quarter			
	1st	2nd	3rd	4th
1992	20	26	24	18
1993	24	30	27	23
1994	26	34	31	25
1995	30	36	35	29

(a) Plot these values on a graph.
(b) Suggest a reason for the seasonal variation shown by your graph.
(c) Calculate the four-point moving averages for these data.
(d) Plot these moving averages on your graph.
(e) On your graph, draw a trend line by eye.
(f) Use your graph to estimate the sales during the first quarter of 1996. [SEG]

21. The table shows the amounts, in £1000s, deposited in a bank on each of 12 weekdays before Christmas.

	Mon	Tue	Wed	Thur	Fri
Week beginning 6/12	250	190	200	215	230
Week beginning 13/12	280	215	235	240	255
Week beginning 20/12	305	245			

(a) On a graph, plot the daily amount deposited.
(b) Calculate the 5-point moving averages for the data.
(c) Explain why a 5-point moving average is appropriate.
(d) Plot the moving averages on the graph and draw the trend line.
(e) Calculate the average daily variation for Wednesday.
(f) Use the daily variation in order to estimate the sum deposited on the next Wednesday. [SEG]

22. The table below shows the number of units of electricity used by a householder during eight successive quarters in 1995 and 1996.

	Electricity consumption (units)			
Year	Quarter 1	Quarter 2	Quarter 3	Quarter 4
1995	1450	1080	730	1280
1996	1630	1220	930	1460

(a) Draw a time series graph to represent the amounts of electricity used over the eight quarters.
(b) (i) What are the main seasonal trends shown by your graph?
(ii) What is the most likely explanation for them?
(c) Calculate appropriate moving averages for the data.
(d) Plot the moving averages on your graph.
(e) Draw by eye the trend line on the graph.
(f) The seasonal effects for Quarters 1 and 2 are as follows:

Seasonal effect	
Quarter 1	Quarter 2
+390	−77.5

Use this information and the trend line to provide seasonally adjusted forecasts for Quarter 1 and Quarter 2 of 1997.

7 Probability

It is remarkable that a science that began with the consideration of games of chance should be elevated to the rank of the most important subjects of human knowledge

Laplace

Probable impossibilities are to be preferred to improbable possibilities

Aristotle

You can be certain that the sun will rise in the morning.

This unit will show you how to

- Work out simple probabilities and expected frequencies
- Draw sample space and tree diagrams
- Use Venn diagrams to calculate probabilities
- Calculate probabilities for independent events
- Calculate probabilities for conditional events

Before you start

You should be able to answer these questions

1 Copy and complete the table to convert between fractions, decimals and percentages.

Fraction	Decimal	Percentage
$\frac{1}{4}$		
		60%
	0.375	
$\frac{17}{20}$		

2 Calculate.

(a) $\frac{1}{4}+\frac{1}{5}$ (b) $\frac{1}{3}+\frac{5}{8}$ (c) $\frac{2}{5}+\frac{4}{9}$

(d) $\frac{1}{6}\times\frac{1}{4}$ (e) $\frac{2}{7}\times\frac{1}{3}$ (f) $\frac{3}{4}\times\frac{5}{9}$

Consider the following statements:

- ✦ There's a fifty-fifty chance a coin lands on tails when it is tossed.
- ✦ It is highly unlikely that pigs will, one day, learn to fly.
- ✦ It is likely that a premier division football team will win the FA cup.

In all of these statements a prediction is made on the outcome of a future event.
Probability is a mathematical measure of how likely an outcome is to happen.

7.1 Simple probability

Words and phrases such as possible, very likely, evens or unlikely are used to describe the chance of an outcome happening.

Events can be shown on a likelihood scale.

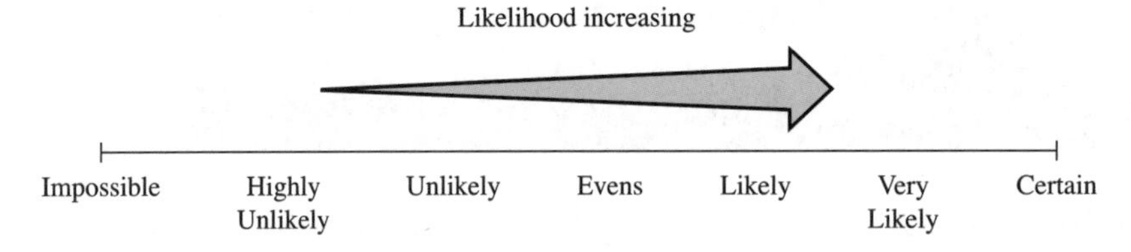

Example

Write these events where you think they should appear on a likelihood scale.
(a) A fair coin landing on heads.
(b) A score of 7 from an ordinary dice.
(c) It will snow in March in the UK.
(d) The sun rising tomorrow morning.

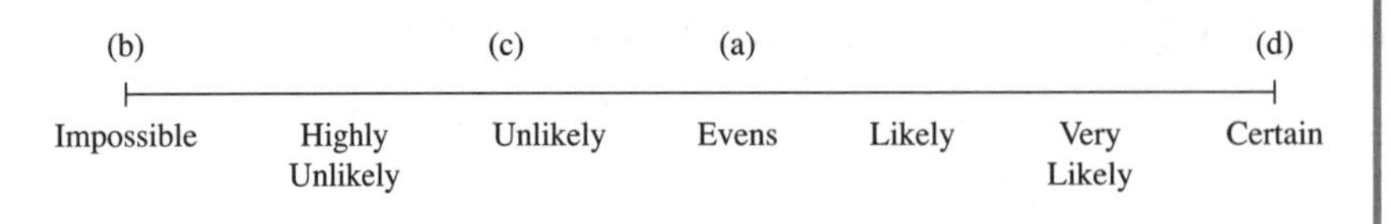

Activity

Where would you place the events 'It will snow in March' and 'An unlocked bicycle being stolen' on the likelihood scale?

What other information would you need that may influence your answer?

When a more exact measure of the chance of an outcome is needed, for example in insurance or medicine, probability is measured on a scale from 0 to 1

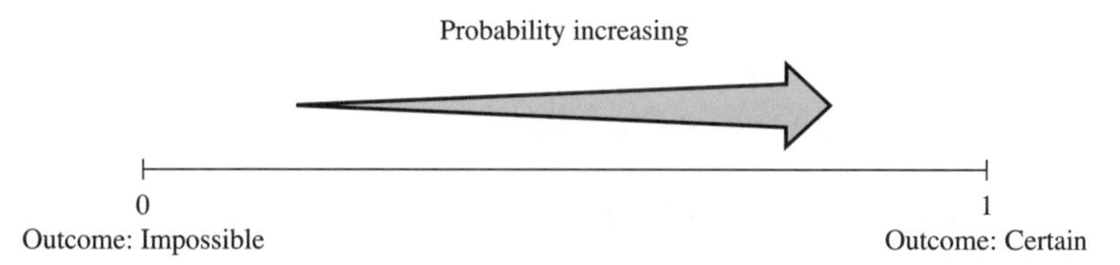

> Outcomes of events range from impossible with a probability of 0 to certain with a probability of 1.
>
> All other outcomes have a probability between 0 and 1.

Probability can be written as a fraction, decimal or percentage

Suppose there is a 70% chance that Spurs will win the FA cup, then you write

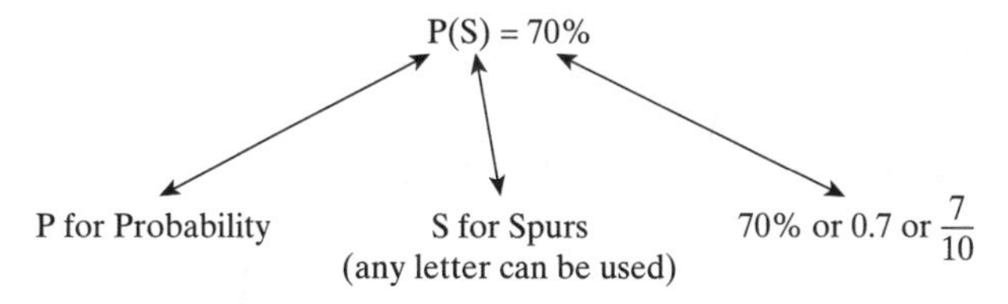

Example

Show these probabilities on a probability scale.

(a) P(S) = 0.7

(b) The probability of heads on a fair coin = $\frac{1}{2}$

(c) P(bank base rate decreasing next month) = 20%

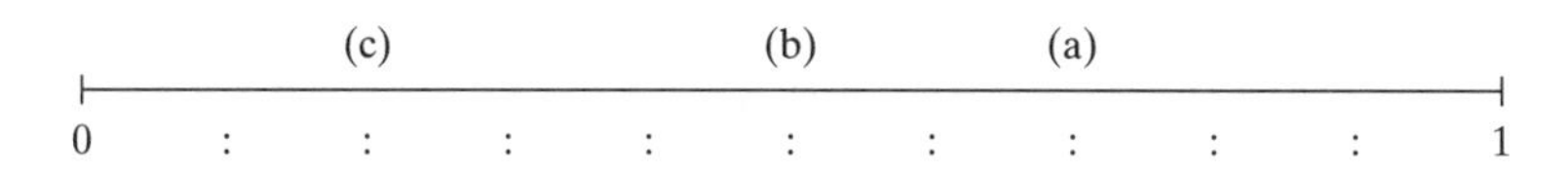

Exercise 7A

1. Choose words from the likelihood scale that best fit each of the following events.
   (a) A fair dice when rolled will land on a '6'.
   (b) A fair coin when spun will land on tails.
   (c) There will be a flood in a town in England next year.
   (d) The next pope elected will be female.

2. Draw a likelihood scale and mark on the scale the following events.
   (a) A card drawn from an ordinary pack of playing cards is a diamond.
   (b) A fair dice when rolled will show an even number.
   (c) A person chosen at random has red hair.
   (d) Today, someone will have a birthday.

3. Write in words $P(X) = 0.4$

4. What is the numerical probability of an event that is (a) certain to happen, (b) impossible?

5. Draw a probability scale and mark on the scale the following probabilities.
   (a) P(choosing a red card from an ordinary pack of playing cards) = 50%
   (b) P(my waking before the alarm wakes me) = 0.8
   (c) P(score 4 on fair dice) = $\frac{1}{6}$

7.2 Equally likely outcomes

Deciding who goes first in a match often depends on the result of the toss of a coin.
The result, head or tail, are the outcomes of the event, tossing the coin.

> If all outcomes of an event are **equally likely** to occur then the probability can be found as the fraction
>
> $$\frac{\text{Possible outcomes}}{\text{Total outcomes}}$$

Example

A bag contains 1 green, 5 red and 6 white marbles. All marbles are the same and equally likely to be chosen. One marble is chosen at random.

Find the probability of choosing a marble that is (a) red, (b) red or white, (c) not red.

(a) $P(R) = \frac{5}{12}$
$5 \longrightarrow$ 5 red marbles
$12 \longrightarrow 12 = (1 + 5 + 6)$ marbles altogether
R is the outcome that a red marble is chosen

(b) $P(R \text{ or } W) = \frac{11}{12}$ $\quad 11 \ (= 5 + 6)$

(c) $P(\text{not } R) = \frac{7}{12}$ $\quad 7 = 12 - 5$ or $\frac{7}{12} = 1 - \frac{5}{12}$

> When all the outcomes are accounted for, the sum of their probabilities = 1
> For an event A, P(not A) = 1 − P(A)

Exercise 7B

1. A card is chosen at random from an ordinary pack of 52 playing cards. Find the probability that the card is
   (a) an ace
   (b) a heart
   (c) the queen of clubs
   (d) a picture card
   (e) not a diamond.

2. A letter is chosen at random from the word STATISTIC. Find the probability of choosing
   (a) a vowel
   (b) the letter T
   (c) not the letter T.

3. A bag contains buttons, identical except for their colour. 4 are brown, 5 are red, 8 are white. Find the probability that a button chosen at random is
   (a) brown
   (b) red or white
   (c) not white.

4. A spinner has 8 equal sections. Two are red, one orange, one white, one green and three blue. Find the probability that when the spinner is spun the pointer lands on
   (a) Green
   (b) Blue or red
   (c) Not red
   (d) Orange, white or blue.

5. A fair dice is rolled. Find the probability of obtaining
   (a) the number 4
   (b) a prime number
   (c) a number that is a factor of 6
   (d) a number that is a multiple of 3
   (e) not the number 1.

6. Four girls compete to be the lead in a school play
   Some of the probabilities of their being chosen are shown in the table.

Paula	Ria	Susie	Tessa
0.25	0.15	0.33	x

   Work out the value of x.

7. Five boys want to be captain of the school football team for the next match.
Some of the probabilities of their being chosen are shown in the table.

Adam	Ben	Charlie	David	Eddie
0	0.14	x	0.35	0.21

(a) Explain what the probability that Adam is chosen = 0 means.
(b) Work out the value of x.

7.3 Relative frequency

If a coin was biased or if a dice loaded to land on a certain number then it is not possible to use equally likely outcomes to calculate probabilities.
To estimate probabilities of unfair or biased events use experimental probability.

Example

A biased coin is thrown 300 times. It lands on tails 190 times.

Estimate the probability of this coin landing on tails (T) on the next throw.

$$P\ (T) = \frac{190}{300}$$

In general the more times the experiment or trial is carried out the more reliable the estimate of probability.

The estimated probability is known as the **relative frequency.**

$$\text{Relative frequency} = \frac{\text{Number of successful outcomes}}{\text{total number of trials}}$$

Example

Emma cracked open 6 eggs from one box from a local farm. 4 of the eggs had double yolks.

Emma cracked open 6 eggs from another box from the same local farm. 1 of these had a double yolk. Estimate the probability of finding an egg with double yolk from another box from the same local farm.

The probability is the relative frequency of the total number of double yolks $= \frac{5}{12} = \frac{4+1}{6+6}$

A graph is helpful to see how relative frequency changes.

Example

Anne collected shells on the beach on 10 days one summer. The table shows the total number of shells collected each day and the number of those shells collected that were black.

Day	1	2	3	4	5	6	7	8	9	10
Total shells collected	20	30	20	10	10	30	20	20	20	20
Black shells collected	8	6	14	8	9	21	4	2	18	4

(a) Add a row to the table to show the relative frequency each day.
(b) Draw a graph to show how relative frequency changes.
(c) Which relative frequency gives the best estimate of the probability of choosing a black shell at random from Anne's collection of shells? Explain why you chose that answer.

(a)

Day	1	2	3	4	5	6	7	8	9	10
Relative frequency	0.4	0.28	0.4	0.45	0.5	0.55	0.5	0.45	0.5	0.47

(Day 1 $\frac{8}{20} = 0.4$; Day 2 $\frac{8+6}{20+30} = 0.28$; Day 3 $\frac{8+6+14}{20+30+20} = 0.4 \ldots$)

(b)

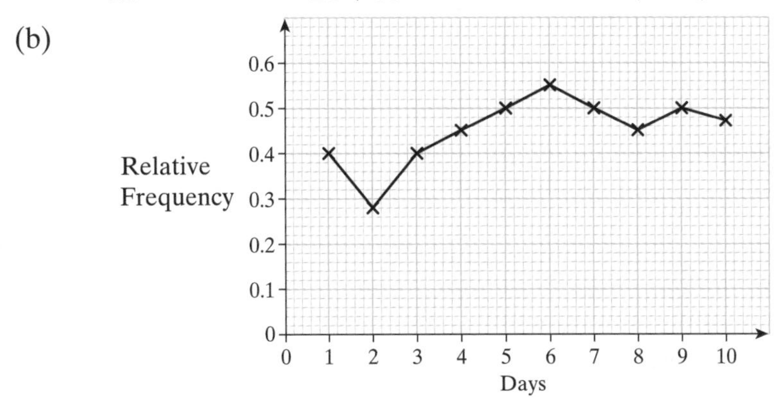

The graph shows relative frequency tends towards a value as more data is included in its calculation.

(c) Relative frequency of 0.47 is the best estimate to use as it uses all the shells collected over the ten days, all the data Anne has.

Activity

Find out if a coin or a dice is biased using relative frequency.

Spin the coin or roll the dice many times and count the number of heads/tails or make a tally of the number the dice lands on. Calculate the relative frequency. The closer your answers are to the answer you expect from using equally likely outcomes the less likely it is that the coin or dice is biased.

Why is it unlikely that the answers will match exactly?

Exercise 7C

1. Amy has a packet of seeds for flowers of mixed colours.
She plants 10 seeds each week for 8 weeks.
The table shows the number of red flowers that grew in each group of seeds.

Week	1	2	3	4	5	6	7	8
Number of red flowers	5	7	4	6	5	6	5	7

(a) Work out the relative frequency for each week.
(b) Write down the best estimate of the probability of getting a red flower.
(c) Draw a graph to show how the relative frequency of getting a red flower changes as the weeks pass.

2. Clive suspects that a coin is biased. He spins the coin and notes how many tails there are in each group of 10 spins. Clive spins the coin 100 times in total. The results are shown in the table.

Group of 10 spins	1	2	3	4	5	6	7	8	9	10
Number of tails	3	4	3	5	4	2	6	3	2	3
Relative frequency										

(a) Copy the table and complete the row for relative frequency.
(b) Write down the best estimate of the probability of the coin landing on tails.
(c) Draw a graph to show how the relative frequency of the coin showing a tail changes. On the same grid, draw a graph to show the relative frequency of the coin showing heads.
(d) Is the coin biased? If yes, which way is it biased? Explain your answer.

3. A four-sided dice is rolled 36 times. These are the outcomes

3	3	4	2	1	3	2	4	3	1	2	4
2	1	3	4	1	2	3	1	2	4	3	2
3	4	1	2	3	4	1	3	1	4	2	4

(a) Work out the relative frequency of the dice landing on 1, 2, 3 and 4.
(b) Is the dice biased? Explain your answer.

4. A spinner has 36 sectors, 18 black and 18 red. The table shows the relative frequency of the spinner landing on black for 10 successive spins.

Spin number	1	2	3	4	5	6	7	8	9	10
Relative frequency of black	0	0.5	0.25	0.5	0.6	0.5	0.57	0.625	0.67	0.6

(a) Draw a relative frequency graph for these results.
(b) What colour did the spinner land on each successive spin?
(c) Is it possible to tell if the spinner is biased? Give a reason for your answer.

7.4 Expected frequency

Probability or relative frequency can be used to work out the expected frequency of something happening.

Expected frequency = total number × probability

Example

A new school is buying scissors for all students. They know that 0.12 of the population is left-handed. There will be 800 students in the school. How many left-handed and right-handed scissors should they buy?

$800 \times 0.12 = 96$

They should buy 96 left-handed scissors and 704 (800 – 96) right-handed scissors.

Exercise 7D

1. The probability that a biased dice will land on a six is 0.22. Estimate the number of times the dice will land on a six when it is rolled 500 times.

2. The probability that a biased coin will land on heads is 0.4. Estimate the number of times the coin will land on heads when it spun 250 times.

3. A biased coin is thrown 72 times. It lands on tails 27 times. Estimate the probability that this coin will land on tails on the next throw.

4. A biased four-sided dice is rolled 160 times. The table shows the outcomes.

Score	1	2	3	4
Frequency	30	28	72	36

(a) Explain why it is twice as likely that the dice will land on a 3 than a 4.
(b) The dice is rolled once more. Estimate the probability that it lands on 2.
(c) The dice is rolled a further 400 times.
How many times would you expect the dice to land on 1?

5. A biased dice is rolled 100 times. The table shows the outcomes.

Score	1	2	3	4	5	6
Frequency	10	16	25	32	12	5

(a) The dice is rolled once more. Estimate the probability that the dice will land on
(i) 1 (ii) 2 (iii) 1 or 2 (iv) 4 or more (v) not 5.
(b) The dice is going to be rolled a further 240 times.
How many times would you expect the dice to land on
(i) 3 (ii) 6.

6. There are 180 students in Year 9 at a school.
(a) In a survey of 40 students from Year 9, 22 owned an iPod.
How many of the whole of year 9 would you expect to own an iPod?
(b) In a survey of 45 students from Year 9, five were left-handed.
How many of the whole of Year 9 would you expect to be left-handed?

7. A small town has 1500 households.
In a survey of 50 households, 34 said they owned two or more cars.
How many of the households in the town would you expect to own two or more cars?

8. A spinner has 12 equal sectors; 4 are black, 4 are white and 4 are red.
The spinner is spun 200 times. The spinner lands on black 73 times.
Is the spinner fair? Explain your answer.

7.5 Tables and diagrams

Tables and diagrams are a useful way of listing all the possible outcomes.

A **two-way table** is used to show the results of a survey.

Example

The two-way table shows the favourite outdoor activity of 50 students.

	Orienteering	Paintballing	Quad Biking	Total
Girls	12	5	6	23
Boys	7	9	11	27
Total	19	14	17	50

One student is chosen at random.

(a) Write down the probability that
 (i) the student's favourite activity is quad biking,
 (ii) the student is a girl who prefers quad biking,
 (iii) the student's favourite activity is not orienteering.

These students were a sample chosen from a larger group of 300 students.

(b) How many of the larger group would you expect to (i) prefer paintballing (ii) be boys?

(a) (i) $\frac{17}{50}$ (ii) $\frac{6}{50}$ (iii) $\frac{31}{50}$

(b) (i) $300 \times \frac{14}{50} = 84$ (ii) $300 \times \frac{27}{50} = 162$

A **sample space diagram** is used to list all possible outcomes for equally likely outcomes.

Example

Two tetrahedral dice are rolled. One dice is numbered 1 1 2 4. The other dice is numbered 0 1 2 3. Their scores on each dice are multiplied. The diagram shows the results.

Multiply	1	1	2	4
0	0	0	0	0
1	1	1	2	4
2	2	2	4	8
3	3	3	6	12

Work out the probability of a score (a) 0, (b) 2, (c) 7, (d) greater than 7.

There are 16 possible scores. Each score is equally likely.

(a) $\frac{4}{16}$ (b) $\frac{3}{16}$ (c) $\frac{0}{16}$ (d) $\frac{2}{16}$

A **Venn diagram** is used to represent data or probabilities.

Example

An office survey of 80 people was carried out to how many people liked tea or coffee.
37 people like coffee only, 18 people like both, 20 people like neither.
Draw a Venn diagram to represent these data.
Work out the probability that a person chosen at random likes:
(a) tea only (b) tea.

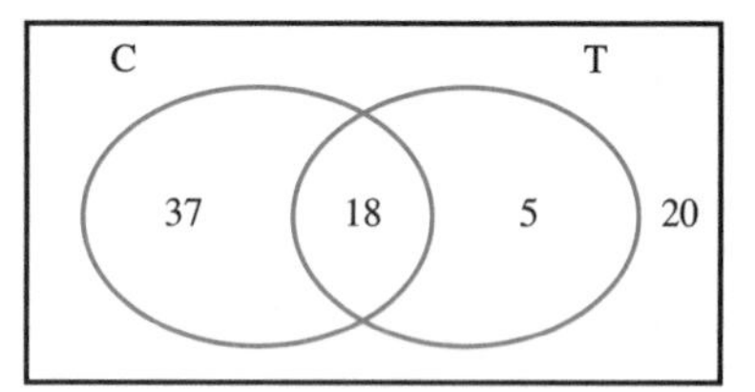

Draw circles for each event.
Fill in the data you know. Always begin with data that is in both, where the circles cross over.
Any numbers that are not in either go outside the circles inside the rectangle.

(a) P(T only) $= \frac{5}{80}$ (b) P(T) $= \frac{23}{80}$ All the data in T circle will count.

If probabilities were entered into the Venn diagram it would look like this:

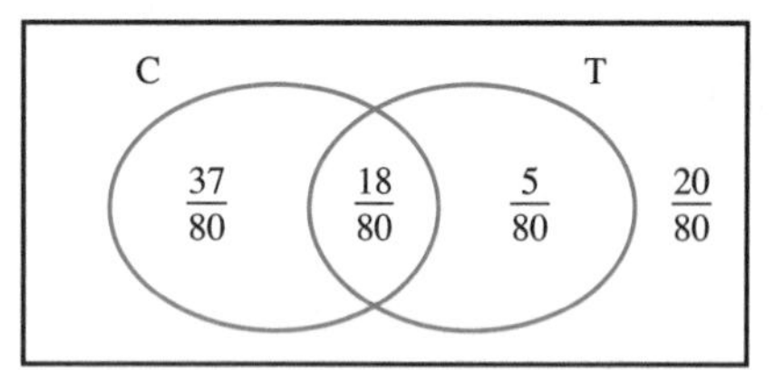

The probabilities all add up to 1.

Example

At St Marks school students study Spanish or French or both or neither.

$\frac{3}{5}$ of the students study Spanish; $\frac{3}{4}$ study French; $\frac{1}{10}$ study neither.

Draw a Venn diagram to represent this data and work out the probability that a student chosen at random studies both Spanish and French.

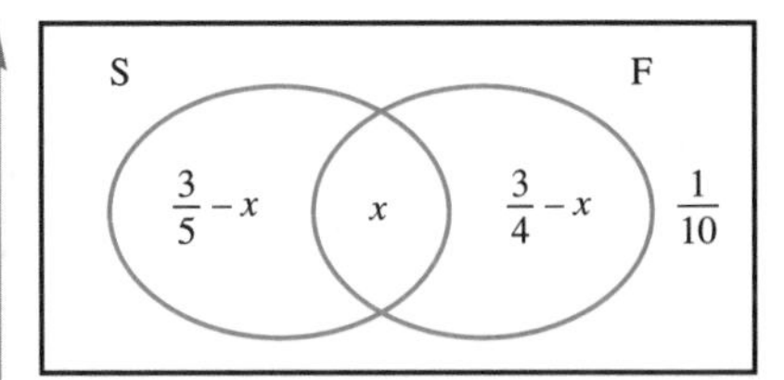

Total probability = 1 and as $\frac{3}{5} + \frac{3}{4} > 1$ these probabilities cannot be only Spanish and only French respectively.
Begin with where the circles cross. Put x if it is unknown. Total Spanish is $\frac{3}{5}$ so only Spanish is $\frac{3}{5} - x$. Do the same for French.

Adding all the probabilities gives $\frac{3}{5} - x + x + \frac{3}{4} - x + \frac{1}{10} = 1$

The probability that a student studies both Spanish and French is x and $x = \frac{9}{20}$.

Exercise 7E

1. The two-way table shows some information about 60 students at a school.

	Holiday in Europe	Holiday in USA	No holiday	Total
Girls	7	15	14	36
Boys	11	8	5	24
Total	18	23	19	60

One student is chosen at random. Write down the probability that the student

(a) holidayed in Europe
(b) did not holiday in Europe
(c) is a girl
(d) is a boy that holidayed in the USA
(e) went on holiday
(f) is a girl that did not go on holiday.

2. The two-way table shows some information about the preferred science subject for 100 students.

	Biology	Chemistry	Physics	Total
Girls	16			
Boys		9	36	
Total	28		60	100

(a) Copy and complete the table.

(b) One student is chosen at random. Write down the probability that the student
(i) is a boy. (ii) is a boy that prefers biology.
(iii) prefers chemistry. (iv) is a girl that prefers chemistry.

3. Two ordinary dice are rolled and the difference between their scores is recorded.
(a) Draw a sample space diagram to show all the outcomes.
(b) Find the probability that the difference between the scores is
(i) 0 (ii) 5 (iii) 1 or 2 (iv) a prime number.

4. Two fair pentagonal spinners, each numbered 0, 1, 1, 2, 3 are spun. Their scores are added.
(a) Draw a sample space diagram to show the outcomes.
(b) Work out the probability that the sum of the scores is
(i) 6 (ii) 1 (iii) an odd number.

5. Two spinners are spun. Spinner S is divided into 8 equal sectors, three are red, two blue, one green, one white and one orange. Spinner T has 5 equal sectors, one of each of the colours red, blue, green, white and orange.
(a) Draw a two-way table to show all the possible outcomes.
(b) Each spinner is spun once. What is the probability that
(i) both show white.
(ii) both show the same colour.
(iii) one shows green and the other orange.
(iv) one shows red and the other blue.

6. The Venn diagram shows the number of boys in a school year that chose A level RS and the number who are visiting Rome on a school trip.

One boy is chosen at random. Find the probability that this boy
(a) Chose RS
(b) Chose RS and is visiting Rome
(c) Visiting Rome, but did not choose RS.

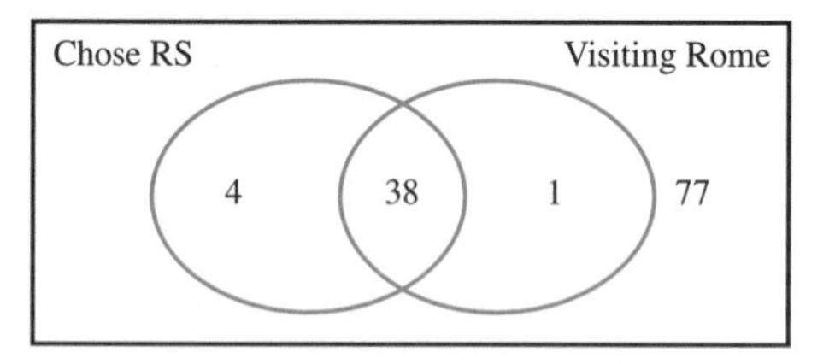

7. A fair dice is rolled. Event M is that the dice lands on a multiple of 2. Event F is that the dice lands on a factor of 6.
(a) Draw a Venn diagram to represent these events.
(b) Work out the probability of these events occurring.
(i) event F (ii) event M and F (iii) neither M or F.

8. In an office 0.78 of the workers are male and 0.36 wear glasses. 0.12 are females who do not wear glasses.
Draw a Venn diagram to represent this situation and use it to find the probability that a person from this office chosen at random is male and wears glasses.

7.6 Probability language

When you have more than one event it is sometimes given a special name. The following example using a fair dice is used to explain these events.
Event S is the dice lands on a square number.
Event M is the dice lands on a multiple of 2.
Event O is the dice lands on an odd number.
Event P is the dice lands on a prime number.

Exhaustive events

Successful outcomes of O are 1, 3, 5 and successful outcomes of M are 2, 4, 6. Together events O and M account for all possible outcomes (1, 2, 3, 4, 5 and 6) when the dice is rolled.
Events O and M are said to be exhaustive events

A set of events is **exhaustive** if they cover all possible outcomes.

Activity

P(A) + (P(not A) = 1

Two dice are rolled together. Let event A be neither dice shows a score less than 4.

Does this mean that 'not A' is the event both scores are more than 4?

(Hints: A diagram may be useful. Language in probability is important.)

Mutually exclusive events

Successful outcomes of S are 1, 4 and successful outcomes of P are 2, 3, 5. There are no successful outcomes that are common to both S and P. S and P are mutually exclusive events.

Events are **mutually exclusive** if they cannot both happen at the same time.

Events O and M are both mutually exclusive and exhaustive.

> When events are both mutually exclusive and exhaustive the sum of their probabilities = 1

The addition law for mutually exclusive events

Events S and P are mutually exclusive.
Together the successful outcomes of events S or P are 1, 4, 2, 3, 5 and
$P(S \text{ or } P) = \frac{5}{6}$ $P(S) = \frac{2}{6}$ $P(P) = \frac{3}{6}$ $P(S) + P(P) = \frac{2}{6} + \frac{3}{6} = \frac{5}{6}$

> If two events A and B are mutually exclusive then the probability of either A or B occurring is the sum of their individual probabilities.
> P(A or B) = P(A) + P(B).

Activity

How could you use probability diagrams to convince someone of the truth of the addition law for mutually exclusive events?

The general addition law

Events S and O are not mutually exclusive. A Venn diagram shows their outcomes.

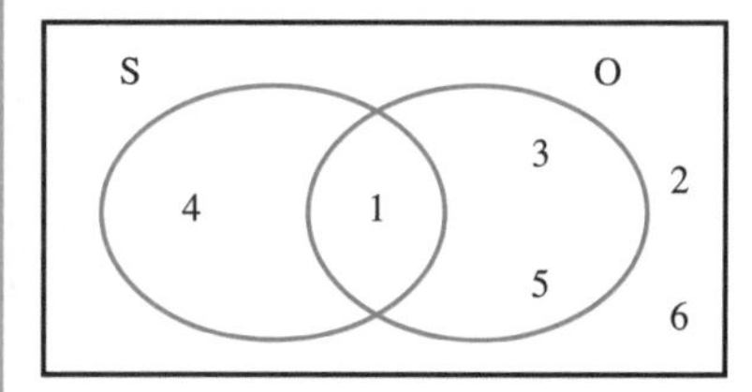

$P(S \text{ or } O) = \frac{4}{6}$; all numbers in the circles.

Adding their individual probabilities would mean counting the intersection twice.

$$P(S \text{ or } O) = P(S) + P(O) - P(S \textbf{ and } O)$$
$$= \frac{2}{6} + \frac{3}{6} - \frac{1}{6}$$
$$= \frac{4}{6}$$

> In general for two events A and B, P(A or B) = P(A) + P(B) − P(A and B)

Exercise 7F

1. In ordinary pack of playing cards:

Event A: An ace	Event D: Diamond	Event G: A number card
Event B: Black card	Event E: King	Event H: Heart
Event C: Red card	Event F: Picture card	

(a) Choose from A to H pairs of events that are
  (i) exhaustive
  (ii) mutually exclusive
  (There may be more than one pair for each answer, list them all.)
(b) Which pairs of events are both mutually exclusive and exhaustive? Explain why.

One card is chosen at random.

(c) Find the probability of choosing with one pick
  (i) A or E (ii) not A (iii) B or H.
(d) Explain why the probability of choosing D or H is the same as event C.
(e) Find the probability of choosing
  (i) A and D (ii) C and F (iii) F or H.
(f) Explain why the probability of choosing E or F is the same as event F.

2. A fair spinner has 8 equal sections numbered 1 to 8.
Event V: Multiple of 4
Event W: Odd number   Event Y: Factor of 8
Event X: Greater than 2   Event Z: Less than 3

(a) Explain why events X and Z are mutually exclusive and exhaustive.
(b) Find the probability of choosing
  (i) V or Z (ii) V or W.
(c) Find the probability of choosing
  (i) X or Y (ii) X or W.
(d) Work out the probability of choosing V or Y and explain why the answer is the same as the probability of just choosing Y.

3. In the national lottery 49 balls are numbered consecutively from 1 to 49.

(a) Find the probability that the first ball to be chosen:
  (i) is a factor of 4 or a multiple of 5
  (ii) ends with a 2 or is a multiple of 10.
  (iii) is a multiple of 4 or a multiple of 6
  (iv) is an even number or a multiple of 8.
(b) (i) Explain why the events P: Prime number and S: Square number are mutually exclusive.
  (ii) Find the probability of choosing P or S.

4. In the game of scrabble there are 100 tiles of which 2 are blank.
For the vowels there are 9 A's, 12 E's, 9 I's, 8 O's and 4 U's.

(a) Find the probability of choosing
  (i) A or E (ii) any vowel (iii) a consonant or U.
(b) Explain why choosing a vowel or a consonant is not exhaustive.

5. A spinner has 20 equal sides; 7 have circles, 5 have pentagons, 4 have squares, 3 have triangles, 1 has a hexagon. The circles and squares are red, the others are blue.

(a) What is the probability that the spinner lands on
  (i) circle or square (ii) triangle, square or circle
  (iii) red or hexagon.

(b) How could you describe these pairs of events
  (i) landing on blue or landing on circle
  (ii) landing on red or landing on blue.

7.7 Independent events and the multiplication law

Imagine that you have two spinners.
One spinner is divided into four equal sections coloured red, yellow, green and blue.
The second spinner is divided into three equal sections, coloured red, white and blue.
Each spinner is spun once. The grid shows the 12 possible outcomes.

The outcome from one spinner cannot affect the outcome from the second spinner.
Each of the twelve possible outcomes shown with a cross has the same chance of occurring.
P(G and W) $= \frac{1}{12}$; from the diagram P(G) $\frac{1}{4}$;
P(W) $= \frac{1}{3}$; $\frac{1}{4} \times \frac{1}{3} = \frac{1}{12}$

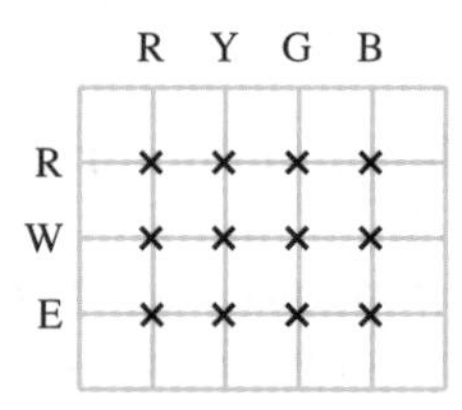

If the outcome of one event does not affect the outcome of the second event then the events are **independent**.

For two independent events A and B, P(A and B) = P(A) × P(B).

Activity

For more than two independent events A, B, C show that P(A and B and C) = P(A) × P(B) × P(C). This is the **General Multiplication Law**.

Tree diagrams

A tree diagram can be used to show the outcomes of events and is a useful tool when calculating probabilities of events.

A tree diagram for the two spinners would be as follows:

Write outcomes at the end of branches.

Outcomes for the second spinner are repeated for each branch from the first spinner.

Write probabilities on each branch.

The sum of the probabilities for each set of branches = 1.
Multiply along the branches to find probability.

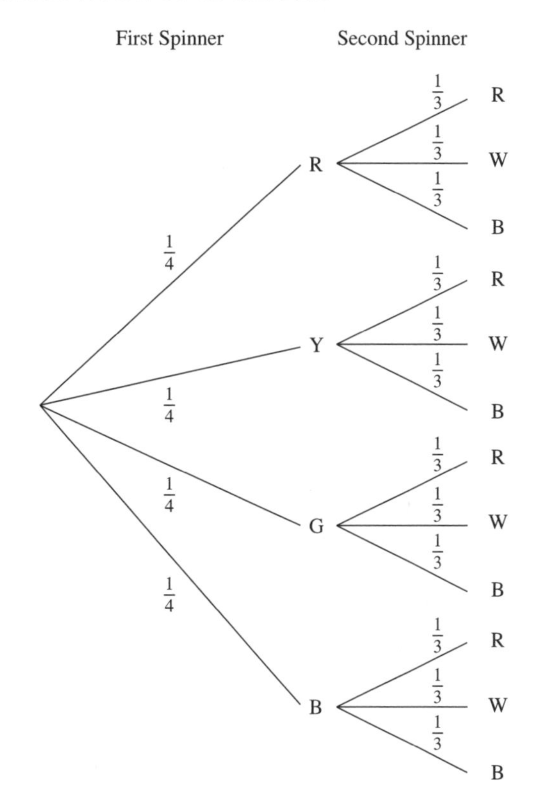

There are two sets of branches that have the successful outcome 'both spinners show the same colour': Red, Red or Blue, Blue.
From the grid, P(same colour) $= \frac{2}{12}$

On the tree diagram P(R,R) $= \frac{1}{4} \times \frac{1}{3} = \frac{1}{12}$; P(B,B) $= \frac{1}{4} \times \frac{1}{3} = \frac{1}{12}$

P(R,R or B,B) = P(R,R) + P(B,B) $= \frac{2}{12}$

> If more than one route is successful, multiply along the branches, then add sets of branches.

Example

Lorna makes two pottery vases. Each vase is made independently. The probability that a vase cracks while it is in the kiln is 0.1.

(a) Draw a tree diagram to show all the outcomes of the vases cracking or not cracking.
(b) Find the probability that both vases will crack while in the kiln.
(c) Find the probability that only one of the vases will crack while it is in the kiln.

(a)

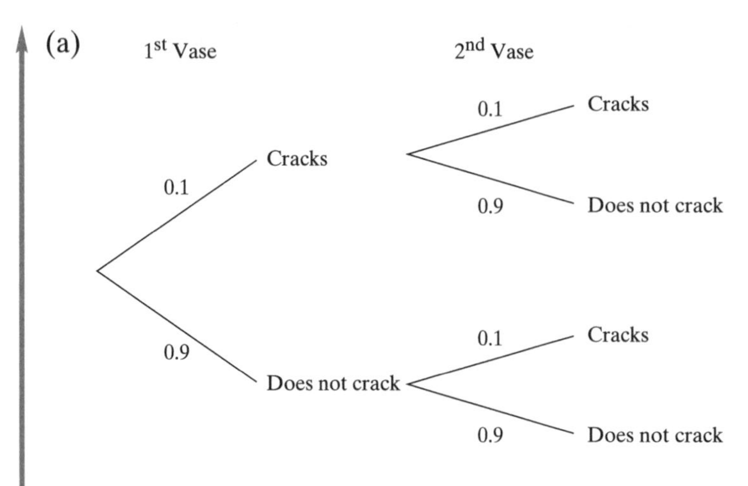

(b) P (crack, crack) $= 0.1 \times 0.1 = 0.01$

(c) P(only one will crack) = P(crack, does not crack) or P(does not crack, crack)

$= (0.1 \times 0.9) + (0.9 \times 0.1)$

$= 0.09 + 0.09$

$= 0.18$

Exercise 7G

1. A dice is rolled twice. Draw a sample space diagram to show all the outcomes.
   (a) Find the probability that on the first roll the dice shows a four and on the second roll the dice shows an odd number.
   (b) Find the probability that both dice show even numbers.

2. A dice is rolled and a coin is spun. Draw a sample space diagram to show all the outcomes and find the probability of an odd number on the dice and a head on the coin.

3. A bag contains 7 purple counters and 5 orange counters. A counter is chosen at random from the bag, its colour noted and replaced in the bag.

   The bag is shaken and then a second counter is chosen at random.
   (a) Copy and complete the tree diagram to show all the possible outcomes.

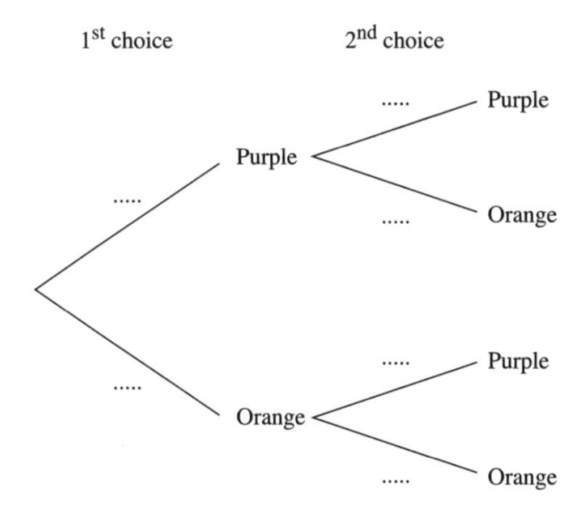

(b) Find the probability of choosing two marbles that are different colours.

4. A bag contains 7 yellow and 3 blue marbles.
A marble is chosen at random from the bag, its colour noted and replaced in the bag.

The bag is shaken and then a second marble is chosen at random.

(a) Draw a tree diagram to show all the possible outcomes.
(b) What is the probability of choosing two marbles the same colour?

5. A spinner has 12 equal sides: five green, four blue, two red and one white. A fair coin is thrown and the spinner is spun.

(a) Draw a tree diagram to show the outcomes.
(b) Find the probability of
  (i) head and green. (ii) tail and white.
  (iii) tail and red. (iv) head and red.
(c) Why are the answers to (iii) and (iv) the same?

6. A spinner has 7 equal sectors. Three are coloured red and four are coloured yellow. The spinner is spun twice.

(a) Draw a tree diagram to show all the outcomes of two spins on the spinner.
(b) Find the probability that on two spins the spinner lands on
  (i) red both times. (ii) red at least one time.
  (iii) one of each colour.

7. Josh makes two model aeroplanes, a grey plane and an orange plane. He flies both the model aeroplanes.
The probability that he crashes a model aeroplane is 0.2.

(a) Find the probability that a model aeroplane does not crash.
(b) Draw a tree diagram to show all the outcomes of both model aeroplanes crashing while being flown.
(c) Find the probability that both model aeroplanes will crash.
(d) Find the probability that only one of the model aeroplanes will crash.

7.8 Conditional probability

Gareth believes that on car journeys when he stops at a red traffic light there will be a higher probability that the next traffic lights he arrives at will also be on red.

Suppose that the probability that Gareth stops at the first set of traffic lights is 0.3.
If Gareth stops at these lights then the probability that he will stop at the second lights is 0.9.
If Gareth doesn't stop at the first set then the probability he stops at the second set is 0.2.

The tree diagram shows the probabilities.

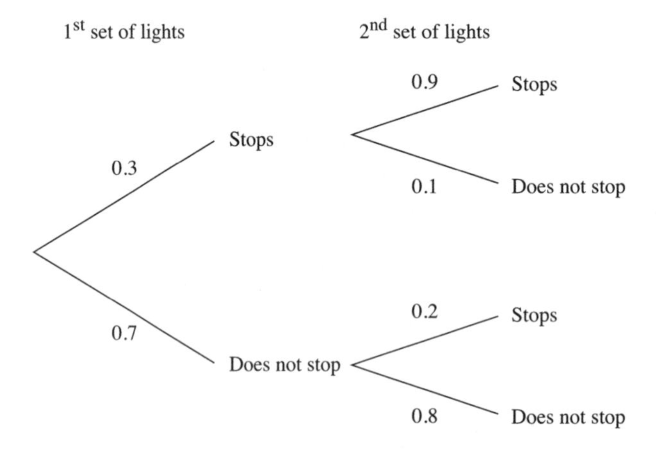

The probabilities on the second sets of branches are **conditional probabilities**; they are conditional on what has already happened at the first set of branches.

The probability that Gareth stops at only one set of lights is

$$\begin{aligned}\text{P(Stops, Does not stop)} + \text{P(Does not stop, Stops)} &= (0.3 \times 0.1) + (0.7 \times 0.2) \\ &= 0.03 + 0.14 \\ &= 0.17\end{aligned}$$

In some problems involving conditional probability take care with the language used and the information that is 'given' as this will change the calculation and the probability of events.
Using diagrams is a good way to sort the information and calculate probabilities.

Example

The table shows the number of boys and the number of girls in Years 12 and 13 at a school. One student is chosen at random. Find the probability that the student is (a) a boy; (b) a boy given that the student is in Year 13; (c) in Year 13 given that it is a boy.

	Year 12	Year 13	Total
Boys	52	78	130
Girls	68	72	140
Total	120	150	270

(a) 130 boys and 270 students in total $P(B) = \frac{130}{270}$

(b) The total here is 150 as Year 13 is given; only use this column.
$P(\text{B given Y13}) = \frac{78}{150}$

(c) The total here is 130 as Boy is given; only use this row.
$P(\text{Y13 given B}) = \frac{78}{130}$

Example

A bag contains 5 white and 3 red marbles. A marble is chosen at random from the bag, its colour noted and **not** replaced in the bag. The bag is shaken and then a second marble is chosen at random.
(a) Draw a tree diagram to shows all the possible outcomes.
(b) Use the tree diagram to find the probability of choosing
  (i) Two white marbles (ii) One marble of each colour.

(a)

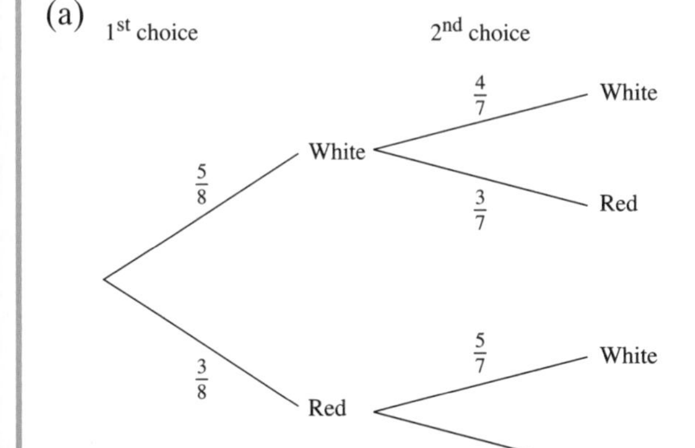

(b) (i) $P(WW) = \frac{5}{8} \times \frac{4}{7} = \frac{5}{14}$

(ii) $P(RW) + P(WR) = (\frac{3}{8} \times \frac{5}{7}) + (\frac{5}{8} \times \frac{3}{7}) = \frac{15}{28}$

Example

60 families live in one street. 15 families have pet dogs and cats. 24 families have just pet cats. 4 families have just pet dogs.

(a) Draw a Venn diagram to show this information
(b) Find the probability that a family chosen at random has
(i) a cat; (ii) a cat given that the family has a pet;
(iii) a cat and dog given that the family has a pet dog.

(a)
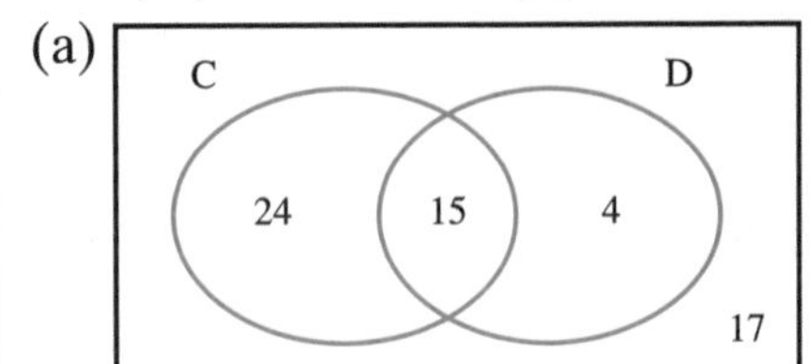

(b) (i) $P(C) = \frac{39}{60}$
(ii) Total is within both circles
$P(C \text{ given pet}) = \frac{39}{43}$
(iii) Total is just circle for dog; use only this circle
$P(C \text{ and } D \text{ given } D) = \frac{15}{19}$

Exercise 7H

1. 24 girls and 36 boys completed a questionnaire.
The probability that a girl completed the questionnaire truthfully was $\frac{7}{10}$. The probability that a boy completed the questionnaire truthfully was $\frac{3}{10}$.

(a) Copy and complete the tree diagram.

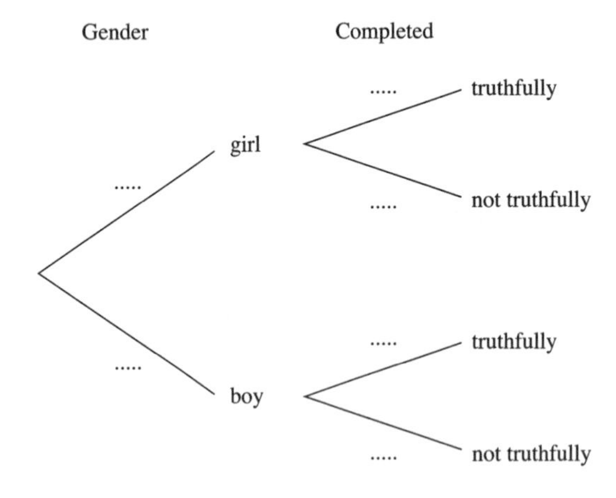

(b) One questionnaire is chosen at random. Work out the probability that the questionnaire is completed (i) truthfully (ii) truthfully given that it was completed by a girl.

2. Richard either drives or cycles to work.
The probability that he drives to work is 0.2.
If Richard drives to work the probability that he is late is 0.4.
If Richard cycles to work the probability that he is late is 0.25.

(a) Draw a tree diagram to show the probability of Richard being late for work.
(b) Work out the probability that on any one day Richard will **not** be late for work.

3. Students at a school study one language French, German or Spanish.
The probability that a student studies French is 0.6, German 0.3 and Spanish 0.1.
The probability that a student who studies French has visited France is 0.7.
The probability that a student who studies German has visited Germany is 0.4.
The probability that a student who studies Spanish has visited Spain is 0.8.

(a) Draw a tree diagram to show the outcomes and probabilities.
(b) One student is chosen at random. Work out the probability that the student:
  (i) studies the language and has visited the country.
  (ii) studies Spanish, but has not visited Spain.

4. A bag contains 7 white counters and 4 black counters.
A counter is chosen at random from the bag, its colour noted and **not** replaced in the bag.

The bag is shaken and then a second counter is chosen at random.

(a) Draw a tree diagram to show all the outcomes and their probabilities.
(b) Find the probability of choosing
  (i) two white counters
  (ii) one counter of each colour
  (iii) at least one white counter.

5. A bag contains 10 lemon and 8 orange sweets.
Reuben chooses a sweet at random and eats it. He then chooses a second sweet and eats it.

(a) Draw a tree diagram to show all the outcomes and probabilities of choosing two sweets.
(b) Find the probability of choosing:
  (i) two orange sweets
  (ii) one sweet of each flavour
  (iii) at least one orange sweet.

6. Bag A contains 4 green (G) marbles and 6 purple (P) marbles.
Bag B contains 7 green and 2 purple marbles.
Alex chooses, at random, a marble from bag A and places it in bag B.
Beth then chooses, at random, a marble from bag B.
(a) Copy and complete the tree diagram to show Alex and Beth's choices.

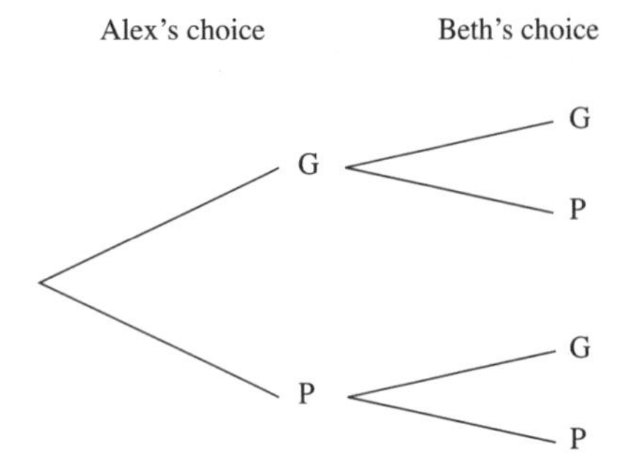

(b) Calculate the probability that Alex and Beth choose a green marble.
(c) Calculate the probability that Beth chooses a green marble.

7. The Venn diagram shows the numbers of people that had a starter (S) and/or pudding (P) at a restaurant one evening.

One person is chosen at random.
Find the probability that they had
(a) a starter and a pudding.
(b) a starter given that they had pudding.
(c) a pudding given that they had a starter.

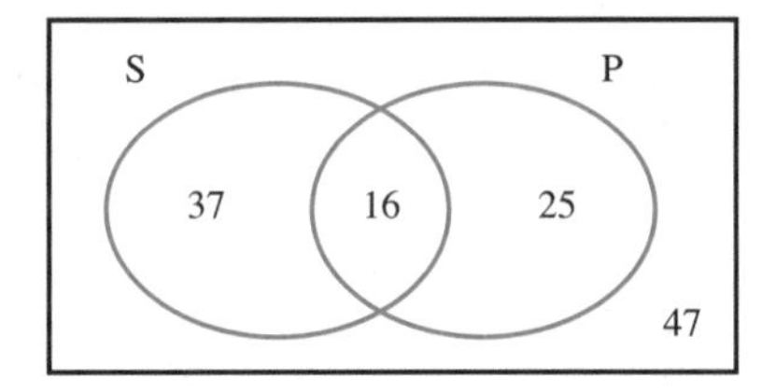

8. 100 people work in an office. 7 are left-handed only, and 10 are colour-blind only and 2 are both left-handed and colour-blind.
(a) Draw a Venn diagram to show this information.
(b) One person is chosen at random. Find the probability that the person chosen is
(i) colour-blind.
(ii) colour-blind given that they are left-handed.
(iii) left-handed given that they are colour-blind.

9. The table shows the number of boys and the number of girls in Years 10 and 11 at a school.

One student is to be chosen at random.
Find the probability that the student is
(a) a boy.
(b) in Year 11 given that a boy is chosen.
(c) a boy given that the student is in Year 11.

	Year 10	Year 11	Total
Boys	57	60	144
Girls	51	52	126
Total	108	112	220

10. A spinner has 24 equal sides. Each side is coloured yellow or black and has either a circle or square on it.
The table shows the colour and the shape drawn on each side.

	Circle	Square	Total
Yellow	4	12	16
Black	6	2	8
Total	10	14	24

The spinner is spun once. What is the probability that the spinner lands on

(a) black.
(b) black given that you know it has a circle.
(c) circle given that you know it is black.

Summary of key points

- For an event with equally likely outcomes:

$$\text{Probability} = \frac{\text{number of successful outcomes}}{\text{total number of outcomes}}$$

- Estimated probability that an event may happen

$$= \frac{\text{Number of successful outcomes}}{\text{total number of trials}}$$

- Events are **exhaustive** if they cover all possible outcomes.
- Events are **mutually exclusive** if they cannot both happen at the same time.
- Sum of probabilities for mutually exclusive and exhaustive events = 1.
- For two events A and B:
  —If they are mutually exclusive then P(A or B) = P(A) + P(B)
  —In general P(A or B) = P(A) + P(B) – P(A and B)
  —If they are independent P(A and B) = P(A) × P(B).
- Conditional probability is the probability of A given that B has already happened.

Links to the Real World

The origins of probability began in the 17th century when a French gambler consulted a mathematician to find out his chances of winning at cards.

Probability is used throughout business to evaluate financial and decision-making risks. Every decision made by management carries some chance of failure, so probability analysis is conducted both formally (using the analytical tools provided by probability theory) and informally (fingers crossed and take a guess).

Insurance companies determine life assurance based on life expectancy through analysis of previous life expectancy, taking into account lifestyle factors such as drinking and smoking.

Decisions in retail business are based upon behaviour in previous sales or production and probabilities of projected outcomes in the future. Other factors also need to be considered. Weather predictions, the probability of sunshine or rain on a particular day, can determine the choice of a seller setting up either an ice-cream or hot dog stand. Long-term weather forecasting can help retail managers decide whether to order more barbeque food or not; whether to stock more umbrellas or more electric fans.

Airlines use probability models to project how many seats to sell in order to ensure that a plane is full on take off. (They usually need to sell more seats than actually exist!)

To ensure time is not wasted, appointments at some companies are made based on past probabilities of people turning up! (More appointments are made than slots that exist.)

Take care not to confuse the odds fixed by bookmakers on the outcome of, for example, a football match with calculated probabilities that are only based on real information. Bookmakers are in business to make a profit and the odds are determined by their subjective view of the chance of winning. These odds can change as the start time for a match approaches and bets are placed by customers.

Revision Exercise 7

1. The table gives the number of pairs of shoes sold by size and width fitting by a local shop.

		Width fitting				
		C	D	E	F	Total
Shoe size	5	3	5	3	2	13
	6	4	7	8	3	22
	7	2	4	5	3	14
	8	1	2	3	1	7
	Total	10	18	19	9	56

(a) What is the probability that a person selected at random buys a pair of shoes of size 5, width D?
(b) What is the probability that a person selected at random buys a pair of size 5 shoes?
(c) What is the probability that a person selected at random buys shoes of width D, given that they bought shoes of size 5?
(d) Two people are selected at random.
What is the probability that they both bought shoes of size 5? [AQA]

2. The probability that John will arrive home late from school on any Monday is $\frac{1}{4}$.
The probability that he will arrive home late from school on any Tuesday is $\frac{1}{5}$.
The events are independent.

(a) Copy and complete the tree diagram below.

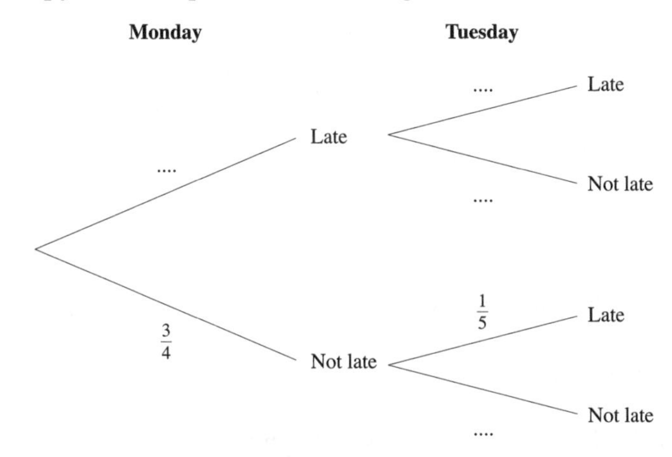

(b) Find the probability that next week he will arrive home late
(i) on both Monday and Tuesday,
(ii) on only **one** of these days. [AQA]

3. In the game of paper, scissors and stone, Chris and Steve place a hand behind their backs. They display their hands, at the same time, as one of the three symbols shown.

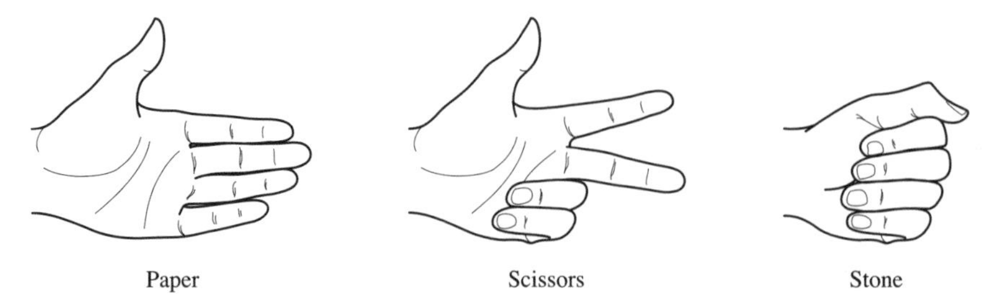

Their choices of symbol are independent.

Chris selects paper with a probability of $\frac{1}{2}$ and scissors with a probability of $\frac{1}{3}$.
Steve selects paper with a probability of $\frac{3}{5}$ and scissors with a probability of $\frac{3}{10}$.

(a) Copy and complete the tree diagram.

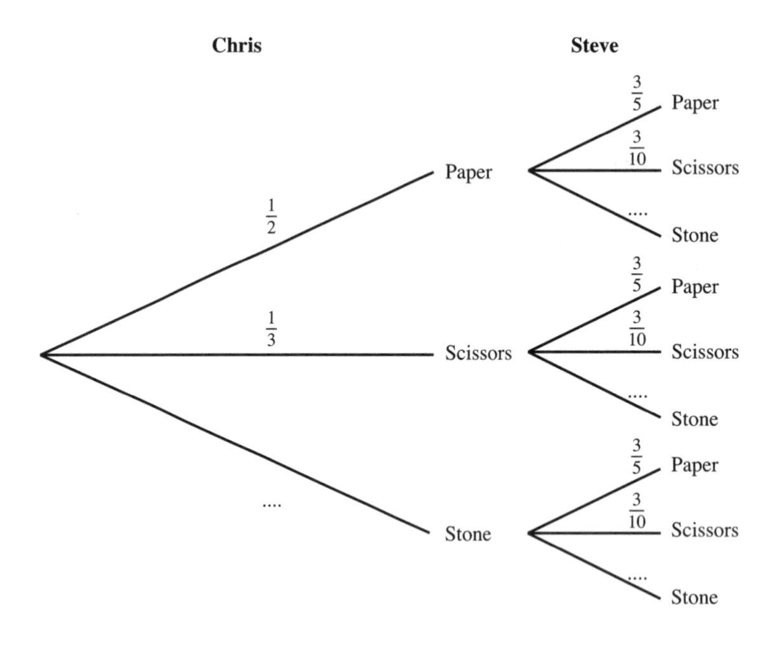

(b) A game is played between Chris and Steve.
Paper beats stone (by wrapping it).
Scissors beat paper (by cutting it).
Stone beats scissors (by blunting them).
The game is a draw if both players display the same symbol.

(i) Show that the probability of a draw is $\frac{5}{12}$.
(ii) Calculate the probability that Chris wins. [AQA]

4. All students at a school study French and Spanish.
The probability that a student is good at French is 0.8
If a student is good at French, then the probability that he/she is good at Spanish is 0.9
If a student is **not** good at French, then the probability that he/she is good at Spanish is 0.3

(a) Copy and complete the tree diagram to show the probabilities when a student is selected at random.

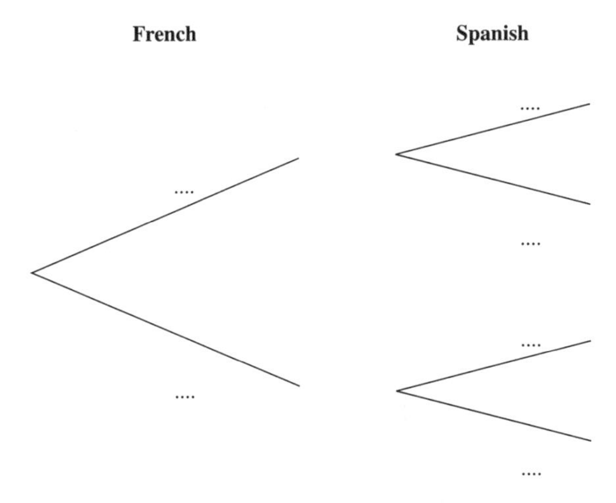

(b) Calculate the probability that a student selected at random is good at French **and** Spanish.
(c) Calculate the probability that a student selected at random is good at Spanish.
(d) 390 students are good at Spanish.
How many of these students would you also expect to be good at French? [AQA]

5. A survey of 24 students was carried out about the number of students who wear glasses and wear earrings.
The diagram shows some of the information from the survey.

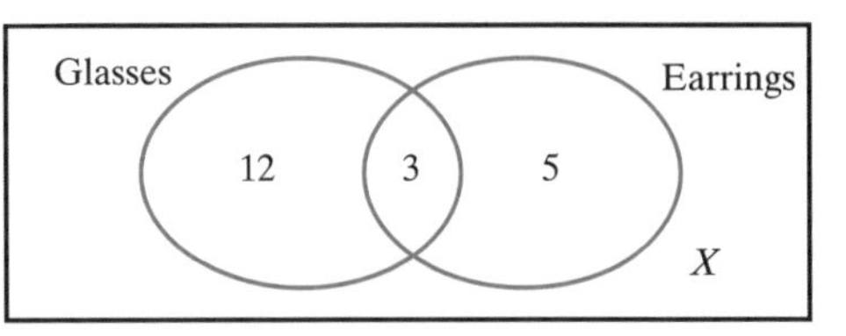

The section labeled **X** has not been completed.
(a) Work out the number that should go in the section labeled **X**.
(b) What can you say about the students in the section labeled **X**?
(c) One student is chosen at random.
What is the probability that the student
(i) wears earrings, but does not wear glasses
(ii) wears earrings and wears glasses.
(d) A student chosen at random wears earrings.
What is the probability that this student also wears glasses? [AQA]

6. (a) Rewrite the following in increasing order of probability.
likely equal chance impossible very unlikely certain

(b) What does it mean when we say that a coin is unbiased?

(c) Two events H and S are defined as:

H Throwing a head with an unbiased coin
S Throwing a six with an ordinary unbiased dice

Mark H and S on a copy of the probability scale to show the probability of each event.

[AQA]

(d) Alfie has two unbiased five-sided spinners, one red and one blue.

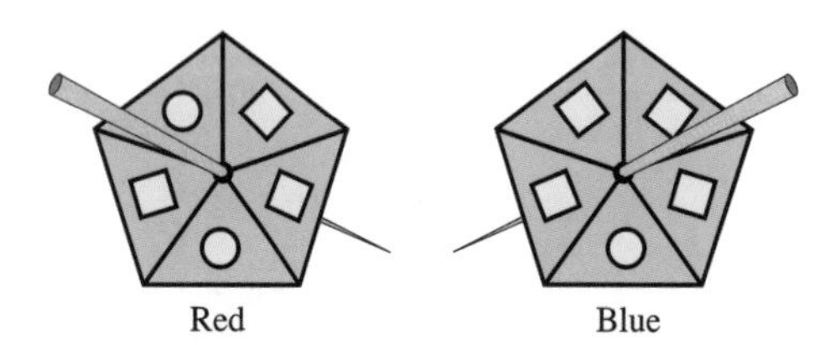

On the red spinner there are three squares and two circles.
On the blue spinner there are four squares and one circle.
Alfie spins one of the spinners. It lands on a circle.

(i) Alfie said the probability of the spinner landing on a circle was 0.2
Was the spinner red or blue? Give a reason for your answer.

(ii) Alfie spins each spinner once.
Copy and complete the tree diagram to show the probabilities when each spinner is spun.

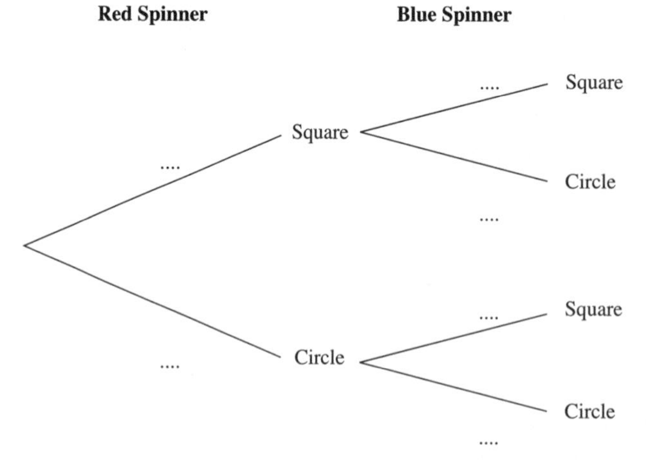

(iii) What is the probability that both spinners land on squares? [AQA]

7. Records for a local library show for each book whether it is in the fiction, non fiction or classics category and whether it is a hard back or soft back version.

When the library closed on Wednesday last week 2700 books were out on loan.
Of the books on loan 72% were in the fiction category.
Of the 620 hard back books on loan 55% were in the non fiction category and 25% in the classics category.
In total 176 classics books were on loan.

(a) Copy and complete the table, entering the number of books on loan in each case.

Category \ Version	Hard back	Soft back	Totals
Fiction			
Non Fiction			
Classics			176
Totals	620		2700

(b) A library record for a book on loan is chosen at random.
Use the table to calculate the probability that the book is
(i) non fiction and a soft back version
(ii) non fiction or a hard back version
(iii) fiction, given that it is a soft back version.

(c) How many of the first 200 books taken out on loan on the following day would you expect to be hard back classics? [AQA]

8. (a) Katie rolls a fair normal dice. She defines events A, B and C:

Event A—the dice shows an odd number.
Event B—the dice shows the number 1.
Event C—the dice shows the number 2 or more.

(i) Copy and label this probability scale, and draw arrows to show the probability of each event.

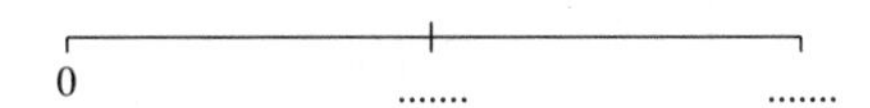

(ii) Choose two events from A, B or C are mutually exclusive.
Given a reason for your answer.

(b) Ben has a fair dice with 10 sides, labelled 1 to 10.
Find the probability that the dice shows either an even number or a number higher than 7. [AQA]

9. Lydia and Roma are testing a spinner they have made to see if it is fair.
The spinner has five equal sections, one each of blue, red, green, yellow and purple.

(a) Roma spins the spinner 10 times.
It lands on red 3 times.
What is the relative frequency for red after these 10 spins?

(b) Lydia spins the spinner 90 times.
It lands on red 12 times.
Explain why Lydia's results should be more reliable than Roma's.

(c) Combine Roma's and Lydia's data to estimate the probability that this spinner lands on red.

(d) Use your result in part (c) to comment on whether or not the spinner is fair.
Give a reason for your answer. [AQA]

10. James conducted an experiment to find out the probability that a drawing pin lands point upwards. He threw a drawing pin 300 times. He recorded the results in this table.

Number of throws	Number of times drawing pin landed point upwards	Relative frequency
First 50	17	0.34
First 100	35	0.35
First 150	54	0.36
First 200	70	
First 250	90	
First 300	111	

(a) Copy and complete the table.

(b) Which of these relative frequency results gives the best estimate of the probability of a drawing pin landing point upwards?
Give a reason for your answer. [NEAB]

11. A pupil threw a coin 40 times and recorded the results on the graph below.

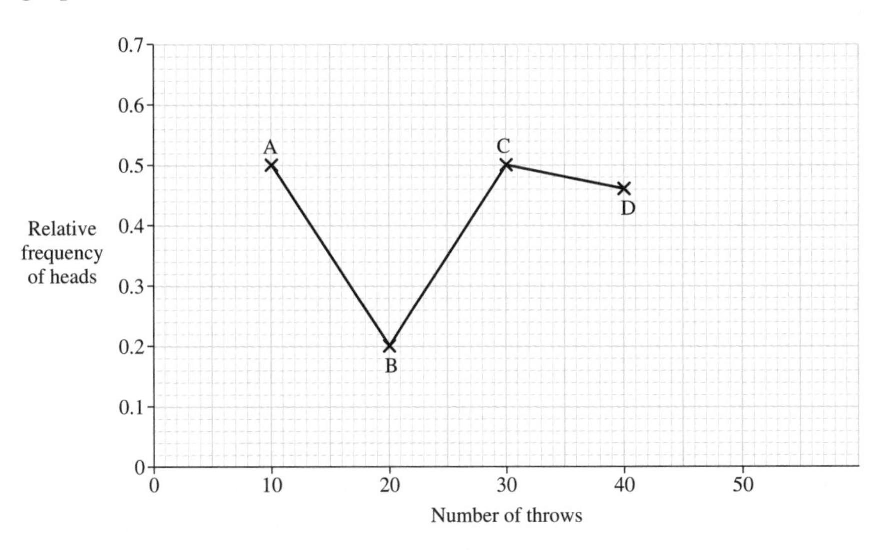

(a) How many heads were obtained in the first ten throws?
(b) One of the points was plotted incorrectly. Which point was plotted incorrectly? Explain your reasoning.
(c) The pupil threw the coin another 10 times so that after 50 throws there were 23 heads. Copy the graph and plot the next point. [NEAB]

12. The pupils in a small school were classified by hair colour and eye colour.

	Brown eyes	Not brown eyes
Fair hair	3	57
Not fair hair	42	38

(a) How many pupils were there in the school?
(b) What is the probability that a pupil chosen at random has brown eyes?
(c) What is the probability that a pupil chosen at random has fair hair?
(d) A pupil with brown eyes is chosen at random.
What is the probability that the pupil has fair hair?
(e) You are told the eye colour of a pupil from this school.
You have to guess whether the pupil has fair hair.
Explain how you would do this. [NEAB]

13. The sweets in a jar are red, yellow or orange.
The probability that a sweet, chosen at random, will be red is $\frac{1}{4}$ and the probability that it will be yellow is $\frac{2}{5}$.
If I choose one sweet at random, what is the probability

(a) that it will be red or yellow,
(b) that it will be orange,
(c) that it will be white?

There are 60 sweets in the jar.

(d) Calculate the number of red sweets.

(e) $\frac{1}{3}$ of the red sweets have soft centres and the rest have hard centres.
How many red sweets have hard centres? [NEAB]

14. In a board game, a counter is moved along the squares by an amount equal to the number thrown on a fair dice.
If you land on a square at the bottom of a ladder you move the counter to the square at the top of that ladder.

	18	17	16
	13	14	15
	12	11	10
	7	8	9
	6	5	4
Start	1	2	3

(a) What is the probability that a player reaches square 4 with one throw of the dice?
(b) What is the probability that a player can reach square 7 with one throw of the dice?
(c) What is the probability of taking two throws to get to square 2?
(d) List the three possible ways to land on square 18 with exactly three throws of the dice.
(e) Calculate the probability of landing on square 18 with exactly three throws of the dice. [SEG]

15. SWEET SIXTEEN

START →

1	2	3	
8	7		5
9		11	12
16	15	14	13

'Sweet Sixteen' is a game for any number of players. To play the game, players take it in turns to throw a fair die and then move their counter the number of places shown uppermost on the die. If a player lands on one of the shaded squares the player must start again. The first player to *land on square 16* is the winner. If a player would move past square 16 on a throw, the player is not allowed to move and misses that turn.

(a) What is the probability that a player lands on a shaded square on the first throw?

(b) A player moves to square 3 on the first throw. What is the probability that the player lands on a shaded square on the second throw?

(c) (i) A player is on square 12 after three turns. Write, in the order thrown, three scores the player could have had.

(ii) In how many different ways could a player have reached square 12 with three throws? Show working to support your answer.

(d) (i) What is the minimum number of turns necessary to complete the game?

(ii) What is the probability of this happening? [SEG]

16. The pupils in a class are classified by gender, hair colour and eye colour. The diagram shows that 7 boys have dark hair and brown eyes.

(a) How many pupils are in the class?

(b) What is the probability that a pupil chosen at random has dark hair?

(c) One part of the diagram is labelled 5. What does the diagram tell you about these 5 pupils?

(d) A girl is chosen at random. What is the probability that she has dark hair?

(e) A pupil with dark hair is chosen at random. What is the probability that the pupil does **not** have brown eyes?

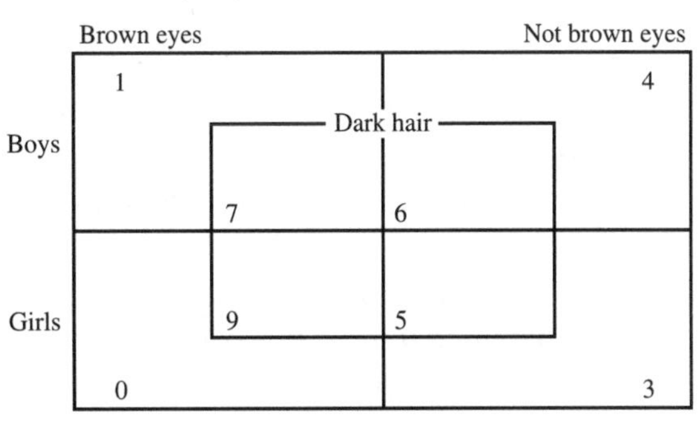

[NEAB]

17. A company decides to tender for 3 contracts, A, B and C. The probability that it will obtain contract A is 0.2, contract B is 0.4 and contract C is 0.3. The contracts are awarded independently of one another.
Calculate the probability that it will obtain
(a) no contracts,
(b) only one contract,
(c) at least **two** contracts. [NEAB]

18. A fair eight-sided dice has 6 red faces and 2 white faces.
The dice is thrown once.
(a) What is the probability of obtaining
  (i) a red face,
  (ii) a white face?
(b) The dice is thrown twice.
  What is the probability that two red faces are obtained?
(c) The dice is thrown four times.
  (i) What is the probability that red is obtained every time?
  (ii) Is it likely or unlikely that red is obtained every time?
[NEAB]

19. In a bag of 50 sweets, 10 are golden toffee, 13 are treacle toffee, 15 are milk chocolate and the remainder are plain chocolate.
Tim chooses one of the sweets at random.
(a) What is the probability that it is a plain chocolate?
(b) What is the probability that it is a toffee?
(c) Sarah chooses from an identical full bag of sweets. The sweet she takes out is a toffee.
  What is the probability that it is a treacle toffee? [NEAB]

20. A green bag contains 8 one pence coins and 5 two pence coins.
A yellow bag contains 9 one pence coins and 6 two pence coins.
A coin is selected at random from the green bag and placed in the yellow bag.
A second coin is then selected at random from the yellow bag and placed in the green bag.
(a) Draw a probability tree diagram illustrating the two selections.
(b) Calculate the probability that the sum of money in each bag is unchanged after the two transfers.

A third coin is then selected at random from the green bag and placed in the yellow bag.
(c) Calculate the probability that the sum of money in each bag is unchanged after the three transfers. [SEG]

21. Three women A, B and C, share an office with one telephone. Calls for the office arrive at random during working hours in the ratios $3:2:1$ for A, B, C respectively.
The nature of their work means that the women leave the office independently at random times, so that A is absent for $\frac{1}{5}$ of her working hours and B and C are each absent for $\frac{1}{4}$ of their working hours.

(a) On occasions when the telephone rings during working hours, find the probability that no one is in the office to answer the telephone.
(b) Use the above information to complete a tree diagram.
(c) (i) On occasions when the telephone rings during working hours, find the probability that a caller wishes to speak to C and is able to do so.
(ii) The phone rings. What is the probability that the office worker requested is available? [NEAB]

22. Parveen plays Roll-Ball at the fairground. She has to roll six balls, all of which must score. When she has rolled four balls the position is shown in the diagram.
So far she has scored

$1+1+2+2=6$

4 1 2 4 4

The winning totals are

6 7 8 9 10

Parveen is equally likely to score any number when she rolls a ball.

(a) Which of the winning totals can she still achieve?
(b) How can she achieve these totals?
(c) What is the probability that the next ball scores 1 or 2?
(d) Fill in the missing probabilities on a copy of the tree diagram.

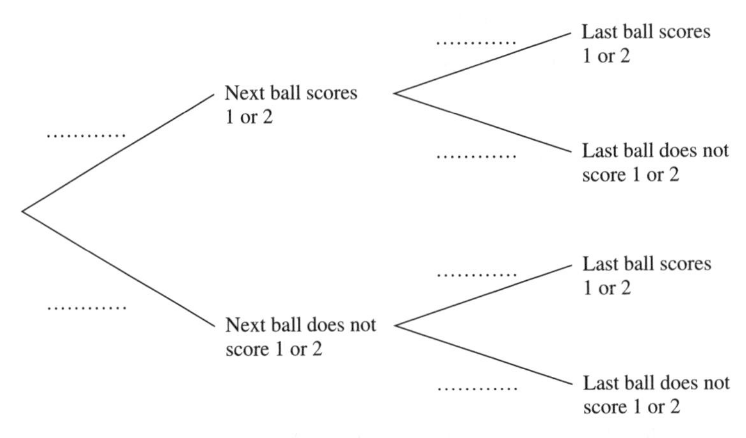

(e) What is the probability that Parveen achieves a winning total? Explain your reasoning. [NEAB]

23. (a) Match one of the following probabilities to each of the events, (i) to (iv), below. Use each probability only once.

$$0, \ \frac{1}{4}, \ \frac{1}{2}, \ 1$$

(i) A card is taken, at random, out of a pack of 52 playing cards. The probability that it is a red card.

(ii) The probability that, if this month is June, next month is July.

(iii) The probability that it will **not** rain for a year in Britain.

(iv) In a bag of sweets there are equal numbers of red, yellow, green and orange sweets. The probability of taking out a yellow sweet, at random.

(b) In a class of 30 children a survey was carried out to find out how many children liked chocolate and how many liked ice-cream. The diagram shows the results, but the region marked A is not filled in.

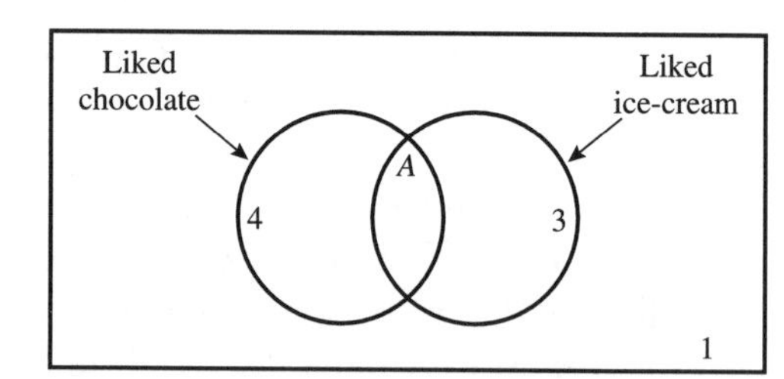

(i) Write the correct number in region A.

(ii) What can you say about the children in region A?

(iii) If one child is chosen at random, what is the probability that the child liked ice-cream but not chocolate?

(iv) One of the children who liked chocolate is chosen at random. What is the probability that the child also liked ice-cream?

[NEAB]

24. The probability that a person passes their driving test at the first attempt is 0.65. If they fail the first time the probability that they pass at the second attempt is 0.8. If they fail the second time the probability that they pass at the third attempt is 0.85.

(a) Copy and complete the tree diagram to illustrate the probabilities when a person takes the driving test three times.

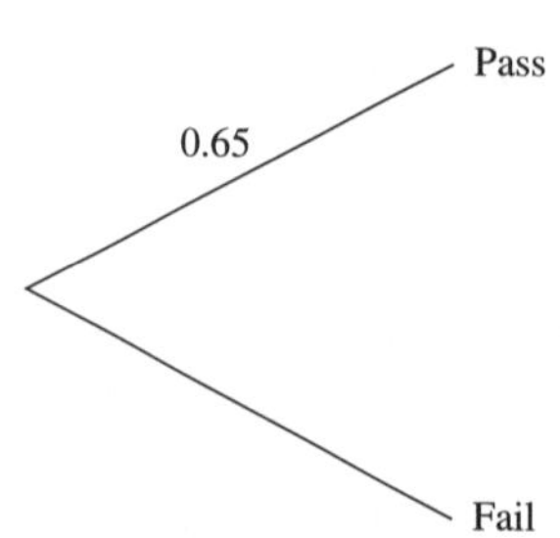

(b) Calculate the probability that a person picked at random

(i) passed at the second attempt

(ii) passed by the third attempt.

[SEG]

25. A vending machine dispenses plain, mint and orange chocolate bars. The machine is full.

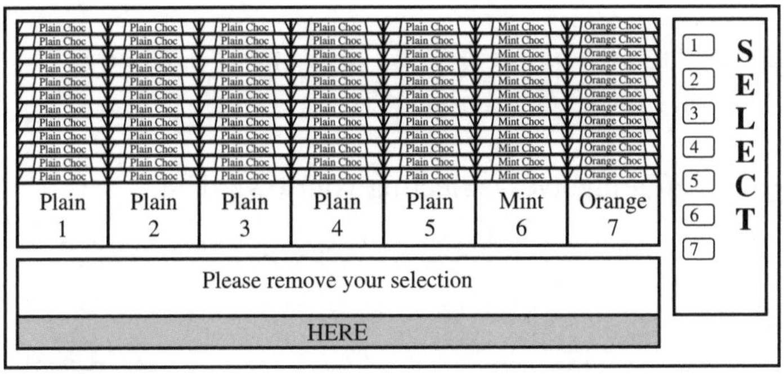

Plain 1	Plain 2	Plain 3	Plain 4	Plain 5	Mint 6	Orange 7

Please remove your selection

HERE

SELECT

The selection system for the vending machine is broken.
It now dispenses a chocolate bar at random from any position containing chocolate.

(a) If one bar is dispensed, what is the probability that it is **not** mint chocolate?

(b) If two bars are dispensed, what is the probability that they are **both** plain chocolate?

The machine is used until there is only **one** bar in **each** of the seven sections.

(c) Draw a tree diagram to show the probabilities and outcomes for the next **two** chocolate bars dispensed.

(d) When there is just one bar left in each section, calculate the probability that **no** plain bars will be dispensed in the next two selections. [SEG]

8 Controlled assessment

The purpose of models is not to fit the data, but to sharpen the questions
Samuel Karlin

Coursework often involves collecting your own data.

This unit will show you how to

- ✦ Write a hypothesis
- ✦ Plan the data collection
- ✦ Analyse collected data

Before you start

You should be able to answer these questions

1 State
(a) a qualitative,
(b) a continuous,
(c) a discrete variable
to do with a pair of spectacles.

2 Design a two-way table to collect age and gender of a group of people.

Statistics is about using scientific methods to collect, organise, summarise, present and analyse data, draw conclusions and hence make decisions.

8.1 Specify the problem

In the controlled assessment you will be given a theme or topic. The controlled assessment has two sections, an investigation and a written assessment. Your investigation will be an aspect on that topic that you want to research.

First you should decide on your research question. Your area of research may need to be broken down into sub-questions.

Example

Noah's favourite fruit was apples. He noted that the size and price of the same type of apple varied considerably between shops and he decided to research the best value for money.

What questions could Noah ask in his research?

First he could compare the size of apples against their price.
Then he could compare the wastage (rotten apples) from each shop.
Finally he could assess the taste and quality of the apples.

Noah could then break down his research into three sub-questions:

- What is the relationship between weight and cost?
- What is the ratio of good and bad apples for different shops?
- Which shops sell the best-tasting apples?

Stating a hypothesis

When you have decided on your area of research you should specify a **hypothesis** to be tested.

Your initial ideas may need refining so that the final hypothesis is easy to research.

> A hypothesis is an idea or theory made on the basis of limited evidence. It is a starting point for an investigation.

A hypothesis should:

- ✦ Be stated clearly.
- ✦ Be testable.
- ✦ Be limited in scope.
- ✦ State the relationship between the variables.

Jenny lives in Hovelton and has two children at Primary school. She wants to research why some children read better than others.

But still, the variables 'reading ability' and 'attitude towards education' need to be better defined.

Exercise 8A

For the following situations write out a workable hypothesis.
State the variables that will be involved and what data you would collect.
There may be more than one acceptable answer for each situation.

1. Matthew, aged 10, received £10 pocket money each month. His older brother, aged 12, was given £12 pocket money each month.
2. Gemma had to choose subjects to study at A level. To help her decide she compared GCSE results with A level results.
3. Charles Dickens wrote books with long sentences and many adjectives because he was paid for his writing according to the number of words it contained. Authors today are paid a percentage of the book price.
4. Gavin wanted a car for his eighteenth birthday. He became aware that he was always looking at cars. Older cars, he noted, were mostly beige or yellow.
5. Ben's mum was always saying, 'Just a minute' and then taking ages before she came to answer him. He wondered if people actually knew how long a minute really was.
6. Boys were always hogging the computer at school. The boys that seemed to spend a lot of time on the computer and talking about the computer games they played at home were also very good at games that involved catching balls.
7. On a school trip visiting churches, Reuben spent some time looking at the gravestones in the churchyards. He knew that nowadays we are meant to be living longer.

8.2 Plan the data collection

For your investigation you will use secondary data. However in the written assessment you may be asked questions about other ways you could have used secondary data or how you would have collected and used primary data to further your investigation.

- If you collect **primary** data, you must keep a record of the process you used to collect the data.
- If you collect **secondary** data, you need to say where it was published. You also need to say who collected it and why it was collected.
- If you conduct an **experiment** you need to explain the method you used to collect the data.

The methods that you can use to collect data are explained in Unit 2.

You should justify your choice of method by explaining why it is appropriate to your research and by comparing it with possible alternatives.

Example

Katherine became vegetarian. She was interested in whether more young people are becoming vegetarian and their reasons.

Discuss how she could use both primary and secondary data in her research.

She could:

- Search the internet, looking at other people's research and then carry out her own survey to see if what she has read is reasonable.
- Carry out a survey based on personal beliefs and then compare her results with a larger published survey.

Remember: Before you carry out a survey you should first carry out a pilot study to check that your survey is going to give you the information you want.

There is more about pilot studies on page 36.

If you carry out a survey that involves a questionnaire, you should include a copy of your pilot questionnaire as well as your main questionnaire.

You should explain any changes you make to your pilot study.

Exercise 8B

For each of the following hypotheses, discuss how you may use primary and/or secondary data.

There may be more than one acceptable answer for each hypothesis.

1. A hungry mouse will learn the route through a maze quicker than a mouse that is better fed.
2. Nowadays women are choosing to have their first child at a significantly older age than women in the 1950s.
3. Orange Smarties taste different from all other coloured Smarties.
4. More road accidents involving a drunk driver result in a death than accidents in which a driver is not drunk.
5. Asian countries are richer than American countries.

6. If it rains on St. Swithin's Day, it will rain every day for the next forty days.

8.3 Collect the data

If you collect lots of data, you will probably need to summarize it in table form. You should design your table to be clear, concise and easy to use for analysis.

Example

Joshua was conducting an experiment to find out how good people were at estimating. He had two identical lengths of string glued to pieces of card.

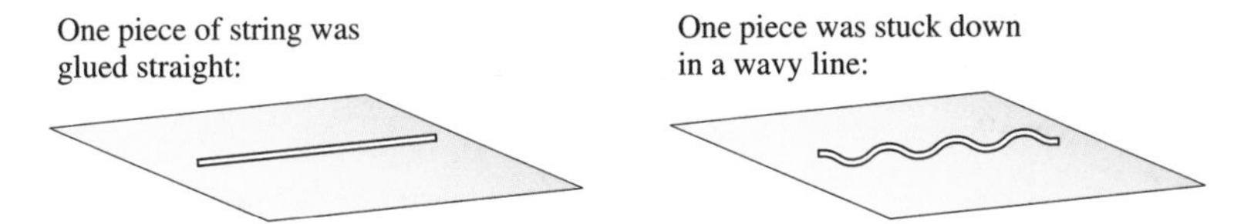

Joshua wanted to research:

1. Is it easier to estimate a length as a straight or a wavy line?
2. Are boys better at estimating than girls?
3. Which age group is best at estimating length?

Design a table to collect all the data that Joshua needs.

Here is a table that Joshua could use.

question 2 → Gender (M/F); question 3 → Age; question 1 → Straight length (cm), Wavy length (cm)

Gender (M/F)	Age	Straight length (cm)	Wavy length (cm)

Age is personal. Joshua may need to specify an age range to collect this data.

Exercise 8C

For each question design a table that will collect all the data needed for the survey or experiment.

1. Alfie listened to many different types of music. He noticed that the length of the tracks often differed with the type of music he played. Alfie wanted to find out (a) if some categories of music tended to produce longer tracks and (b) whether there was a difference in length of tracks produced now compared with ten years ago.

2. Earl read in a book that height was related to arm span and hand span was related to wrist measurement. He decided to carry out a survey to see if there was any truth in these statements.

3. Freya's mum had become very forgetful as she got older. Freya decided to carry out an experiment to see how many objects placed on a tray people of various ages could remember.

4. Penelope was opening a restaurant. As part of her market research she wanted to find out whether there was any variation in (a) the number of table bookings and (b) numbers per table for different days of the week.

5. Supermarkets sell their own-label products alongside brand-named and economy versions. It is not always possible to detect differences from the ingredients listed. Is it possible to distinguish between the products by taste alone?

6. Claire had been tinting her hair blonde for the past three years. She was aware of the phrase 'dumb blonde', and felt that she had been treated differently since becoming blonde. She wanted to conduct research to see (a) if there was any truth in the phrase and (b) whether or not the phrase was related to age.

Choose **any two** of these questions to suggest ways in which the research can be extended. Extend your table and state why you would want to collect the extra data.

8.4 Represent and analyse the data

Statistics are no substitute for good judgement.
Henry Clay (1777–1852)

By now you should have:

- Decided on your research question.
- Formed your hypothesis.
- Planned your research.
- Collected your data and organized it.

You can now begin to represent and process your data.

Representing your data

You should illustrate your data with statistical diagrams.

Your choice of diagrams should always be the most suitable for the data.

Analysing your data

To analyse the data fully you will need to select and calculate appropriate measures of location and spread.

You will need to refer back to Units 3 and 4 for pictorial representations and for summary statistics.

Example

Look back at Joshua's experiment on page 277.

(a) What diagrams could Joshua use to illustrate his data?

(b) What analysis could Joshua perform on his data?

(a) Joshua could illustrate his data with:

- ✦ A scatter diagram of straight length error against age.
- ✦ A scatter diagram of wavy length error against age.
- ✦ Histograms showing the distribution of errors, separated by gender.
- ✦ Box-plots of the data for girls and boys.

(b) To analyse the data, Joshua could:

- ✦ Calculate means and standard deviations of the errors in estimation.
- ✦ Sort his sample by gender and repeat the calculations.
- ✦ Sort his sample into age groups and repeat the calculations.
- ✦ Find Spearman's rank correlation coefficient between the straight and wavy line errors.

Note: There are other representations and calculations that Joshua could use.

If you have a lot of data then it is sensible to use computers for both graphical work and computations. You will need to select which type of graph to use and which calculations are to be carried out (don't just print off all that the program allows) and give reasons for your choices. See Units 3 and 4 for more information.

8.5 Interpret and conclude

A conclusion is the place where you got tired of thinking.
Arthur Bloch (Matz's Maxim)

In your investigation you should summarise your results and your findings as you progress through the investigation. You should interpret your tables, diagrams and calculations by referring back to the original hypothesis. Your conclusions should be ongoing throughout your work and also in a final summary.

It is especially important to interpret and discuss graphical work and calculations that have been carried out by a computer.

In the written assessment section of the controlled assessment you will be asked questions relating to your investigation. You may be asked:

- ✦ What other diagrams you could have drawn?
- ✦ What other calculations you could have carried out?
- ✦ What other sampling methods you could have used?

In each of these you will be expected to explain why they would be appropriate.

You will be asked questions in the written assessment about:

- The limitations of your investigation.
- Evaluating your findings of your investigation.

In these you may be asked to give reasons.

Summary of the process

The processes involved in statistical research are cyclical in nature.

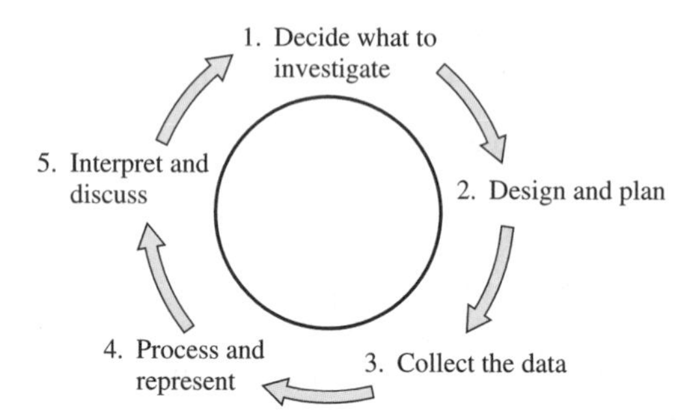

The area of research chosen to investigate should involve:

> The design and plan of an overall strategy. This should identify aims, hypotheses, data and variables.

> The selection and collection of appropriate data, including a description of the data type and sampling method.

> Processing and representing the data should include
> - making comparisons and contrasts through measures of location and spread,
> - drawing tables and graphs,
> - sorting and resorting the data.

> Interpretation and discussion should relate results, tables and graphs to the original hypothesis.

This may lead to:

> A decision to investigate further.

Controlled assessment – Investigation

'Aboriginals have excellent memory recall of the layout of their land to avoid getting lost. People can be trained to improve memory and recall.'

The database in Appendix 1 gives information on the number of objects recalled, the time taken to recall the objects and the first object recalled from three square grids containing 9, 16 and 25 objects respectively. On each of the grids the objects were black and/or white except for one coloured object.

Using your knowledge of statistical methodology and the database in Appendix 1, design an appropriate hypothesis on the topic of memory and recall.
Investigate your hypothesis and draw a conclusion.

You may find the following websites useful.

<http://en.wikipedia.org/wiki/Memory>
<http://human-factors.arc.nasa.gov/cognition/tutorials/ModelOf/index.html>
<http://www.bbc.co.uk/science/humanbody/mind/surveys/memory/>
<http://www.mathsisfun.com/games/memory/index.html>

Controlled assessment – Written assessment

Section A

1. Explain why one of the calculations carried out as part of your investigation and one of the diagrams drawn were considered suitable for analysing the data.
Suggest another calculation or diagram you could have used, explaining why it would also be appropriate. *(5 marks)*

2. Outline any additional information about the data/data collection given in the database that you would have found useful in your investigation, and suggest ways in which you could have used the additional information to improve your investigation. *(5 marks)*

Section B

You have been asked to expand your investigation into memory by collecting a sample of primary data.

3. Explain how you would collect the data for this survey to expand your investigation.
Your answer should include:

- a detailed description of an appropriate sampling method that you could use.
- an explanation of how you would collect the data from the sample, including reasons for your choice. *(5 marks)*

4. Suggest two calculations you could do to explain the primary data you would collect. Explain how the calculations could help support the hypotheses you proposed in your original investigation. *(5 marks)*

Summary of key points

- State a hypothesis.
- Plan an investigation to collect data.
- Choose appropriate graphs and calculations.
- Summarize your results and draw conclusions.

Links to the Real World

This is the information age. The internet has allowed vast quantities of secondary data to become readily available to anyone and everyone. Modern society depends on information as a resource. People rely on information to make decisions and recommendations in many fields. One of the biggest collectors of information is the government.

The media (newspapers, television, radio) tends not to present the general public with lists or tables of numbers, but instead to analyse, interpret and translate into visual, written or verbal forms–using diagrams and headlines that summarise. Making an easily understood report that highlights and communicates key points through a written report and diagrams is the job of the statistician.

Throughout business and industry, organisations rely on the work of statisticians to help in decision-making about chance and risk. These are some jobs in which you can use your statistical skills:

- an environmental statistician in a research institute
- a medical statistician working on trials of new treatments
- a market research statistician for a corporate organisation, ensuring products and services fulfil consumers' wants and needs
- an actuary in an insurance or healthcare company.

Without reliable information, people can make poor decisions that sometimes have serious consequences.

Exam practice paper: Foundation tier

1. Ruby is studying snakes for a project on endangered species. Give an example of each of the following variables connected with snakes.

(a) A continuous variable. *(1 mark)*
(b) A discrete variable. *(1 mark)*
(c) A qualitative variable. *(1 mark)*

2. A person is chosen at random.
The events X, Y, Z are defined as:

X The person was born after the year 1999.
Y The person was born on a weekday.
Z The person was born in March.

Draw a probability scale:

0 ———————————————— 1

Mark on it X, Y and Z to show the probability that each event could represent. *(3 marks)*

3. The bar chart represents the expenditure of the Design Technology department in a school.

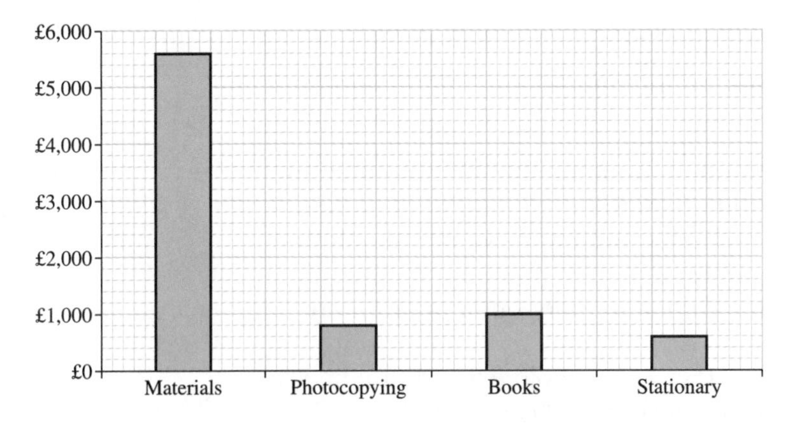

(a) How much did Design Technology spend on materials? *(1 mark)*
(b) How much did the department spend altogether? *(2 marks)*
(c) Draw a pie chart to show the expenditure of the Design Technology department. *(5 marks)*

4. A shop labels its kids clothes in one of two ways, by a letter or by a number.

Size	XXS	XS	S	M	L	XL	XXL
Height (cm)	99–102	102–112	112–124	124–140	140–145	145–152	152–157
Waist, Regular (cm)	52–55	53–56	56–60	60–62	61–64	64–66	66–69

Size	3	4	5	6	7	8	10	12	14	16
Height (cm)	91–99	99–107	107–114	114–124	124–135	135–140	140–145	145–152	152–157	157
Waist, Regular (cm)	52–53	53–55	55–57	57–58	58–60	60–61	61–64	64–66	66–69	69–71
Waist, Slim (cm)	47–48	48–50	50–52	52–53	53–55	55–56	56–58	58–61	61–64	64–66

Chloe and Ellie wanted to buy a dress.

(a) Chloe is 95 cm tall. What number size dress should she buy? *(1 mark)*

(b) Ellie is exactly 35 cm taller than Chloe, what letter size dress should she buy? *(2 marks)*

(c) Ellie also wanted to buy a pair of trousers. Her waist size is 55 cm. What size trousers should she buy? *(1 mark)*

5. Donna is carrying out a survey to find what type of fast food people prefer. She stands next to a fish and chip shop and asks customers the question:

'Do you think fish and chips is good value for money?'

(a) Why is Donna's sample of people likely to be biased? *(1 mark)*

Donna decides to carry out her survey amongst office workers in her town.

(b) Describe a better method of sampling that Donna could use. *(2 marks)*

(c) Why is Donna's question biased? *(1 mark)*

(d) Write a question to find preferred fast food as it should appear on a questionnaire. *(2 marks)*

(e) Suggest one reason for Donna to carry out a pilot survey. *(1 marks)*

6. The table gives four categories of household expenditure and the price index for 1997 for three of them (1996 = 100).

Category	Index
Food	110.2
Clothing	107.5
Heat and light	
Housing	98.0

(a) The price index for heat and light increased by 7.9%. State the price index for heat and light. *(1 mark)*

(b) Which category was more expensive in 1996 than in 1997? *(1 mark)*

(c) If the food bill for a household in 1996 was £2200, how much would you estimate they spent in 1997? *(2 marks)*

7. A quick crossword had 25 clues. Luke drew tally charts to show the length of each answer.

Across

Answer length	Tally
5	卌
6	||||
7	|||
8	|
9	

Down

Answer length	Tally
5	卌
6	||||
7	||
8	
9	|

(a) Design a two-way table and use it to display these data. *(5 marks)*
(b) Find the range of answer length for the clues. *(2 marks)*
(c) Calculate the mean answer length for the clues. *(3 marks)*

On the same day the cryptic crossword had a mean answer length of 7.5 letters and a range answer length of 7 letters.

(d) Make two comparisons between the answer length of the clues in the quick and cryptic crosswords. *(2 marks)*

8. Suggest two ways in which the presentation of this graph can be improved.

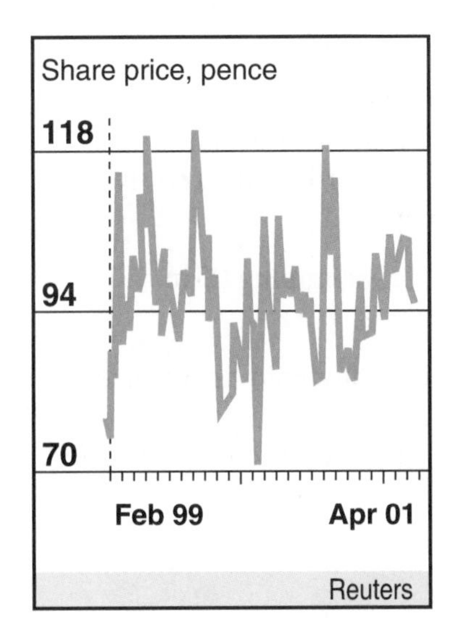

(2 marks)

9. Fifteen 8-year-old boys took part in a reaction-timing experiment. Their results in seconds were

6.0, 5.2, 4.4, 7.7, 7.2,
7.2, 8.3, 7.5, 6.9, 3.1,
8.2, 5.5, 7.3, 6.1, 7.2.

(a) Draw a stem and leaf diagram to represent these data. *(4 marks)*
(b) Use your diagram find the median and upper and lower quartile times. *(3 marks)*
(c) Draw a box and whisker plot to represent the reaction times of the boys. *(3 marks)*
(d) Comment on the skewness of the data. *(1 mark)*

A group of 8-year-old girls took part in the same experiment. Their median and interquartile reaction times were 6.5 seconds and 2.8 seconds respectively.

(e) Compare and contrast the reaction times of the girls and the boys. *(2 marks)*

10. Joss began swimming training twice a week. He recorded his time, in seconds, for 25 m breaststroke at the start of training and kept a record of his subsequent 25 m breaststroke times at time trials.

Time trial	Oct. 1999	Jan. 2000	Mar. 2000	May 2000	Sept. 2000	Nov. 2000	Jan. 2001
Time (s)	30.43	26.10	27.96	27.01	25.19	24.50	24.50

(a) Draw a scatter diagram to show this data. *(2 marks)*
(b) Comment on the correlation shown by your graph. *(1 mark)*
(c) Which time do you think has been recorded incorrectly? *(1 mark)*
(d) Draw a line of best fit on your diagram. *(1 mark)*

Joss will be awarded a bronze badge for swimming 25 m breaststroke when his time is 24.3 seconds.

(e) Use your line to estimate when Joss may gain his bronze badge. *(1 mark)*
(f) Would it be sensible to extend your trend line much further? Give a reason for your answer. *(1 mark)*

11. Mo believed he was telepathic. To test this Mo sits in a room and concentrates on a colour chosen from a choice of four, green (G), orange (O), red (R) and yellow (Y).
His sister Sadie sits in a different room and is asked to choose the colour that her brother is concentrating on.

(a) If they are guessing, what is the probability of getting a matched pair? *(1 mark)*
(b) In 200 attempts, how many matching pairs would you expect them to get if they were just guessing? *(2 marks)*

The results of the first twenty attempts are shown in the table:

Attempt	1	2	3	4	5	6	7	8	9	10	11	12	13	14	15	16	17	18	19	20
Mo	G	O	R	G	O	R	R	Y	Y	O	O	O	R	G	Y	Y	R	O	G	Y
Sadie	Y	O	G	R	O	G	O	R	Y	G	R	Y	G	R	Y	O	G	R	G	O

(c) Estimate the probability of getting a matching pair using the results of
(i) the first five attempts, *(1 mark)*
(ii) the first ten attempts, *(1 mark)*
(iii) all 20 attempts. *(1 mark)*
(d) Use your results to part (c) to comment on Mo's belief that he is telepathic. *(2 marks)*

12. Peter was training for the London to Brighton cycle ride. Peter wore a wrist heart monitor to measure his pulse during training.

(a) What method is being used to collect the data? *(1 mark)*

Peter noted the reading on the wrist heart monitor at five-minute intervals.

Time (minutes)	5	10	15	20	25	30	35	40
H (heart rate)	130	134	142	144	146	148	145	140

(b) Plot these data. *(2 marks)*
(c) In which time interval did Peter's heart rate appear to be increasing at the greatest rate? *(1 mark)*

13. The table gives the market price quarterly figures for the United Kingdom domestic expenditure on goods and services.

Year	Quarter	Domestic expenditure (£ millions)
1990	1	82.9
	2	85.0
	3	89.6
	4	92.9
1991	1	85.8
	2	89.3
	3	94.5
	4	98.3
1992	1	*data unavailable*
	2	94.2

(a) Draw a time series graph to represent these data. (*2 marks*)

(b) Draw a trend line by eye. (*1 mark*)

(c) Use your trend line to estimate the domestic expenditure for the first quarter of 1992. (*1 mark*)

(d) Suggest a reason for the seasonal variation apparent in the fourth quarter of each year. (*1 mark*)

Total (*80 marks*)

Exam practice paper: Higher tier

1. A group of 14-year-olds take part in a reaction-timing experiment. Their results are shown below.

Girls		Boys
8 4	8	2 3
9 9 5 3 2	7	2 2 2 3 5 7
5 2 0	6	0 1 9
6 1 1	5	2 5
3 2	4	4
	3	1

Key: 3 | 1 means $\frac{31}{100}$ seconds

(a) Find the median and upper and lower quartiles for the boys. *(3 marks)*

The median and upper and lower quartiles for the girls are $\frac{65}{100}$, $\frac{79}{100}$ and $\frac{51}{100}$ seconds respectively.

(b) On the same scale, draw box and whisker plots for the girls and the boys. *(5 marks)*

(c) Comment on any similarities and differences between the reaction times of the girls and boys. *(2 marks)*

2. Ms Babs, the new headteacher of an 11–18 secondary school, decided to change the school uniform. To decide on colour and style she wanted to know the preferences of pupils at the school.

(a) Give one reason why a pilot survey should be carried out. *(1 mark)*

(b) Give a reason for not including sixth formers in the survey. *(1 mark)*

The numbers of pupils in years 7 to 11 are:

Year	7	8	9	10	11
Number	134	134	112	112	108

(c) If a stratified sample of 100 is to be surveyed, calculate how many pupils in each year group you would need to ask. *(5 marks)*

(d) Explain why it would be difficult to choose a sample of 150 stratified by age. *(3 marks)*

3. Thomas, my tabby cat, spends his days in the kitchen or on the bed. I am at home 4 days of the week. When I am at home Thomas is four times more likely to be on the bed than in the kitchen. If I am not at home during the day Thomas is in the kitchen.

(a) If I am at home, what is the probability that Thomas is on the bed? *(1 mark)*

(b) Draw a tree diagram to show the probabilities of where Thomas spends his days. *(3 marks)*

(c) Calculate the probability that Thomas will spend his day in the kitchen. *(3 marks)*

4. A finance analyst rated the performance of ten banking institutions. (The actual name was withheld.) The table below gives these ratings and the amount of assets, to the nearest £500 million, held.

Banking institution	Performance rating	Assets (£m)
A	1	14800
B	2	51000
C	3	19500
D	4	8500
E	5	12000
F	6	8500
G	7	20000
H	8	34000
I	9	20500
J	10	7000

(a) Calculate a value for Spearman's coefficient of rank correlation for these data. *(6 marks)*

(b) Comment on the relationship between assets and performance rating. *(1 mark)*

(c) If the actual assets were known, what effect, if any, would this have on your calculation of rank correlation?

Is this likely to change your answer to part (b)? Give a reason for your answer. *(3 marks)*

5. The energy, E required to make an object move at different velocities, v, is believed to be given by the equation $E = 0.5mv^2$ where m is the mass of the object.
An experiment was carried out to test this theory. The results were:

E	2	4	6	8	10	12	15	20
v	0.9	1.3	1.6	1.8	2.0	2.2	2.5	2.9

(a) Draw a scatter diagram of E against v^2. *(4 marks)*

(b) Draw a line of best fit. *(1 mark)*

(c) Use your line to estimate the mass of the vehicle used in the experiment. *(3 marks)*

6. Pie charts are to be drawn to represent the sales of different departments of a retail company in 2006 and 2007. Total sales in 2006 were £56 000 and in 2007 total sales were 82 000. The radius of the pie chart for 2006 is 4 cm. What radius should be used for the pie chart drawn to represent 2007? *(3 marks)*

7. The speeds of 200 vehicles travelling along a stretch of road are summarized in the table below.

Speed, v (kmph)	Number of vehicles
$30 \leqslant v < 50$	12
$50 \leqslant v < 65$	18
$65 \leqslant v < 80$	78
$80 \leqslant v < 95$	54
$95 \leqslant v < 115$	23
$115 \leqslant v < 130$	12
$130 \leqslant v < 160$	3

(a) Draw a histogram to represent these data. *(5 marks)*
(b) Use your diagram to estimate how many cars were travelling at speeds greater than (i) 48 kmph, (ii) 112 kmph. *(6 marks)*
(c) What is the likely speed limit for the road?
Give a reason for your answer. (48 kmph = 30 mph, 112 kmph = 70 mph) *(2 marks)*

8. Sixty first class and forty second class letters were posted. The number of days they took to arrive is summarized in the table.

Number of days to arrive	First class	Second class
1	48	4
2	6	22
3	3	12
4	2	0
5	1	2

(a) Calculate the mean and standard deviation of the number of days it took the first class letters to arrive. *(5 marks)*

The mean and standard deviation for the second class letters are 2.35 and 0.853 days respectively.

(b) The diagram shows the frequency distribution of the number of days it takes 2nd class letters to arrive.

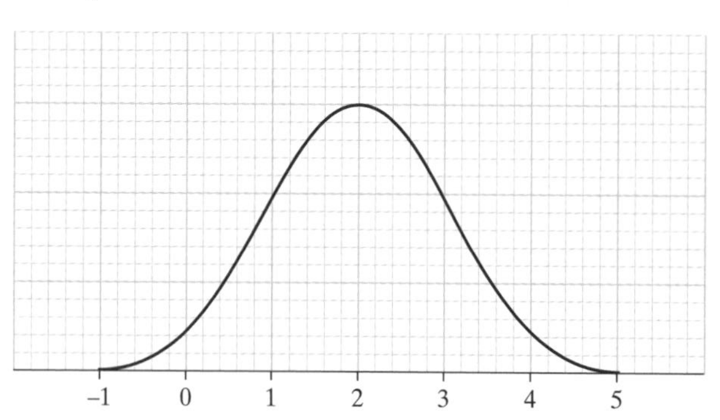

Copy the diagram and on the same grid draw a diagram to show the frequency distribution for the number of days it takes 1st class letters to arrive. *(2 marks)*

(c) Compare and contrast the time it took for the first and second class letters to arrive. *(2 marks)*

9. As part of a survey the following data on the number of children in 120 families was recorded.

Number of children	Number of families
1	16
2	35
3	25
4	18
5	14
6	9
7	3

(a) Write down the median number of children per family. *(1 mark)*

(b) Draw a step cumulative frequency polygon to represent these data. *(4 marks)*

(c) Find the interquartile range of the number of children per family. *(2 marks)*

(d) Explain why the interquartile range is only an approximate measure of spread for this distribution. *(1 mark)*

10. The table gives four categories of household expenditure, the weight assigned to each category and the price index for three of them.

Category	Index	Weight
Food	104.2	150
Clothing	103.5	60
Heat and light		45
Housing	98.0	170

(a) The price index for heat and light increased by 7.9%. State the price index for heat and light. *(1 mark)*

(b) Calculate a weighted price index for these items of household expenditure. *(4 marks)*

(c) What does this index tell you about overall household expenditure? *(1 mark)*

11. The table gives the market price quarterly figures for the United Kingdom domestic expenditure on goods and services.

Year	Quarter	Domestic expenditure (£ millions)
1990	1	82.9
	2	85.0
	3	89.6
	4	92.9
1991	1	85.8
	2	89.3
	3	94.5
	4	98.3
1992	1	90.6
	2	94.2

(a) Draw a time series graph to represent these data. *(2 marks)*

(b) Calculate appropriate moving averages. *(3 marks)*

(c) Plot these moving averages and draw a trend line. *(3 marks)*

(d) Use your line to predict the domestic expenditure for the third quarter in 1992. *(3 marks)*

(e) (i) Calculate the average seasonal variation for the first quarters of the years. *(3 marks)*

(ii) Hence estimate the domestic expenditure for the first quarter of 1993. *(2 marks)*

Total *(100 marks)*

Appendix 1: Database information

Investigation of memory based around party game

Square grids containing objects were shown to each person in the survey for a set amount of time. Each person was shown three different grids, one containing 9 objects, one with 16 and one with 25 objects.

On the grid containing 9 objects all the objects were black and/or white. On the grids containing 16 and 25 objects all the objects were black and/or white except for one.

The number of objects recalled and the time taken to recall them by each person was recorded.

The first object recalled for each grid for each person was also recorded on the database, as was the coloured object and the object placed in the top left corner of each grid.

The grids were:

3×3

Dolphin	Pen holder	Sharpener
Bracelet	Key ring	Necklace
Ink	Pen refill	Paperclip

4×4

Tape	Whale	Key chain	Anklet
Flower	Alan key	Bus pass	Lipstick brush
Padlock	Mints	Coloured Necklace	Socks
Zebra	USB pen	Mirror	Paperclip

5×5

Rabbit	Card wallet	Rubber	Cotton bud	Black pen
Stapler	Pencil	Key	Hair clip	Cotton reel
Balloon	Battery	Lego brick	Clock	Chalk
Phone	Sharpener	Purse	Hair oil	White paint
Coloured Ball	Black paint	Elastic band	Hankie	Button

		3 × 3 Grid			4 × 4 Grid			5 × 5 Grid		
		Object top left - Dolphin			Object top left - Tape			Object top left - Rabbit		
		Coloured object - None			Coloured object - Necklace			Coloured Object - Ball		
Name	Age	Time seconds	Number recalled	1st object recalled	Time seconds	Number recalled	1st object recalled	Time seconds	Number recalled	1st object recalled
Ellie	15	7	9	Bracelet	31	14	Tape	74	13	Ball
Jessica	15	12	9	Dolphin	66	8	Tape	103	20	Rabbit
Jane	15	7	9	Dolphin	20	14	Tape	64	15	Rabbit
Sarah	15	14	7	Dolphin	14	16	Flower	58	9	Battery
Samantha	15	10	9	Ink	28	16	Whale	58	18	Rabbit
Laura	15	10	9	Bracelet	23	16	Whale	50	16	Elastic band
Emma	15	6	9	Sharpener	24	7	Mirror	35	13	Ball
Sophie	15	12	9	Dolphin	33	16	Padlock	64	14	Button
Rebecca	15	7	9	Ink	25	7	USB	60	13	Phone
Caroline	15	5	9	Paperclip	18	13	Mints	47	17	Rabbit
Helen	15	7	9	Dolphin	20	16	USB	42	17	Ball
Liz	15	25	6	Dolphin	89	12	Necklace	121	9	Ball
Rosanna	15	10	9	Ink	21	16	Whale	55	12	Pencil
Steph	15	21	9	Ink	34	10	Padlock	43	9	Ball
Grace	15	11	9	Ink	24	12	Flower	48	15	Key
Beth	15	9	9	Ink	44	11	Anklet	68	15	Pencil
Shirley	15	9	9	Dolphin	27	14	Whale	46	21	Rabbit
Lorna	15	8	9	Ink	30	16	Tape	42	25	Ball
Sam	15	8	9	Ink	23	12	USB	48	18	Hankie
Lucy	15	9	9	Sharpener	34	16	Padlock	48	23	Ball
Charlotte	15	9	7	Dolphin	37	13	Whale	59	20	Ball
Elspeth	15	8	9	Dolphin	28	12	USB	54	21	Ball
Hiab	15	11	9	Bracelet	22	16	Whale	38	25	Ball
Cheryl	15	12	9	Dolphin	32	8	Anklet	74	12	Ball
Briony	15	10	9	Dolphin	37	9	Whale	79	18	Ball
Joan	15	9	8	Dolphin	38	10	Whale	88	18	Rabbit
Kerry	15	12	9	Ink	46	13	Whale	95	16	Ball
Georgia	11	17	7	Dolphin	57	7	Zebra	84	7	Ball
Stephanie	11	11	9	Dolphin	31	12	Tape	83	12	Ball
Ellen	11	6	9	Ink	16	16	Flower	93	13	Ball
Katherine	11	12	9	Ink	29	8	Tape	73	3	Ball
Yasmin	11	8	9	Dolphin	24	16	Zebra	95	14	Ball
Trisha	11	9	9	Dolphin	41	13	USB	60	16	Ball
Hilary	11	12	9	Dolphin	42	9	Whale	92	12	Rabbit
Amy	11	19	9	Ink	47	7	Tape	81	10	Rabbit
Naomi	11	14	9	Key ring	44	13	Whale	76	8	Ball
Harriet	11	12	9	Paperclip	29	10	Whale	67	16	Paint
Shireen	11	14	9	Dolphin	49	13	Tape	106	14	Hankie
Danielle	11	7	9	Ink	22	10	Tape	56	11	Rabbit
Hannah	11	11	7	Ink	37	10	Whale	77	12	Ball
Becky	11	21	9	Dolphin	51	9	Tape	116	11	Ball
Heather	11	17	9	Necklace	22	8	Flower	46	8	Hankie
Shelagh	11	31	6	Dolphin	56	14	Anklet	121	23	Key
Lauren	11	13	9	Sharpener	41	12	Anklet	59	13	Pen
Elizabeth	11	15	9	Key ring	42	11	Flower	67	15	Ball
Candice	11	25	9	Dolphin	68	16	Whale	60	17	Stapler
Claire	11	7	7	Dolphin	33	12	Anklet	44	11	Phone
Helena	11	16	9	Dolphin	20	16	Tape	91	18	Ball
Holly	11	11	9	Ink	47	10	Anklet	62	10	Hankie
Charlize	11	13	7	Paperclip	51	11	Necklace	58	16	Rabbit
Mo	11	10	9	Dolphin	50	10	Zebra	79	12	Ball
Imogen	11	12	9	Dolphin	42	12	Whale	120	16	Ball
Alex	11	11	9	Ink	45	12	USB	113	13	Ball
Doris	11	13	8	Necklace	34	11	Whale	114	15	Ball

Answers

1 Data all around

Before you start 1

1. $\frac{3}{10}, \frac{21}{50}, \frac{1}{2}, \frac{3}{4}, \frac{89}{100}$
2. *Drawings of scaled lines*
3. (a) 17:13, (b) 3:2, (c) 9:4, (d) 3:2

Exercise 1A

1. People who garden as a hobby are more likely to grow vegetables.
2. Half, 50%, is average. 37% is less than half.
3. (a) You do not know where those questioned live. May be hoping for increased business.
(b) Air traffic also increased, need to know the proportion of fatalities.

Exercise 1B

1. (a) £1, (b) 5p, 10p, 20p, 50p; British silver coins
2. (a) 35%, (b) Ireland, (c) 11%
3. (a) Shredded Wheat, (b) Rice Krispies, (c) Shredded Wheat or Shreddies
4. (a) Gymnastics, swimming (hard) or Yoga, (b) Rowing & swimming (hard), (c) Tennis & badminton, (d) Very good (instead of beneficial) strength

Exercise 1C

1. (a) Thick line, drop shadow, false zero; (b) Scale does not begin at zero; (c) Years not linear; (d) No scale given.
2. No, need scale on vertical axis.
3. Do not know what is represented on horizontal axis, data may not be recorded at equal intervals.
4. Zenith Suppliers, sales gradient £400 000 (Arcwell £80 000).
5. (a) Vertical axis begins at 100000 and is not scaled; (b) Impression given of greater increase; (c) Actual sales or vertical scale.
6. First graph gives an impression of greater variation in sales and Spring sales appear almost negligible.

Exercise 1D

1. (a) (i) 1:3, (ii) 1:9, (b) No, area of picture more prominent than the values.
2. Have their areas in proportion to the total sales.
3. Horizontal scale not linear. Height of wheelie bins is difficult to read. The 3-D picture gives a different impression to the height. Only reported non-collections, what about non-reported?

Revision Exercise 1

1. (a) (i) 41 (ii) Women have a greater life expectancy than men (b) Better nutrition; better healthcare
(c) (i) Life expectancy at birth is lower than at 1 year (ii) There is a higher risk of children dying at birth or in their first year than in later years.
2. (a) 3-D picture gives a different impression from the height of each house, as the comparison of area is much larger than the actual values suggest. (b) 4.5 cm
3. (a) 8 (B) Boys, tent, 3; Girls, caravan, 4; Total, caravan, 13.
4. (a) Mixed (b) 5 (c) Similarities – smallest percentage of both groups is 65 and over; Largest percentage of both groups is aged 35–64. Difference – more than half the White ethnic group is aged 35 and over; less than half the Indian ethnic group is aged 35 and over.
5. (a) 18% (b) Two people (c) Rounding errors (d) Complete bar chart for 2001: one person 0–28, two people 28–63, three people 63–79, four people 79–93, five or more 93–100 (e) Similarity – two and three person households make up about half of each total. Differences – larger percentages of one person households in 2001; smaller percentage of five or more person households in 2001.

6. (a) Vertical scale does not start at zero; Horizontal scale is not linear
   (b) There are fewer drivers in the over 79 years age group so proportion of drivers involved in crashes needs to be looked at; Graph only shows number or fatal crashes, not other types of crash.
7. (a) Income Tax; (b) £21.7 billion; (c) £23.1 billion.
8. 50% is average; 40% (less than half) is less than average.
9. (a) 60%; (b) 1995; (c) 20%; (d) North; (e) 88p; (f) 68p.
10. No horizontal scale/labels; 92.62 higher than 96; Width of line so large that exact coordinates are obscure; Thick line (17.48 could be read as 10)
11. (a) 6%; (b) 32–34; (c) Any difficulty less than individual column entries; (d) $3 + 2 + 3 < 14$.
12. Misleading title; false zero; sloping lines; unequal distances between numbers on horizontal scale.
13. False zero; suggests that growth has tripled when not actually doubled; do not know about intervening years.
14. Areas not proportional to data.
15. (a) Ratio of areas is 1:4; (b) 5.04 cm.

2 Data collection

Before you start 2

1. (a) (i) 23 (ii) 4, (iii) 10; (b) (i) 卌| (ii) 卌卌|||| (iii) 卌卌卌卌 (iv) || (v) 卌|
2. (a) 4 (b) 19 (c) 23 (d) 11 (e) 33 (f) 67
3. (a) $\frac{6}{40}$ (b) $\frac{10}{40}$ (c) $\frac{3}{40}$ (d) $\frac{8}{40}$ (e) $\frac{11}{40}$ (f) $\frac{16}{40}$ (g) $\frac{33}{40}$

Exercise 2A

1. (a) Discrete (b) colour.
2. Texture of hair.
3. Continuous.
4. (a) (i) colour (ii) length
   (b) (i) type of fish (ii) number in the shoal
   (c) (i) how realistic (ii) playing time.
5. (a) (i) position (ii) time taken
   (b) (i) postage cost (ii) parcel weight
   (c) (i) eggs (ii) sugar.
6. Descriptive, judgemental, assigned a number rather than countable.
7. Discrete.

Exercise 2B

1. Secondary.
2. (a) Secondary (b) Jason, more data used.
3. Primary, need to know if people actually like/will buy it.
4. Use hand span data so that kettle is comfortable for majority of population to hold.
5. Explanatory – leg length, Response – time taken.
6. Personal interview, needs to find out what people want/would use.
7. Only need to ask people living in new houses.

Exercise 2C

1. All of this type of elastic band. Test to destruction.
2. Need to be aware of what workers would want and population is small, population is everyone who works there.
3. (a) Sample, too many to look at every house.
   (b) Census, small number, likely to be individual in a village.
4. Everyone living within range of floodlight beam plus everyone who may be affected by increased traffic/parking at evening matches.

Exercise 2D

1. (a) Town residents in work, (b) likely to travel by rail, (c) random.
2. (a) Children at the school, (b) not in proportion, (c) stratified.
3. (a) Whole population, (b) one area, possibly not in employment, (c) stratified (or opinion poll).
4. (a) Population of Britain, (b) one area, (c) stratified.
5. (a) Married people in Scotland, (b) Churchgoers more likely to marry in church, (c) systematic.
6. (a) All schoolchildren, (b) only one school, (c) stratified by age/gender (or clusters of other schools).
7. (a) All bulbs manufactured by Glowalot, (b) Only one month's production is tested, (c) tests to destruction, systematic.
8. (a) All smokers, (b) poor people may not be able to afford return postage/does not include the homeless, (c) cluster.
9. 20 women, 30 men
10. Year 3–12 or 11, Year 4–11; Year 5–9; Year 6–8 or 9; total must be 40
11. Number each block and use random sampling method to choose say 6 blocks; repeat this process numbering each flat in all the chosen blocks to choose 12 flats; repeat this process numbering each student in all of the chosen flats to choose 60 students.

Exercise 2E

1. 'A lot' is undefined. Give choices of number of hours per day.
2. Leading. Rewrite with choices poor to very good.
3. Mix of units plus gap between five feet and 2 metres. Re do choices with no gaps.
4. (b) should appear before (a) and (a) should read 'If yes , what do . . . ' and have choices.
5. Young, middle-aged, old are undefined. Replace with age ranges.
6. Gaps in choices. Replace with 0, 1–3, 4–6, daily.
7. Questionnaire should include age/year group and preferred flavours of crisps. Whole school is population. Sample should be stratified and about 10% of total. Pilot survey could identify which flavours to include.
8. Pilot questionnaire should include open questions to see which features people identify and how much they would pay if they buy one. (a) Whole population could be sampling frame. (b) Random or stratified.

Exercise 2F

1. Matched pairs.
2. Data logging.
3. Data logging.
4. Control group.
5. Capture – recapture method.
6. Before-and-after.
7. Capture – recapture method.
8. 300.
9. 400.
10. (a) (i) Assign H and T to straight on and one of HH and TT to left and the other to right turn (a) (ii) Assign digits 0–7 in this ratio: Right turn: Left turn: Straight on = 1:1:2 (b) Assign digits 0–9 in this ratio: Right turn: Left turn: Straight on = 1:3:6; Use random number tables or similar to carry out the simulation.

Exercise 2G

1. (i) Class tally chart for pets, (ii) Class tally chart for bicycle colour.
2. Frequencies: 2, 5, 2, 2, 3, 3, 2, 1
3. Tally chart with 6 rows (for the numbers on a dice).
4. Tally chart with 5 rows (for each vowel).

Exercise 2H

1. £120.50; £119.50.
2. £125; £115.
3. 750.5g; 749.5g.
4. 755g; 745g.
5. 1010g (1.01kg); 990g (0.99kg).
6. 47.5km; 42.5km.
7. 26.5cm, 25.5cm if nearest cm; 26.05cm, 25.95cm if nearest tenth cm; . . .

8. 40.5 m, 39.5 m (nearest m); 42.5 m, 37.5 m (nearest 5 m); . . .
9. 9.75 m, 9.65 m (nearest 10 cm); . . .
10. 35.5 g, 34.5 g (nearest g); . . .

Exercise 2I

1. Frequencies: 6, 8, 10, 9, 7
2. Frequencies: 4, 4, 11, 5, 4

3.

Height, h cm	Frequency
$100 < h \leqslant 105$	1
$105 < h \leqslant 110$	2
$110 < h \leqslant 115$	3
$115 < h \leqslant 120$	6
$120 < h \leqslant 125$	2
$125 < h \leqslant 130$	2
$130 < h \leqslant 135$	3
$135 < h \leqslant 140$	2

4.

Mass, m grams	Frequency
$0.7 < m \leqslant 0.8$	2
$0.8 < m \leqslant 0.9$	3
$0.9 < m \leqslant 1.0$	5
$1.0 < m \leqslant 1.1$	3
$1.1 < m \leqslant 1.2$	5
$1.2 < m \leqslant 1.3$	1
$1.3 < m \leqslant 1.4$	1
$1.4 < m \leqslant 1.5$	1

Exercise 2J

1. (a) 37 (b) 7 (c) 8.
2. Almost double the next heaviest coin.

Weight in g	Year			
	1996	1997	1998	1999
9.6–10.0	4	1	0	0
10.1–10.5	0	2	4	0
10.6–11.0	0	0	0	3

The older coins tend to be lighter than the newer coins.

3.

	Across						
		3	4	5	6	7	8
Down	3						
	4						
	5						
	6						
	7						
	8						

4. Two-way table, gender and types of music; own data.

5.

	Lines					
		8	9	10	11	12
Verses	1					
	2					
	3					
	4					

Revision Exercise 2

1. Q1: Number of hours is undefined; Long period of time to recall. Q2: Does not include the category 'unemployed' or 'retired'. Q3: Leading question – they may not have enjoyed listening.
2. (a) Choices overlap; Does not includes 'under £1000' (b) Return postage paid (prepaid return envelopes); Replies entered in a prize draw; Follow-up telephone calls.
3. (a) 29, 44, 56, 51, 38, 07 (b) 4 boys, 2 girls
4. (a) Type of music (b) Length of track; download speed
5. (a) To identify what types of music to include in the questionnaire. (b) Using a list of pupil's names, randomly choose a starting point, then use a regular pattern (say every ten pupils) to choose the sample. (c) Ask the same number of pupils from each year group, choosing the same number of boys and girls in each group.
(d) It is a quick method to choose a random sample (e) No sampling frame is needed.
6. (a) Approx. 2140 (b) Return the fish to the lake; catch another 300 fish to see how many are ringed.
7. (a) 45 (b) Simple random sampling: assign a number to each student in the Sixth Form; use random number tables, a calculator or a computer to choose a sample, ignoring duplicate numbers.
8. (a) Leading question; does not give option of undecided. (b) A statement, with an opinion scale or tick boxes: strongly agree, agree, no opinion, disagree, strongly disagree.
9. (a) Stratified sampling of the men. (b) No women would be surveyed; in some sections the majority of workers are men and in others the majority are women. (c) (i) 2 (ii) 3 (d) Tick boxes: strongly agree, agree, no opinion, disagree, strongly disagree; Opinion scale from disagree to agree.
10. (a) (i) The choices do not overlap or leave gaps (ii) There are clearly defined categories; the data is easy to summarise.
(b) Included a pre-paid reply envelope; telephone survey or personal interview.
(c) Pilot survey
(d) No choices are given, e.g. less than one month. Does not specify whether the food eaten is a snack or a meal.
11. (a) Primary; (b) Number of children, amount spent; (c) Journey time.
12. (i) Weight of an ingredient or cooking time; (ii) number of eggs or lemons; (iii) Taste.
13. (a) Frequencies 3, 10, 5, 2; (b) 4.
14. Method 2; sampling frame involves (almost) all groups of people (adults).
15. (a) Quicker/cheaper; (b) All likely to want it, limited sampling frame; (c) Random sample sampling frame everyone within local area; (d) Suitable question with at least 3 non-overlapping choices with no gaps.
16. (a) Census includes whole population, sample only some; (b) Test to destruction;
(c) Census too large/ saves time/ saves money.
17. (a) Questions are short/relevant/closed/not leading, personal/unbiased/easy to understand, answer;
(b) (i) Large coverage/fewer staff/cheaper/answer questions at leisure; (ii) non return/loss/no help given;
(c) (i) Personal/do not like giving weight; (ii) Clear wording, 3 non-overlapping groups, no gaps.
18. Where did you go on holiday last year? Britain [] Europe [] Elsewhere [] Did not go on holiday [].
If you went on holiday last year, was your accommodation: Hotel [] Self-catering [] Camping [] Other [].
19. Measure a sample of people in the morning and again that same evening, using same means of measuring.
20. (a) Not random allocation, only given to girls, no control, only children, only his patients;
(b) Use a control group, random allocation, equal numbers boys and girls.
21. (a) May be other reasons that people lose/do not lose weight; (b) Paired same gender, similar weight, height, lifestyle etc; (c) To keep all other factors the same.
22. (a) $\frac{20}{50}$; (b) High non-response, short people less likely to respond;
(c) Tick the box giving your height. At least 3 non-overlapping and no gaps alternatives.
23. (a) Names in hat, choose 80 or number all 500 students and select 80 using random numbers;
(b) $\frac{80}{500} = 0.16$, sample 16, 12, 20, 16, 16; (c) Interviewer chooses (appropriately classified members from each year) up to the required number.
24. (a) Time short, Sample small, Business people unlikely at 11am, No criteria for choice, Interviewer bias;
(b) (i) Number and select every nth; (ii) Divide population by some criteria, select in proportion to total;
(iii) Stratified ensures selection across each group;
(c) In which age group are you? (3 groups not overlapping, no gaps).
25. (a) Quick/cheaper/easier; (b) All men/women/same floor; (c) 20, 10, 20; (d) 4;
(e) Number 1 to 20, choose every 5th random start 1–5.
26. (a) P Taylor, D Peters, B Quarishi; (b) All boys; (c) Stratified by gender.

3 Summary statistics

Before you start 3

1. (a) 15; (b) 3.5; (c) 8.5
2. (a) 7.5; (b) 25
3. (a) 20, 60; (b) 50, 150; (c) 57.5, 172.5
4. (a) 27; (b) 4

Exercise 3A

1. (a) (i) 3; (ii) 5; (iii) $5\frac{1}{3}$; (b) (i) 17; (ii) 13; (iii) 12; (c) (i) 8; (ii) 13; (iii) $13\frac{8}{15}$; (d) (i) 28 and 45; (ii) $35\frac{1}{2}$; (iii) 38.1; (e) (i) 4.3; (ii) 4.7; (iii) 4.77
2. (a) Median 15.7; no mode and median is not affected by the one extreme value; (b) Median 2005 or mean 2005.56; no mode; (c) Median or mean 105; two modes; (d) Mode 44; this is a very common value and the other values are evenly spread either side.
3. (a) Mean 9; median 7; mode 7; (b) (i) 7; (ii) $\geqslant 7$; (iii) 9; (iv) 21; (c) (i) 2 or 5; (ii) 5
4. 824.4 kg
5. (a) 52.9 g; (b) $158\frac{4}{9}$ cm

Exercise 3B

1. (a) (i) 4; (ii) 6; (iii) 6.59; (b) (i) 6 and 7; (ii) 6; (iii) 5.77
2. 41.5 matches
3. (a) (i) 10.22 (ii) 12; (iii) 10; (b) Manufacturer choice: mode as its highest of the three averages
4. (a) (i) $10 < t \leqslant 20$; (ii) $20 < t \leqslant 30$; (iii) 23.5; (b) (i) $5 < t \leqslant 10$; (ii) $10 < t \leqslant 15$; (iii) 14.7
5. (a) Between two classes; (b) £17
6. (a) $37\frac{1}{3}$; (b) $20 < M \leqslant 40$; (c) $40 < M \leqslant 60$; (d) Mean would increase as new amount much higher and the mean uses all the values; median and mode remain unchanged a they are not affected by extreme values.
7. (a) $180\frac{4}{9}$ mg; (b) 279.73 mm; (c) 2:10:03 (2 hours 10 minutes 3 seconds)

Exercise 3C

1. (a) 5.85%; (b) 6.05%
2. 6.44%
3. Loss 16.5%
4. 13.4%
5. Increase 2.76%
6. (a) 4.38; (b) 5.33; (c) 2.58
7. Multiplying by zero would give a zero answer (this could not be correct)

Exercise 3D

1. (a) 24, 13; (b) 51, 17; (c) 40, 16; (d) 36, 14; (e) 22, 9.5; (f) 31, 9
2. (a) 6, 4; (b) 6, 3; (c) 5, 1; (d) 7, 2

Exercise 3E

1. (a) 21, 4.58; (b) 47.85, 6.92; (c) 175.89, 13.26; (d) 0.148, 0.38
2. (a) 3.945, 1.986; (b) 1.215, 1.102
3. (a) 152.75, 12.36; (b) 155, 12.45
4. (a) 0.1944, 0.441; (b) 185.15, 13.61; (c) 0.017325, 0.132; (d) 19.712, 4.44; (e) 5.2, 2.28; (f) 24.42, 4.94

Exercise 3F

1. (a)

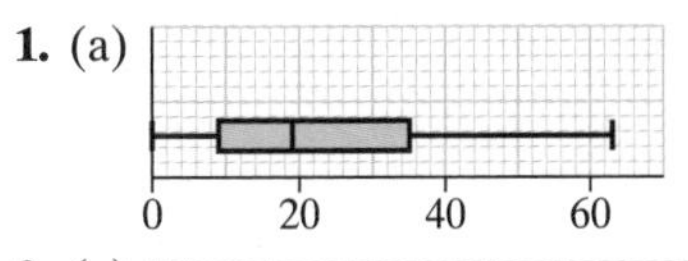

(b) Positive skew
(c) 0.2 agrees with part (b)
(d) Yes, 59 and 63

2. (a)

(b) Y has a higher average; smaller range; smaller IQR; skewed. X is not skewed.
(c) X (i) 0.055; (ii) 0.166; (iii) 0
Y (i) 0.345; (ii) 0.627; (iii) 0.273

3. (a) Similarities: same median, same range; Differences: Dentists have a smaller IQR, Doctors data skewed; (b) No; (c) Doctors −0,375, Dentists 0
4. (a) Similar IQR, Smokers larger range, higher median, data skewed; (b) Smokers Yes – highest value; (c) Smokers −0.45, Non-smokers 0
5. 0.77; positive skew
6. −0.48; negative skew

Exercise 3G

1. (a) (i) A; (ii) B; (b) A – 40, B – 50, C – 70. Median and mode are equal.
2. f(x)

B C A

0 10 20 30 40 50 60 70 80 90 100 x

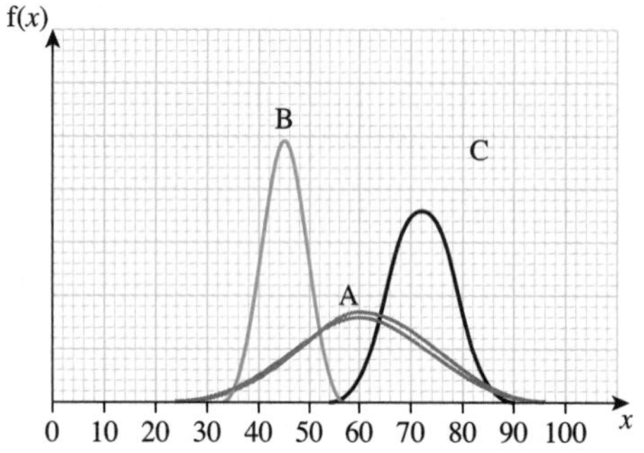

3. (a) (i) 1.6 m; (ii) 1.96 m; (b) 1.66 m – 1.9 m
4. Paper 1 – The mark is about mean +2 sd. If the mark was from Paper 2 then it would be outside of mean +3 sd.
5. Ryan, as his range extends up to 3.44, whereas Josh's errors are almost all in the range 2.04 to 2.76.
6. (a) Physics – Jenny −0.6, Karen −0.8, Louise 2; Chemistry Jenny – 0.125, Karen 0.5, Louise 2; (b) Louise

Exercise 3H

1. A There is some variation, which is not excessive although the range is increasing. It may be assumed that the machine is functioning properly.
   B There is an increase in the sizes. The machine may need adjusting. The range is also close to the action limit. Further samples may need to be checked.
   C The means are mostly above the target mean. The final two readings are above the warning level. The machine should be stopped and checked.
   D The means are mostly below the target mean. Further samples should be checked.
2. (a) Ensure that the contents do not fall below that stated on box (4 kg).
   (b) Mean graph – increasing, more consistent after reset; Range graph – not very consistent, but range very small compared to overall contents. Samples are all below the action limit.
3. Average to ensure correct amount of the item; Range to ensure consistency of measurements.

Revision Exercise 3

1. (a) £52 000 (b) (i) £65 400 (ii) The mean is affected by the extreme value (£129 500).
2. (a) 0.074 kg (c) The mean weight has been rising over the past five hours. The range is below, but close to, the acceptable range. Check machinery.
3. (a) 120.3, 9.51 (b) The duration of almost all films would be expected to be within 3.09 standard deviations of the mean (149 mins). (c) On average, romance films are longer than adventure films, but there is more variation in the length of adventure films.
4. (a) 4, 11, 9, 1 (b) 1 sweet (c) 1.28 sweets.
5. (a) Standardized scores: Mathematics −1.5, Statistics −2. Better at Mathematics.
   (b)

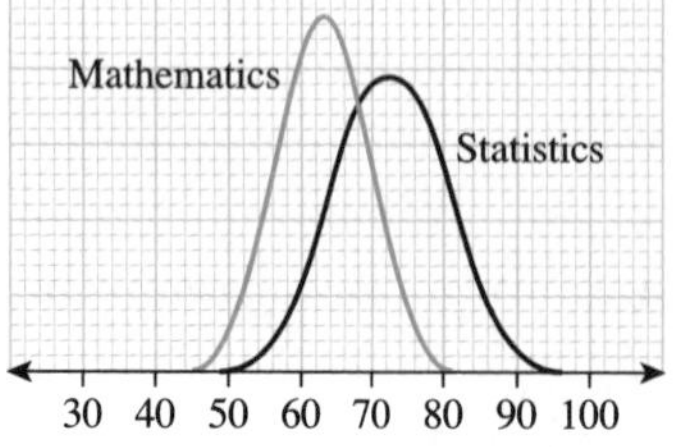

Mathematics Statistics

30 40 50 60 70 80 90 100

6. (a) 31.5, 9.52
   (b) 32.4, 9.09)
   (c) (i) The total mark increased, so the mean increased.
   (ii) 32 is closer to the mean than 23 so the standard deviation has increased.
7. (a) 23, 28, 18, 6, 3, 2 (b) 80 (c) 184 (d) 2.3 (e) 2
8. (a) 180.5 s (b) 243 s
9. Full-fat (Semi-skimmed: mean + 2 s.d. is 574 ml; Full-fat: mean + 2 s.d. is 576 ml)
10. (a) (i) 7 (ii) 10 (iii) 9 (iv) 8.5 (b) Affected by the extreme value (3) (c) Joshua gave lower, but more consistent, enjoyment scores.
11. (a)

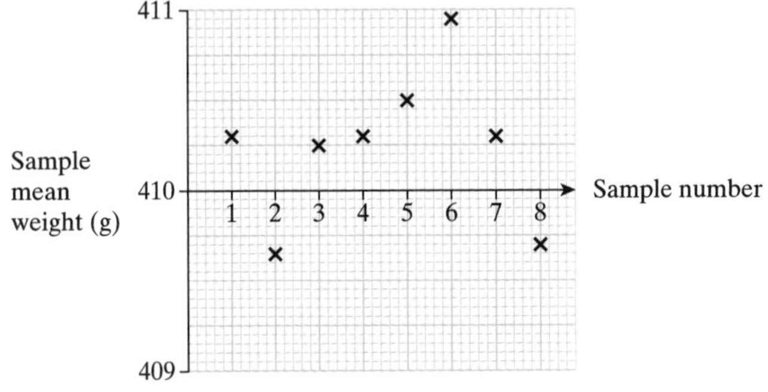

   (b) After sample 6. This was above the upper action limit, after which the sample weights return to acceptable limits.
12. (a) 6.23, 4.61
   (b) (i) Increases (ii) Remains the same
   (c) (i) (ii)

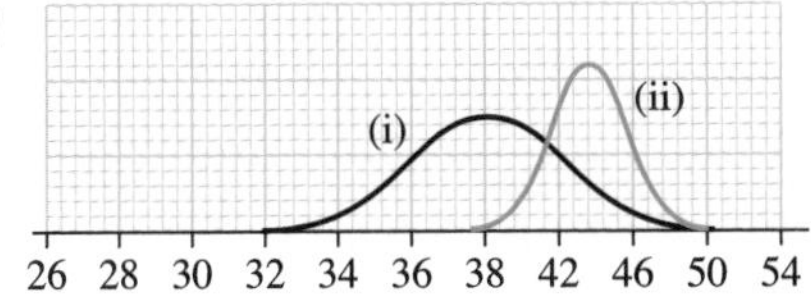

   (iii) 50% (iv) 0%
13. (a) £220 (b) £12 (c) Higher, the extreme value (£225) will affect the mean.
14. (a) 7, 5, 4, 2, 1, 1 (b) mode
15. (a) 2 (b) 9, 1 (c) 8 (d) Outlier or extreme values
16. (a) (i) 5.3; 6.6 (b) (i) 1.06, 0.897
17. (a) 93.9s, 46.1s
18. (a) 34 (b) 10.9
19. (a) (i) 51 (ii) 2.07
20. (a) £28, 300, £10, 005 (b) −1.59, 0.05
21. (a) (i) 1.5 (ii) 0.98 (b) 0.36, 0.65
22. (a) 1.5 (b) 1.53 m
23. (b) better at History
24. (a) 5.5 (b) 0.76 (c) (i) 0.39 (ii) 5.7

4 Representation of data

Before you start 4

1. (a) 90; (b) 120; (c) 92
2. (a) (i) 43; (ii) 59; (b) (i) 3.6; (ii) 0.9
3. (a) (i) 2.8 Euros; (ii) 6.3 Euros; (b) (i) £2.80; (ii) £5

Exercise 4A

1. (a) Daily national; (b) 10; (c) 10; (d) 110
2. **Transport**

Car	
Bus	
Walk	
Cycle	
Other	

Key: = 10 people

3. (a) Many correct answers can be given;
   (b) **Number of cars manufactured in 2006**

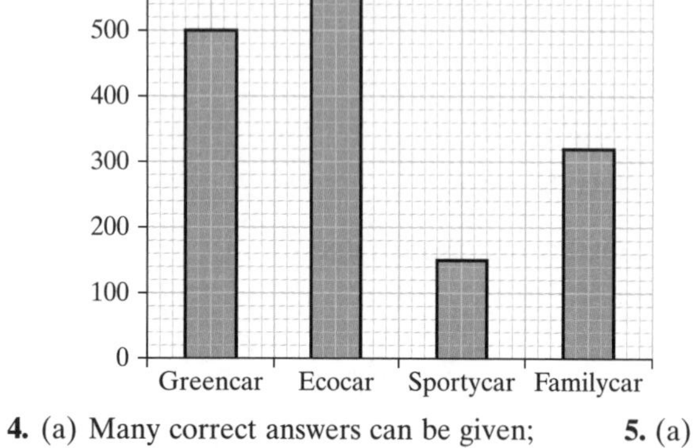

4. (a) Many correct answers can be given;
   (b)

Bigfeet Cycles Sales in June

Frequency
14
12
10
8
6
4
2
0
Road Mountain BMX Hybrid
Bike Type
Women
Men

5. (a) **Renewable energy 1996 - 2000**

1000 tonnes of oil equivalent
3500
3000
2500
2000
1500
1000
500
0
1996 1998 2000 2002 2004
Year
Biofuels
Hydro
Wind

(b) Hydro

Exercise 4B

1. (a) Baths, showers, hand washing; (b) 4100 megalitres per day
2. (a) Leisure, recreation, holidays; (b) Rail; (c) No, the mode of transport chart represents the transport choices of all visitors, not just business visitors.
3. (a)

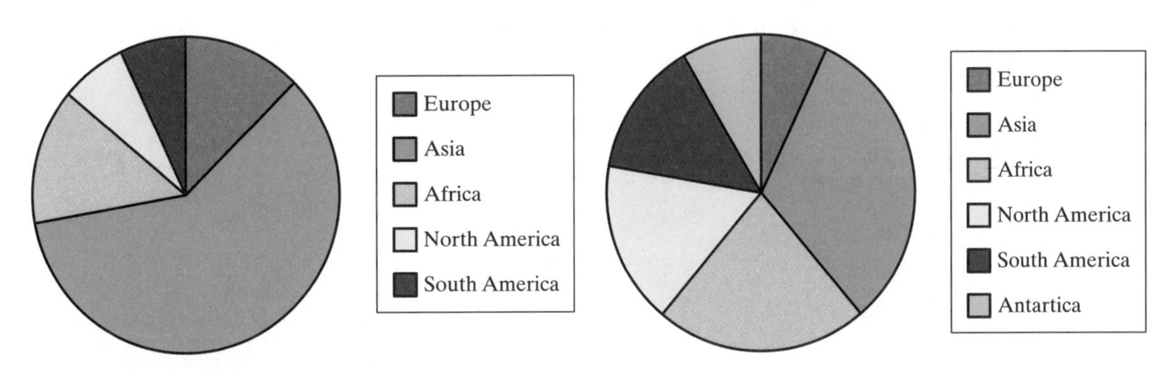

4. (a) The area would be four times larger – area should be in proportion; (b) 7.07 cm
5. (a) 6.53 cm; (b) 3.83 cm

Exercise 4C

1. The graph shows more 4's were rolled.

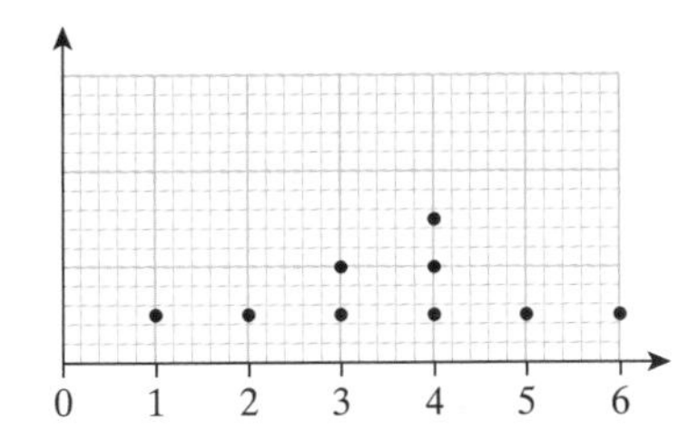

2. (a)

8	8 9
9	1 2 4 8
10	1 3 4 5 6 7 8 8 9
11	0 2 4 6 6 7 7 8 9
12	1 5 6 7 9
13	1 3

Key: 10|1 means 101

(b)

80 85 90 95 100 105 110 115 120 125 130 135 x

(c) Slight negative skew

3. (a)

1	0 0 0 2 3 4 5 6 6 8 9
2	1 1 3 3 5 6 8
3	0 1 2 3 3 5 5 7 9
4	0 0 2 7 8
5	0

Key: 2|1 means 21

(b)

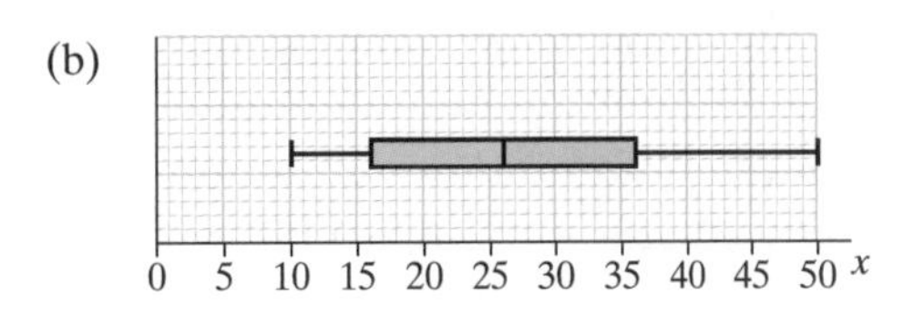

(c) Box shows no skew

4. (a)

A		B
8 7	3	
9 7 5 4 4 3 2 1	4	1 4 8
8 6 6 5 3 2 1	5	3 3 4 6 7 7
2 1	6	1 3 5 6 9
	7	0 2 2 5 9

Key : 1|5|3 means 51% in test A, 53% in test B

(b)

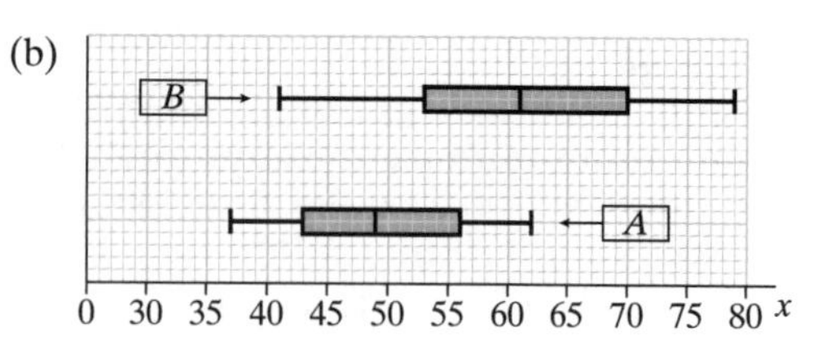

(c) Similarity: Both have slight negative skew;
Difference A has lower median or A has smaller range or A has smaller IQR

Exercise 4D

1. (a)

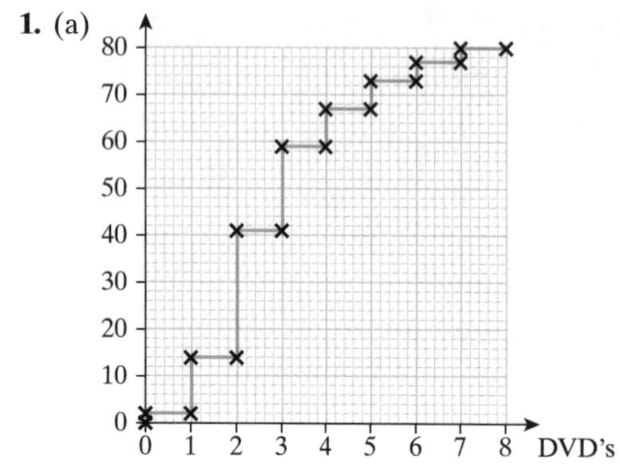

(b) Median = 2; IQR = 2

2. (a)

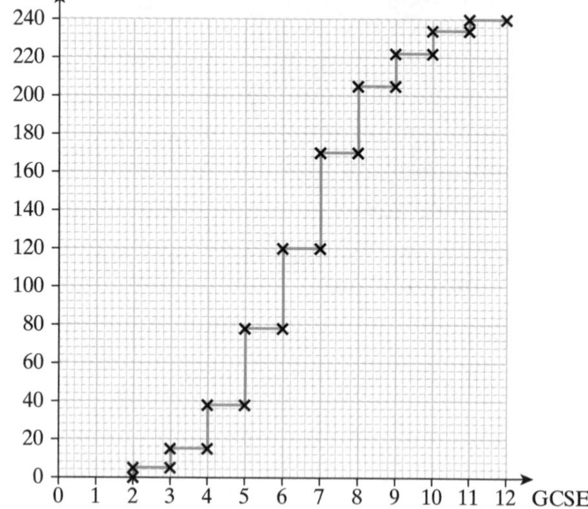

(b) 10th percentile = 4
90th percentile = 10
middle 80% = 6

3. (a)

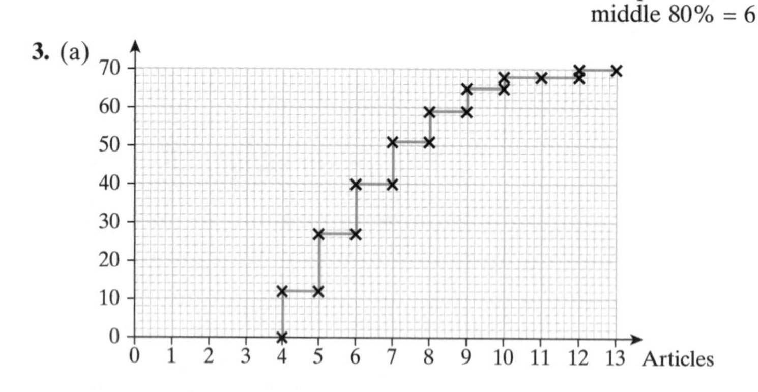

(b) 2nd decile = 5
8th decile = 8
interdecile range = 3

Exercise 4E

1. (a) (i) 152.5 cm; (ii) 52; (b) (i) 157 cm; (ii) 6;

(c)

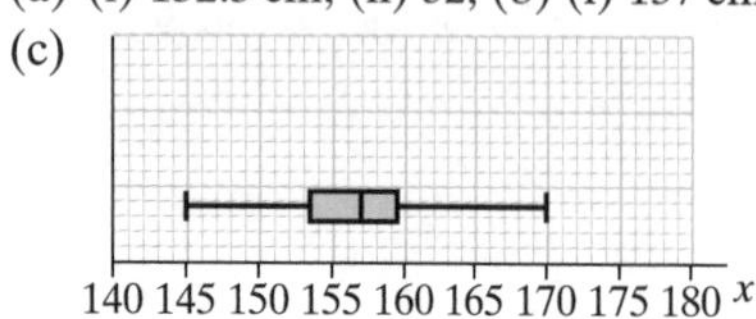

(d) Medians are similar; Boys have greater IQR

2. (a)

Height, h cm	$h < 80$	$h < 100$	$h < 120$	$h < 140$	$h < 160$
Cumulative frequency	7	37	89	110	120

(b) (c) (ii)

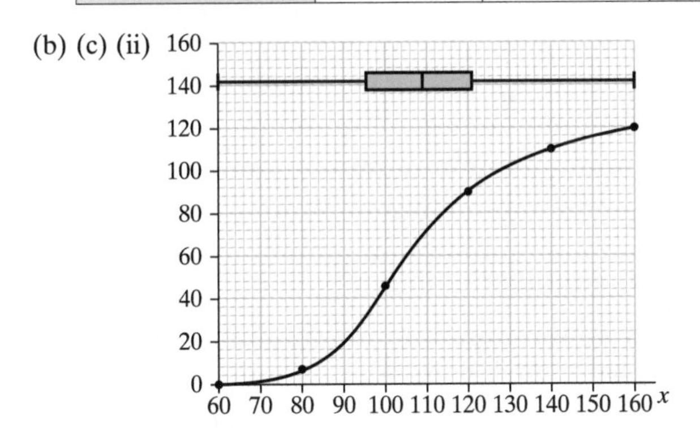

(c) (i) Median 108.5, IQR 24 (c) (ii) No skew (d) 20 (e) 18 (f) (i) 93 cm (ii) 124 cm (g) 31

3. (a)

Time, t minutes	$t < 10$	$t < 20$	$t < 30$	$t < 40$	$t < 50$	$t < 60$
Cumulative frequency	4	15	44	81	108	120

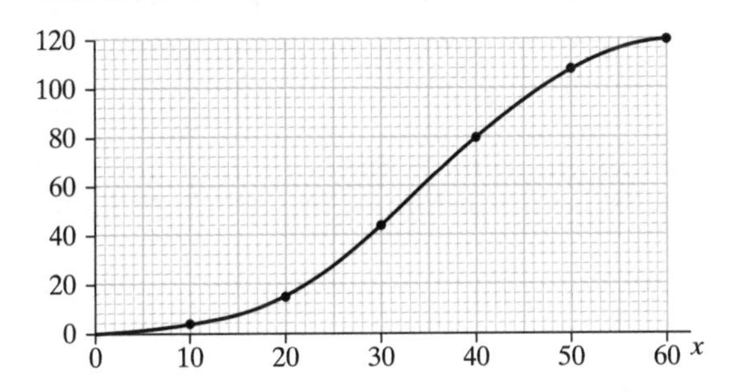

(b) Median 34 mins IQR 16 mins
(c) On average took longer to complete sudoku and times for sudoku more varied.

4. (a)

Time, t minutes	$t < 10$	$t < 20$	$t < 30$	$t < 40$	$t < 50$	$t < 60$
Cumulative frequency	9	36	78	108	128	140

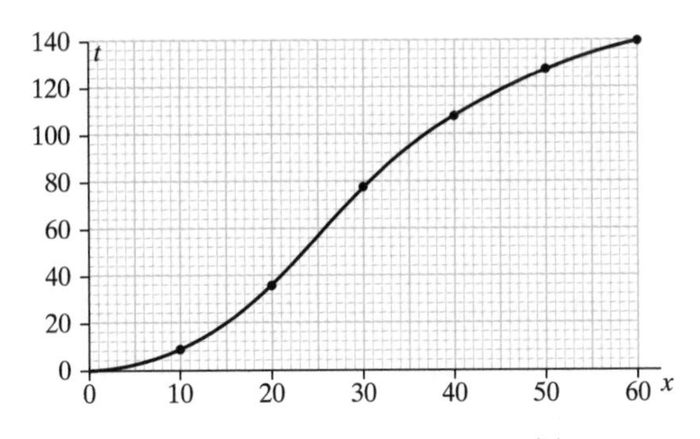

(b) Median 28; IQR 20 (c) (i) 12; (ii) 49 (d) 37

Exercise 4F

1. (a) Weekday

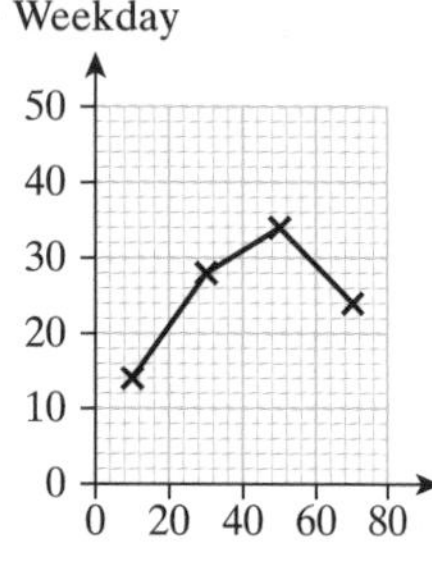

Saturday

(b) (i) Weekday $40 < a \leqslant 60$; Saturday $20 < a \leqslant 40$; (ii) Weekday 80; Saturday 80
(c) Same range of ages, higher modal age on weekday.

2. Same modal class for number of miles travelled as both peak in class 40–60, however more longer journeys in January than December, plus slightly more miles travelled overall.

3. (a)

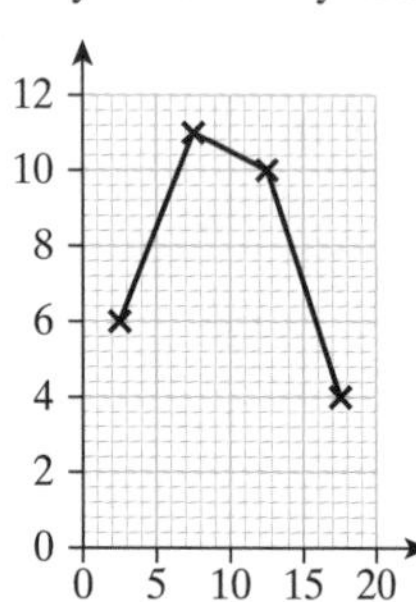

(b) Similarity: Same modal class
Difference: Greater range of times in August

4. (a) Duracomp

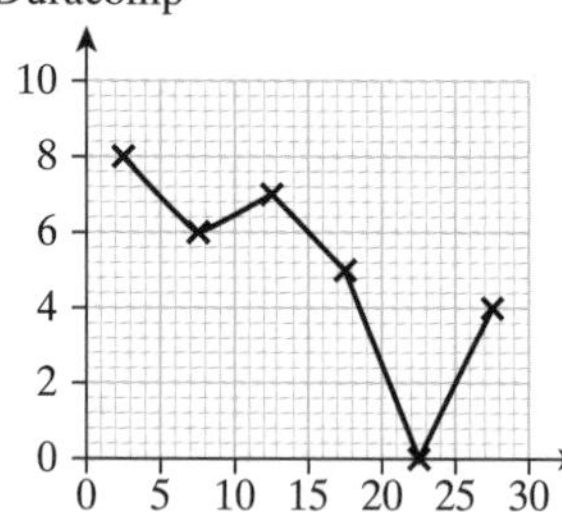

Powerblast

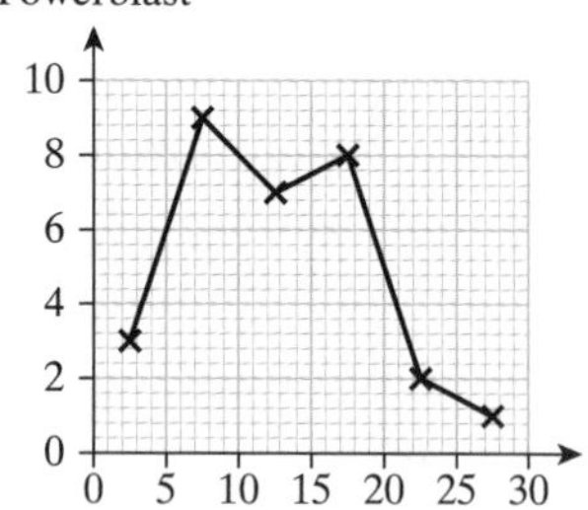

(b) Modal class greater for Powerblast; median in same class; Powerblast has a higher mean. Buy from Powerblast.

Exercise 4G

1. (a)

Time, t seconds	$1 \leqslant t < 3$	$3 \leqslant t < 4$	$4 \leqslant t < 5$	$5 \leqslant t < 6$	$6 \leqslant t < 9$
Class width	2	1	1	1	3
Frequency	12	17	19	11	18
Frequency density	6	17	19	11	6

(b)

(c) $4 \leqslant t < 5$ (d) Positive skew

2. (a)

Time, t, minutes	$10 \leqslant t < 20$	$20 \leqslant t < 40$	$40 \leqslant t < 60$	$60 \leqslant t < 90$	$90 \leqslant t < 120$
Class width	10	20	20	30	30
Frequency	8	16	28	39	9
Frequency density	0.8	0.8	1.4	1.3	0.3

(b)

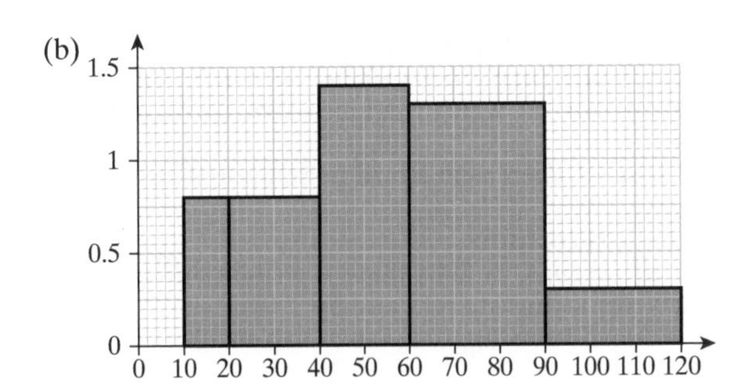

(c) $40 \leqslant t < 60$
(d) Negative skew

3. (a) Missing frequencies 6; 10; 14

(b)

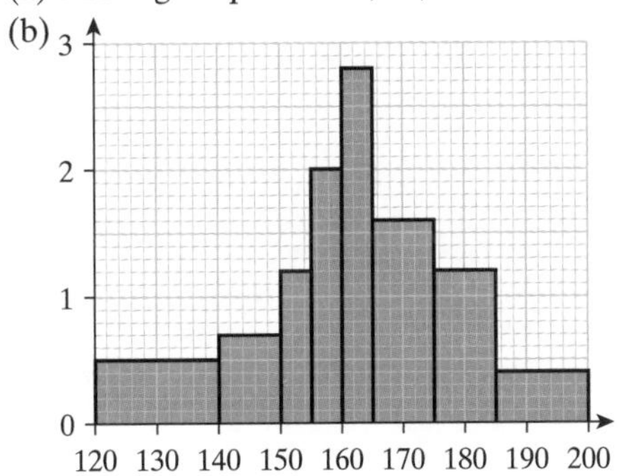

(c) $160 \leqslant g < 165$
(d) Positive skew

4. (a) Missing frequencies 10, 8

(b)

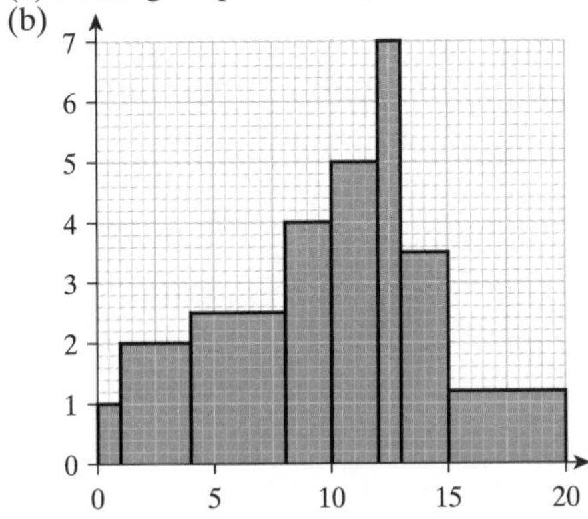

(c) $12 \leqslant h < 13$
(d) Negative skew

5. (a) An end value for the last class. Suitable values would be minimum 65 with maximum of 80.
(b) Graphs using their end values

Exercise 4H

1. (a) Correct population pyramid drawn.
(b) Similarity: Modal class age is the same for both men and women
Difference: Higher percentage of women are over 70.

2. (a) Correct population pyramid drawn.

3. Bangladesh has much higher proportion of younger population than Austria.
Bangladesh has almost equal proportions of men and women in all age groups while Austria does not.
Only about 10% of the population of Bangladesh live beyond age 50, which is a much lower proportion of the population compared with Austria.

4. Difference: Greater proportion of Kenya population is under 40 whereas in Brazil population is more evenly distributed across age groups.
Similarity: Almost equal proportion of male and female in both countries.

5. 1891 greater proportion of population are in the younger age groups, by 2001 there is a slight middle-aged bulge. 1891 very few people living beyond 80, by 1951 they are living into 80's and by 2001 living into 90's and over 100. Proportion of population that are aged less than 5 years approximately half in 2001 compared to 1891.

Exercise 4I

1. (a) London; (b) 0–2%
2, 3 Correctly shaded maps

Revision Exercise 4

1. (a) 80 (b) 50 (c) 3 loaves (d) 190

2. (a)

Stem	Leaves
5	3
6	2 4 8 9 9
7	0 2 4 5 5 6 8
8	1 2

Key 6|2 means 62

(b) Median 72, LQ 68, UQ 76

(c)

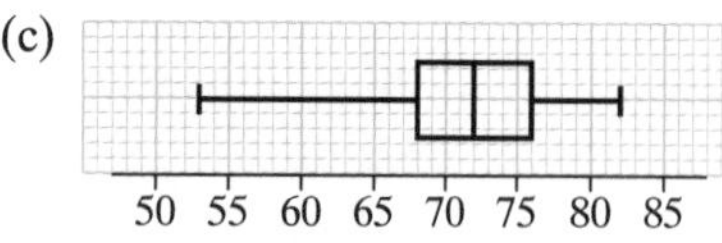

3. (a)

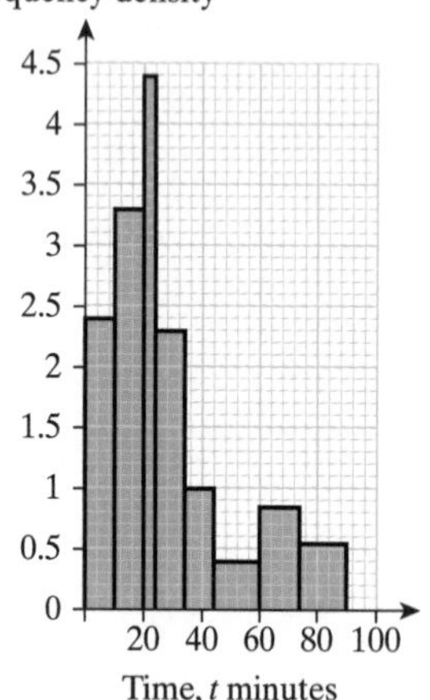

(b) Positive skew (c) Median and mode

4. (a) 80 (b) 110 (c) Three-quarters of a symbol (d) 350

5. (a) Chart correctly plotted
(b) (1) 80 (b) 150 (c) Fewer irons sold; more toasters sold

6. (a)

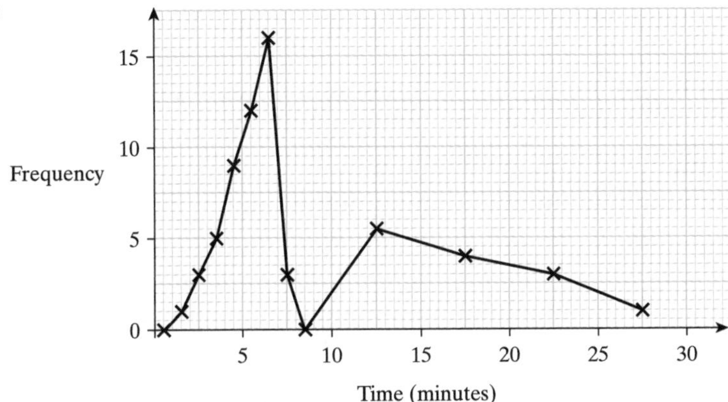

(b) $6 \leqslant t < 7$ (c) (i) 10 (ii) 34 (d) Positive skew

7. (a) Correct shading drawn (b) Bottom left-hand corner

8. (a)

Stem	Leaves
0	0 3 5 6 7 9
1	0 2 3 4 6
2	2 4 5 6
3	3
4	5
5	
6	0 4

Key: 6|0 means 60

(b) Median 14, LQ 7, UQ 26 (c) George III, Victoria (d) Monarchs' range of reigns is greater, and the middle 50% of reigns are more varied than the Popes'. The Monarchs' reigns have a stronger positive skew than the Popes', but on average Monarch's reign is longer than a Pope's.

9. (a) 3299 (b) Men 197°, children 84° (c) 63500

10. (a)

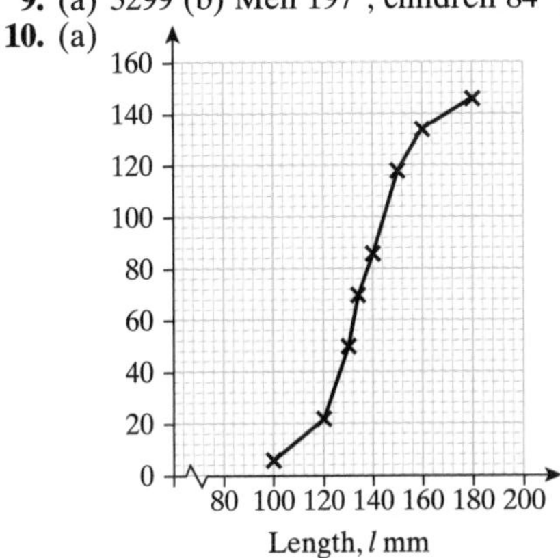

(b) 48 mm (c) Avoids using extreme values, plus there is no upper bound shown.

11. (a) Bartley (b) 6

12. (a) Values 14, 55, 68, 87, 96, 100 (b) Cumulative frequency graph with values plotted at upper bounds. (c) (i) 18 (ii) 13 (iii) 34 (d) 54 years (e) (i) box and whisker plot with values as above (ii) On average 10 am passengers were younger, 5 pm distribution is symmetrical, 10 am had positive skew.

13. (a) Cumulative frequency step polygon with values plotted at mid-points of groups at 3, 3, 11, 29, 51, 78, 96, 1114, 120 (b) Median 13, second decile 11, eighth decile 14, interdecile range 3. (c) On average the girls remembered fewer words but their recall was more varied.

14. (a) Each small square represents 0.1 (b) (i) 22 (ii) 10 (iii) 5 (c) Frequency densities for other groups: 0.4, 1.5, 3. (d) 202.9 g

15. (a) Frequency polygon with values 1, 3, 5, 1. (b) Longlast, on average they last longer.

16. (a) Larger population in total (b) 50–54 (c) 0.7 million.

17. (a) 27 (b) £220 000
18. (a) 90 (b) 34
19. (a) (i) 16.5% (b) (ii) 14.7%
20. (a) 2700 (b) 900, 1300, 1500, 1200, 700, 300, 100 (c) 26 years (d) 19 years
21. (a) 86 (b) 213 (c) 11.5 per year
22. (a) 80, 60, 40, 60
23. (a)

Stem	Leaf
2	8
3	5 5 6
4	0 2 2 5 6 7 8
5	0 4 4 6 9
6	0 1 3 3 4 9
7	1 1 3 5
8	1

Key: 7|1 means 71

(b) (i) 54 (ii) 22

24. (a) 86 (b) 4.5 (c) 5.3, 3.7 (d) 4.2 (e) 0.0879
25. (a)

Stem	Leaf
2	3 4
3	6 9
4	3 3 4 4 8 9
5	1 4 5 5 5 6 6
6	5 7 7
7	3 8
8	4

Key: 7|3 means 73

(b) (i) 55 (ii) 43, 67

26. (a) Pie chart with angles Gas 111°, Electricity 79°, Council Tax 104; Telephone 66° (b) 10.02 cm
27. (a) (i) 5.25 (ii) 5.75, 4.8 (c) Negative skew (d) Faster times on average, positive skew
28. (c) 18.5s
29. (b) £83 444, £20 421 (c) 40 (d) (i) 1991 (ii) 16% decrease
30. (c) (i) 43.4 (ii) 52.1 (iii) 34.1 (d) (i) 8.7, 9.3 (e) 28 good, 37 average, 60 poor
31. (b) (i) 2 (ii) 6 (c) 60
32. (b) (i) 35 (ii) 20.1 (c) 40.25, 16.89 (d) There are four extreme values

5 Correlation and regression

Before you start 5

1. Isosceles triangle.
2. 22.08
3. (a) $y = 3x + 1$ (b) $y = \frac{x}{2} + 3$ (c) $y = -\frac{x}{4} + 2$ (d) $y = -3x - 1$

Exercise 5A

1. B
2. A
3. C
4. Sketch, negative correlation, temperature (x-axis) gas used (y-axis).
5. Sketch, positive correlation, age (x) weight (y).
6. Sketch, no correlation, height (x) amount spent (y).

Exercise 5B

1. Correlation.
2. Causality.
3. Third variable.
4. Correlation.
5. Causality.

Exercise 5C

1. Scatter graph, height (x) arm span (y), mean point (144, 138.5) line of best fit with positive gradient.
2. Scatter graph, age (x) weight (y), mean point (44.1, 9.2) line of best fit with negative gradient.
3. Scatter graph, published price (x) book club price (y), mean point (10, 7.4) line of best fit with positive gradient.
4. Scatter graph, Number of absentees / number of thefts, no correlation mean & line of best fit inappropriate.

Exercise 5D

1. Strong positive correlation.
2. Strong negative correlation.
3. Strong positive correlation.
4. No correlation.

Exercise 5E

1. Answer in range 138 cm–141 cm.
2. (a) Approximately 9g; (b) Answer in range 4.8g–5.8g; (a) is more reliable, within the plotted points.
3. (a) Answer in range £21–£22; (b) approximately £8; (b) is more reliable, within the plotted points.
4. (a) £17; (b) £2; (c) £0, line of best fit has reached x-axis.
5. (i) ~3600; (ii) ~5250; (iii) 0–100; (ii) unrealistic, 12 year olds should not be driving.
6. Pregnancy unlikely to be this long, no longer premature, but very overdue.

Exercise 5F

1. (a) (i) their line using one point and (144, 138.5); (b) (i) increase in arm span with height (ii) unrealistic.
   (a) (ii) their line using one point and (44.1, 9.2); (b) (i) decrease in weight with age (ii) unrealistic.
   (a) (iii) their line using one point and (10, 7.4); (b) (i) book club price factor of published price (ii) realistic if 0.
2. (a) $y = 0.4x - 2.2$, not appropriate for less than £5.50
   (b) $y = -800x + 6600$, not appropriate for age less than 17 yrs.

Exercise 5G

1. Plot $\frac{1}{s}$ (x-axis) T (y-axis) points (1, 89) (0.5, 46) (0.33, 30) (0.23, 25) (0.2, 20) (0.17, 16) (0.14, 13) (0.125, 11) (0.11, 10) (0.1, 9). (i) ~62 °C; (ii) ~20 °C; (iii) ~1 °C.
2. (a) Plot $\sqrt{A}$ (x-axis) C (y-axis) points (1.41, 39.3) (2, 42) (2.45, 44) (2.83, 45.4) (3, 46) (3.16, 46.4).
   (b) ~15 cm. Unreliable outside plotted points; growth rate may change.
3. Plot S^2 (x-axis) C (y-axis) points (784, 20) (900, 21) (1225, 24) (1600, 30) (2500, 35) (3025, 42). a = 0.01; b = 12.

Exercise 5H

1. 0.29; closest to zero.
2. A 0.78; B (−)0.81; C (−)0.39; 1.32 not a coefficient as greater than 1.
3. $r_s = 1$; same rank order for each test.
4. $r_s = 0.25$; very little agreement.
5. $r_s = 0.814$; high degree of agreement.
6. $r_s = -0.579$; weak negative correlation, the longer the time the less errors; employ C quickest with not too many errors.

Revision Exercise 5

1. (a) (i) Diagram 2 (ii) Diagram 1 (b) Value of car
2. (a) As thickness increases the amount of heat escaping decreases; (b) As temperature increases in NZ the amount of coal sold in the UK increases; (c) Part (a).
3. Line of best fit drawn though (17, 184) (b) (i) 230 tonnes (ii) 360 tonnes (c) (i) More reliable, within plotted points (d) 9 tonnes, 800 (f) If sector areas are above 1400 square metres the timber felled is about equal; above this pine forests give proportionally more timber than natural woodland. Increasing the area of a pine forest increases the amount of timber more quickly than in a natural woodland. (g) 0.946, high degree of agreement (h) Least 189, greatest 280.
4. (a) Points plotted on scatter diagram (b) Negative (c) 18 (d) Own line through (27, 28) (e) 12 calls (f) Because the line of best fit does not pass through 45 text messages so may give a more accurate average.
5. (a) −0.839 (b) John put more value on those items that the expert thought less valuable and vice versa.
   (c) (i) −0.02 (ii) 0.92

6. (b) Negative (c) (i) 9 (ii) Own line through (9.4, 9) (d) (i) 5 days (ii) 15 days (e) (i) More reliable within plotted points.

7. (a) Plot (20, 10) (25, 21) (30, 18) (35, 24) (40, 28) (45, 30) (50, 34) (55, 40) (60, 45) (65, 50); (b) 42.5; (c) (i) (42.5, 30); (e) Aged 57, within the plotted points; (f) B.

8. (a) Plot (63, 141) (13, 14) (34, 43) (80, 170) (51, 95) (14, 21) (45, 72) (74, 152) (24, 31) (82, 171); (b) (48, 91); (c) Line through mean and (20, 24.5); (d) (i) £179; (ii) –£11; (iii) £119.50; (e) Order (iii), (i), (ii); interpolation, extrapolation, not possible.

9. (a) 108 kg; (b) 168 cm; (c) Player (172, 98); (d) Positive; (e) (i) greater than 84–86; (ii) > 190 cm.

10. (a) Plot (167, 101); (b) Line through mean point; (c) ~ £62; (d) (i) Beetall, £55 gets a camera with a higher usual price; (ii) Difference is greater.

11. B, Perfect positive; A, Negative; C, No correlation.

12. (a) $y = 1.55x + 0.05$; (b) If straight line distance is zero then so is journey distance; (c) For each km away from the school you have to journey 1.55 km.

13. (a) Plot (7.8, 29) (8.1, 28) (6.4, 26) (5.2, 20) (7, 24) (9.9, 35) (8.4, 30) (6, 22) (7.2, 25) (10, 36); (b) 27.5; (d) $y = 3.2x + 3$; (e) ~30; (f) Extrapolation.

14. (a) Straight line not appropriate; (b) Extrapolation not recommended, Growth has stopped.

15. (a) Plot (18, 37) (36, 54) (45, 63) (22, 42) (69, 84) (72, 91) (13, 33) (33, 49) (60, 79) (79, 98) (10, 32) (53, 70); (b) (42.5, 61); (c) Line must pass through mean and given point; (d) (i) £83; (ii) £102; (e) (i) interpolation; (f) 0.981; (g) per unit increase in production cost.

16. (a) Y; (b) X, ~ $^{-}0.95$; Z, ~ +0.7

17. (a) 0.6; (b) Weak or moderate agreement.

18. (a) $^{-}0.52$; (b) (i) $^{-}0.52$ closer to $^{-}1$ than 0.45 is to $^{+}1$.

19. (a) Rank 1 1 2.5 5 4 2.5 6; (b) (i) C; (ii) Ranks must remain unchanged.
Rank 2 1 3.5 5 3.5 2 6

20. (a) First judge awards higher points than the second judge; (b) (i) 0.95; (ii) Strong agreement.

21. (a) 0.714; (b) 35; (c) (i) 49; (ii) 52; (d) 1.

22. (a)

Sales	1	2	3	4	5	6	7	8	9	10
Grants	1	4	6	2	7	5	8	3	9	10

(b) 0.71; (c) Positive correlation; (d) Anything < £107.5 million.

23. (a) 0.188; (b) Ranks for attendance figures for 1986 more similar to 1991, than 1981 is to 1991.

24. (a) 0.396; (b) Little agreement between the two jumps; (c) (i) No correlation; (ii) Strong positive correlation; (iii) Mistake made in the calculation.

25. (a)

Sunshine	4	6	8.5	10	8.5	5	3	2	7	1
Temperature	6	10	9	8	2	4.5	7	3	1	4.5

(b) 0.2; (c) Almost no correlation; (d) (i) Sunshine & temperature not related; (ii) inverse relationship between sunshine & temperature.

6 Other summary statistics

Before you start 6

1. (a) 19.4 (b) 22.
2. (a) 60% (b) 73.3%
3. (a) 8:15 (b) 30:13
4. Points plotted correctly

Exercise 6A

1. Time series graph & trend line; missing bill £64.
2. Time series graph & trend line; includes Christmas shopping period.
3. Time series graph & trend line; long weekend away by staff.
4. Time series graph & trend line; Trend line suggests decrease in attendance; week 3 could have coincided with school half term holiday; consider latest film releases, time of year, school holidays.

Exercise 6B

1. (a) 4-point moving averages: £47.25, £48.50, £49.63, £51.75, £53.25, £54.25, £55.88; (c) £60; (d) similar possibly more accurate; (e) £24–£25; (f) £86–£87.

2. (a) Profit is given half yearly that is two values per year; (b) Moving averages: £25500, £25500, £27500, £29250, £29750, £30500, £31750, £32500, £33250; (d) Jan. – June £29500; July – Dec. £41000.

3. (a) 5-point moving averages: 5.2, 5, 5, 5.2, 5.4, 5.6, 5.6, 5.8, 5.6, 5.4, 5.2; (d) Monday ~12; Tuesday ~4.
4. (b) 3-point moving averages: £361.67, £365, £370, £380, £381.67, £386.67, £395, £401.67. (d) ~£410; (e) ~ −£51.25; (f) ~£373.75.

Exercise 6C

1.

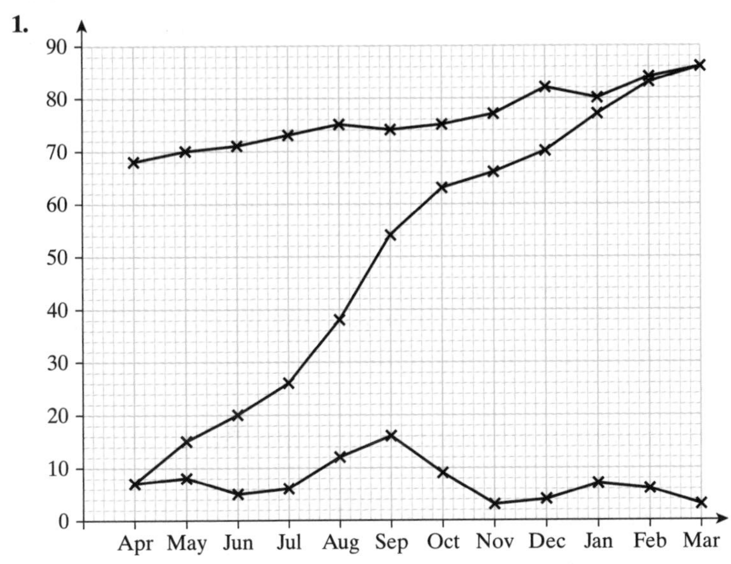

2.

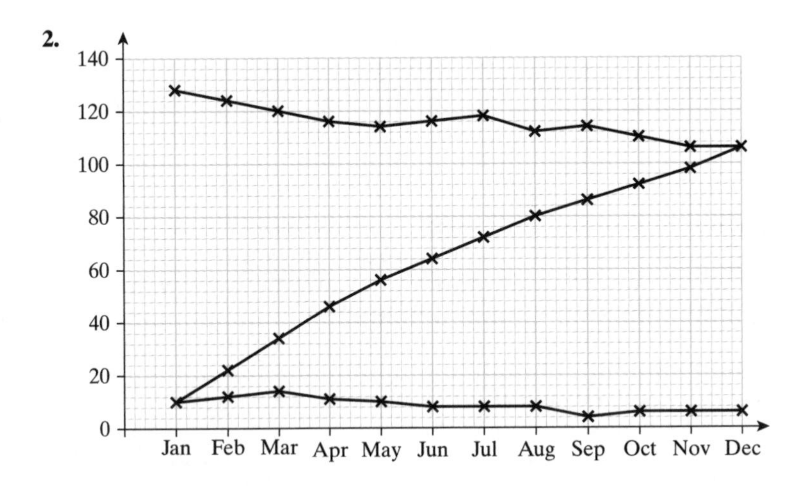

3. (a) (i) 240 (ii) 100; (b) 890; (c) 2100
4. (a) (i) 22 000 (ii) 30 000; (b) 134 000; (c) 450 000; (d) Overall decreasing until December.

Exercise 6D

1. 108.3%
2. 106.47%
3. 91.67%
4. £4.90
5. £75
6. (a) 1992; (b) Prices always increase; (c) £20.16; (d) £140; (e) 113.3
7. (a) Washing machine 140, dishwasher 130; (b) WM; (c) DW; (d) Actual increase for DW greater although % increase smaller as original price greater to begin with.

Exercise 6E

1. (a) increase; (b) small decrease then increase; (c) no change; (d) increase, no change then decrease; (e) increase, decrease, no change.
2. 166.67, 125, 116, 120.69
3. 60, 69.4, 72, 80.56; annual decrease, but % decrease smaller each year; 1996 index – 30, 70% decrease in 3 years, only 28% over the previous year.
4. 100, 105, 106.67, 107.14, 113.3
5. 100, 120, 148.8, 184.5, 202.96; more than doubled.

Exercise 6F

1. 154.43
2. 82.13
3. 106.9
4. 79.54
5. 124.65
6. Gilding metal 81.43; Dutch metal 82.74; Gilding metal costs changed the most.
7. 80.61; 170.65; 91.46; 79.45; 81.69. Cost decreased, almost doubled, then decreased for the next three years.
8. 82.38; 157.36; 90.89; 85.62.

Exercise 6G

1. Negative until late 1980's and from 1990 till late 1990's. Positive late 1980's until 1990 Close to balance from late 1990's.
2. Negative throughout most of 1990's; Positive in 2000, otherwise close to balance.
3. Strongly positive through late 1980's/early 1990's. Otherwise fairly close to balance.

Exercise 6H

1. 217.5
2. (a) 150 (b) 30.
3. 496
4. 106
5. 16.8; distortion of true figure as not all the women will be of child bearing age.

Exercise 6I

1. (a) Crude rate lower for Antville; standardised rates similar; (b) Antville as more younger people
2. (a) Crude rate higher Clawtown; standardised rates similar; (b) Clawtown as greater crude rate
3. Earlsham crude rate double; standardised rates similar; Mark is more likely to find employment in Frissom
4. Grocaster higher crude rate; standardised rates similar; fewer accidents in Henbury.

Revision Exercise 6

1. (a) As shown (b) 20.0 (c) Greenfield – the crude birth rate is higher than the crude death rate.
2. (a) 18.0 (b) Takes into consideration the age distribution of the population.
3. (a) 1999, 2001 (b) (i) £6000 (ii) £6780 (c) 2000 (d) 2.7%
4. (a) 76, 75.4 (b) Averages correctly plotted (c) 123 000
5. (a) (49.4) (b) Takes into consideration the age distribution (c) Stokeham; lower standardized unemployment rate.
6. (a) Graph correctly plotted (b) The overall values are rising; The number of visits peaks each year in Q3.
7. (a) (i) index = 194.2 (ii) Both categories had high / large index values (b) (i) 109.2, 122.7, 95.5, 97.7 (ii) Increase 9.2% or 22.7%; Decrease 4.5% or 2.3%
8. (a) $2 \times 2.5 + 4 \times 1 + 12 \times 4 + 1 \times 5 = 62$; (b) £72; (c) 116.1; (d) 33.3%; (e) Labour costs rising at a significant higher rate.
9. (a) Cost is 5% higher than in 1994; (b) (i) £32.40; (ii) £2.40; (c) 116.
10. (a) 112.5 (b) £600 (c) 25% (d) 11.1%.
11. (a) 125; (b) 61.8p; (c) Price increases by a factor 1.2.
12. (a) (i) 75; (ii) 150; (b) Same as 1988.
13. (a) (i) $((250 \times 208) + (305 \times 77) + (358 \times 38) + (308 \times 149) + (391 \times 67))/539$; (ii) 320.7; (iii) 107.2; (b) Reduction in index value, high relative price increase, significant weighting.

14. (a) 1973, (b) Higher (expected 68); (c) Exercise / nutrition / medicine / ...
15. (a) 24 (b) 19 (c) 7505.
16. (a) Plot year (x) car production (y) points (1984, 900) (1986, 1000) (1988, 1250) (1990, 1290) (1992, 1290) (1994, 1500) (1996, 1690);
(b) Suitable line crossing axis between 740 and 840;
(c) (i) ~930 000; (ii) ~1820 000.
17. (c) 23.7; (d) High, increases smaller in later years.
18. (a) 1992; (b) School closed for summer holiday; (e) Turnover is falling.
19. (b) 105, 108.25, 109.75, 112.25, 116, 116.5, 120, 123.75; (d) £179.
20. (b) Weather / Longer days / Growing season / Spring enthusiasm; (c) 22, 23, 24, 24.75, 26, 26.5, 27.5, 28.5, 29, 30, 30.5, 31.5, 32.5; (e) £330 000–£370 000.
21. (b) 217, 223, 228, 235, 240, 245, 250, 256; (c) Weekly takings; (e) ~£13 500; (f) £256 000–£263 000.
22. (b) (i) Peak demands in Q1 and Q4; (ii) Winter seasons; (c) 1135, 1180, 1215, 1265, 1310; (f) Q1 ~ 1810, Q2 ~ 1382.5.

7 Probability

Before you start 7

1.

Fraction	Decimal	Percentage
$\frac{1}{4}$	0.25	25%
$\frac{6}{10}$	0.6	60%
$\frac{3}{8}$	0.375	37.5%
$\frac{17}{20}$	0.85	85%

2. (a) $\frac{9}{20}$; (b) $\frac{23}{24}$; (c) $\frac{38}{45}$; (d) $\frac{1}{24}$; (e) $\frac{2}{21}$; (f) $\frac{5}{12}$

Exercise 7A

1. (a) Unlikely; (b) Evens; (c) Likely; (d) Very unlikely
2. (c) (a) (b) (d)

Impossible ———————————————— Certain

3. Probability of X occurring is 0.4
4. (a) 1; (b) 0
5. (c) (a) (b)

Impossible ———————————————— Certain

Exercise 7B

1. (a) $\frac{1}{13}$; (b) $\frac{1}{4}$; (c) $\frac{1}{52}$; (d) $\frac{3}{13}$ (e) $\frac{1}{4}$
2. (a) $\frac{1}{3}$; (b) $\frac{1}{3}$; (c) $\frac{2}{3}$
3. (a) $\frac{4}{17}$; (b) $\frac{13}{17}$; (c) $\frac{9}{17}$
4. (a) $\frac{1}{8}$; (b) $\frac{5}{8}$; (c) $\frac{3}{4}$; (d) $\frac{5}{8}$
5. (a) $\frac{1}{6}$; (b) $\frac{1}{2}$; (c) $\frac{2}{3}$; (d) $\frac{1}{3}$; (e) $\frac{5}{6}$
6. 0.27
7. (a) No chance of being chosen; (b) 0.3

Exercise 7C

1. (a) Relative frequencies: 0.5; 0.6; 0.53; 0.55; 0.54; 0.55; 0.54; 0.56; (b) 0.56
   (c)

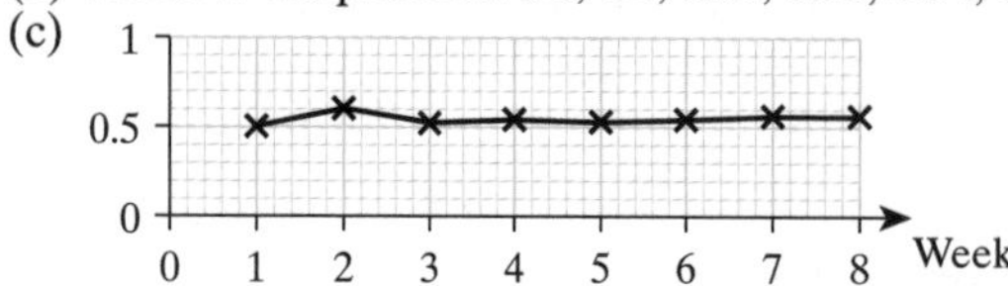

2. (a) Relative frequencies: 0.3; 0.35; 0.33; 0.375; 0.38; 0.35; 0.39; 0.375; 0.356; 0.35;
   (b) 0.35
   (c)

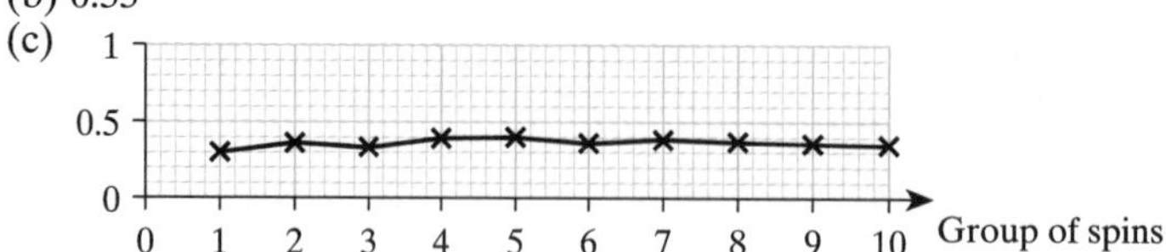

   (d) Yes, Heads, P(H) consistently > 0.5
3. (a) 0.2, 0.25, 0.27, 0.25; (b) No, all probabilities are approximately equal
4. (a)

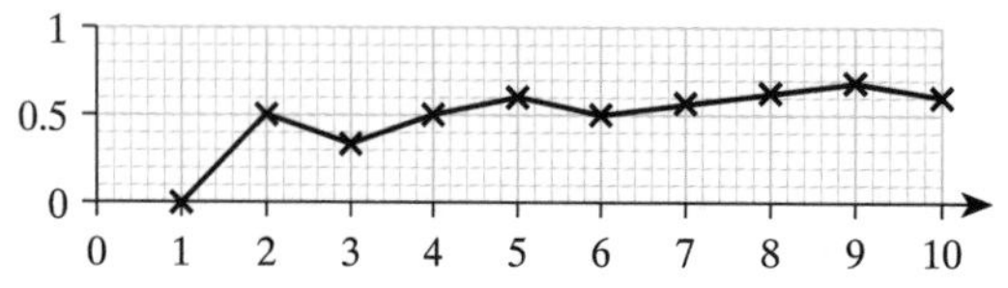

   (b) R B R B B R B B B R
   (c) No, not enough results

Exercise 7D

1. 110
2. 100
3. $\frac{3}{8}$
4. (a) $72 = 2 \times 36$; Relative frequency of 3 is twice as high as that of 4
   (b) $\frac{7}{40}$; (c) 75
5. (a) (i) 0.1; (ii) 0.16; (iii) 0.26; (iv) 0.49; (v) 0.88; (b) (i) 60; (ii) 12
6. (a) 99; (b) 20
7. 1020
8. Yes; $\frac{4}{12} \times 200 = 66\frac{2}{3}$ which is close to 73

Exercise 7E

1. (a) $\frac{3}{10}$; (b) $\frac{7}{10}$; (c) $\frac{3}{5}$; (d) $\frac{2}{15}$; (e) $\frac{41}{60}$; (f) $\frac{7}{30}$
2. (a)

	Biology	Chemistry	Physics	Total
Girls	16	3	24	43
Boys	12	9	36	57
Total	28	12	60	100

   (b) (i) 0.57; (ii) 0.12; (iii) 0.12; (iv) 0.03

3. (a)

	1	2	3	4	5	6
1	0	1	2	3	4	5
2	1	0	1	2	3	4
3	2	1	0	1	2	3
4	3	2	1	0	1	2
5	4	3	2	1	0	1
6	5	4	3	2	1	0

   (b) (i) $\frac{1}{6}$; (ii) $\frac{1}{18}$; (iii) $\frac{1}{2}$ (iv) $\frac{4}{9}$

4. (a)

	0	**1**	**1**	**2**	**3**
0	0	1	1	2	3
1	1	2	2	3	4
1	1	2	2	3	4
2	2	3	3	4	5
3	3	4	4	5	6

(b) (i) $\frac{1}{25}$; (ii) $\frac{4}{25}$; (iii) $\frac{12}{25}$

5. (a)

	R	**R**	**R**	**B**	**B**	**G**	**W**	**O**
R	RR	RR	RR	RB	RB	RG	RW	RO
B	BR	BR	BR	BB	BB	BG	BW	BO
G	GR	GR	GR	GB	GB	GG	GW	GO
W	WR	WR	WR	WB	WB	WG	WW	WO
O	OR	OR	OR	OB	OB	OG	OW	OO

(b) (i) $\frac{1}{40}$; (ii) $\frac{1}{5}$; (iii) $\frac{1}{20}$; (iv) $\frac{1}{8}$

6. (a) $\frac{7}{20}$; (b) $\frac{19}{60}$; (c) $\frac{1}{120}$

7. (a)

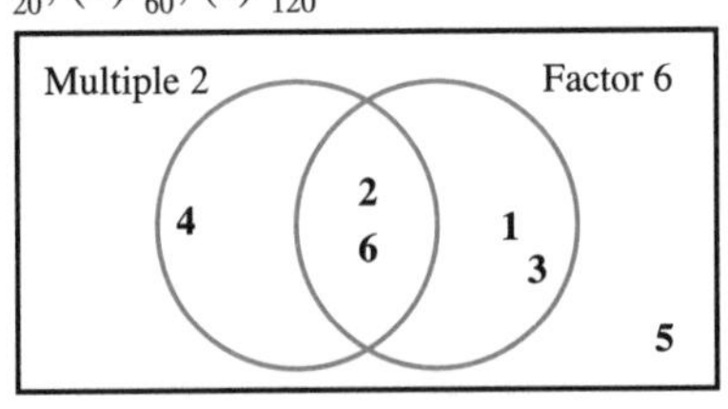

(b) (i) $\frac{2}{3}$; (ii) $\frac{1}{3}$; (iii) $\frac{1}{6}$

8.

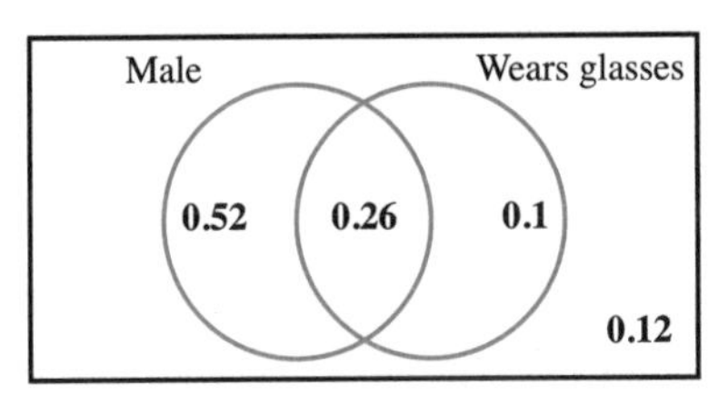

P(male & wears glasses) = 0.26

Exercise 7F

1. (a) (i) B and C, F and G (ii) A and F, B and C, B and D, B and H, D and H, A and G, A and E, E and G, F and G;
(b) B and C; F and G: all outcomes accounted for, but none appear in both;
(c) (i) $\frac{8}{52}$; (ii) $\frac{48}{52}$; (iii) $\frac{39}{52}$;
(d) Diamonds and Hearts together account for all red cards;
(e) (i) $\frac{1}{52}$; (ii) $\frac{3}{52}$; (iii) $\frac{22}{52}$;
(f) All kings are picture cards

2. (a) Cover all outcomes, but none in both;
(b) (i) $\frac{1}{2}$; (ii) $\frac{3}{4}$;
(c) (i) 1; (ii) $\frac{7}{8}$;
(d) $\frac{1}{2}$, for this set of numbers all multiples of 4 are factors of 8

3. (a) (i) $\frac{12}{49}$; (ii) $\frac{9}{49}$; (iii) $\frac{16}{49}$; (iv) $\frac{24}{49}$;
(b) (i) Prime numbers cannot be square numbers; (ii) $\frac{21}{49}$

4. (a) (i) 0.21; (ii) 0.42; (iii) 0.6;
(b) There are two blank cards which are neither vowel or consonant

5. (a) (i) $\frac{11}{20}$; (ii) $\frac{7}{10}$; (iii) $\frac{3}{5}$;
(b) (i) Mutually exclusive; (ii) Exhaustive and Mutually exclusive

Exercise 7G

1. (a) $\frac{1}{2}$; (b) $\frac{1}{4}$
2. $\frac{1}{4}$
3. (a)

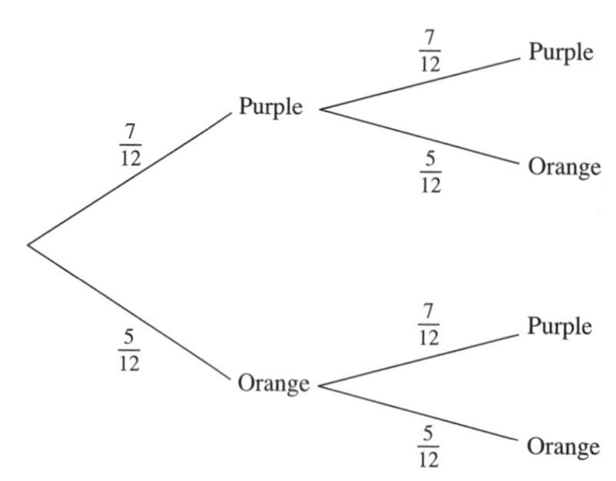

(b) $\frac{35}{72}$

4. (a)

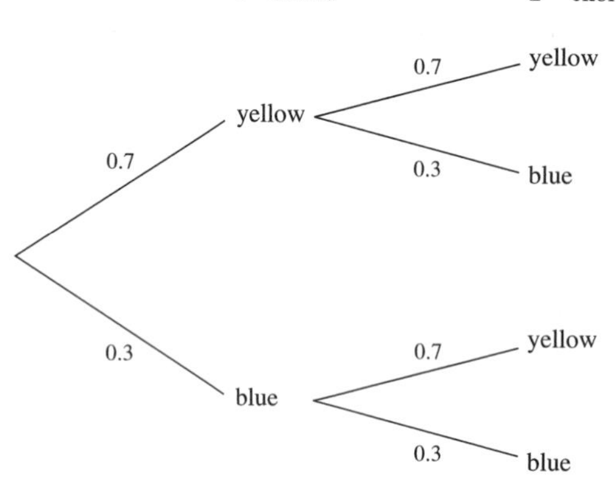

(b) 0.58

5. (a)

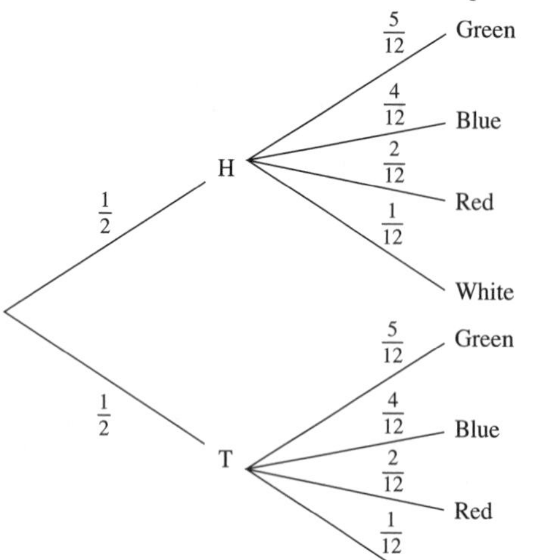

(b) (i) $\frac{5}{24}$; (ii) $\frac{1}{24}$; (iii) $\frac{1}{12}$; (iv) $\frac{1}{12}$
(c) Probability of H and T are equal

6. (a)

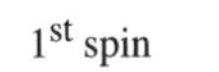

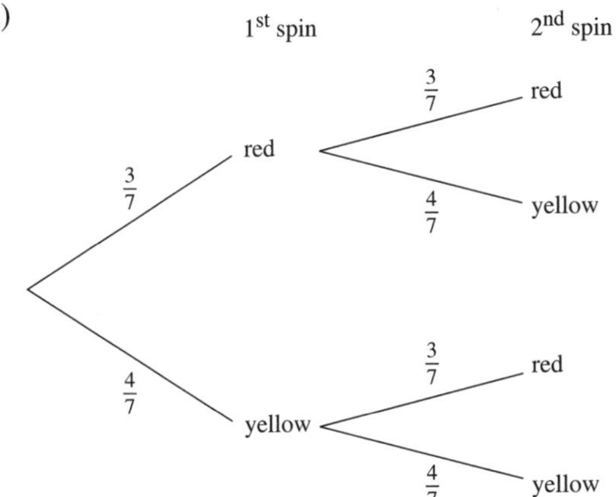

(b) (i) $\frac{9}{49}$; (ii) $\frac{33}{49}$; (iii) $\frac{24}{49}$

7. (a) 0.8
(b)

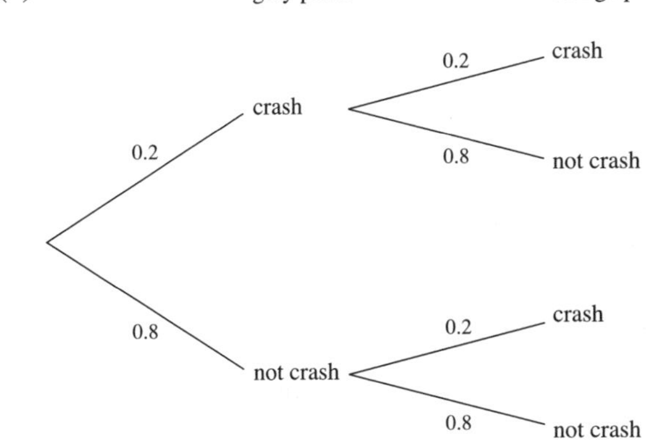

(c) 0.04
(d) 0.32

Exercise 7H

1. (a)

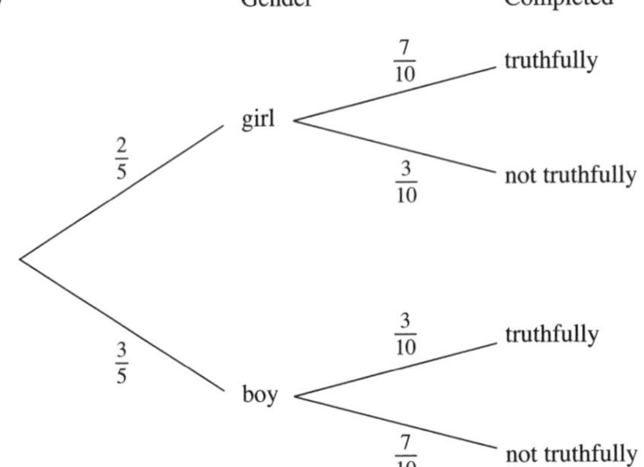

(b) (i) $\frac{23}{50}$; (ii) $\frac{7}{10}$

2. (a)

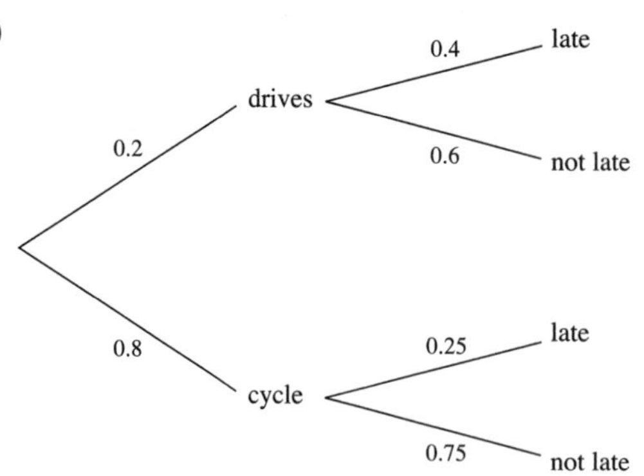

(b) 0.72

3. (a)

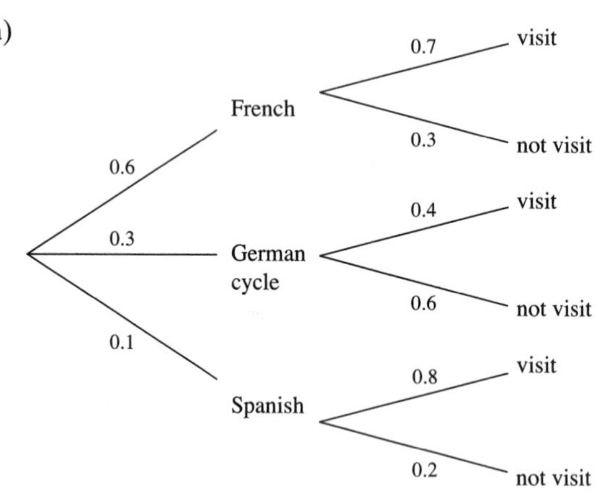

(b) (i) 0.62; (ii) 0.02

4. (a)

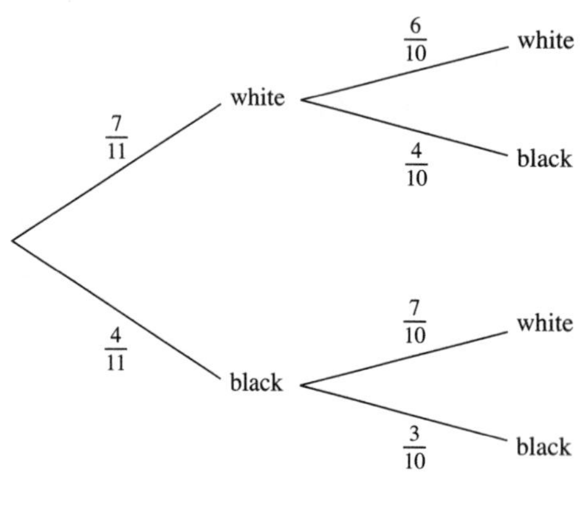

(b) (i) $\frac{21}{55}$; (ii) $\frac{28}{55}$; (iii) $\frac{49}{55}$

5. (a)

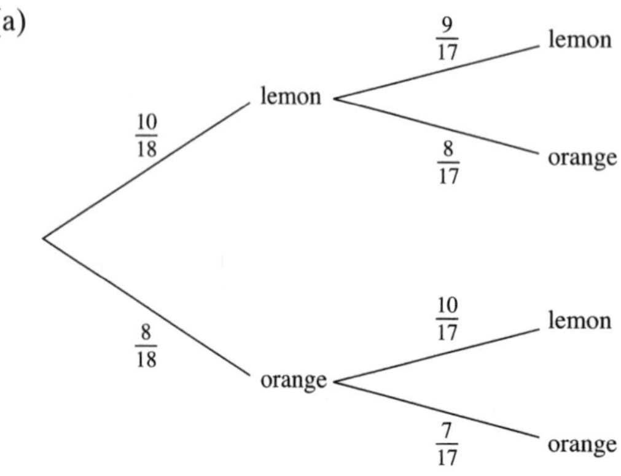

(b) (i) $\frac{28}{153}$; (ii) $\frac{80}{153}$; (iii) $\frac{12}{17}$

6. (a)

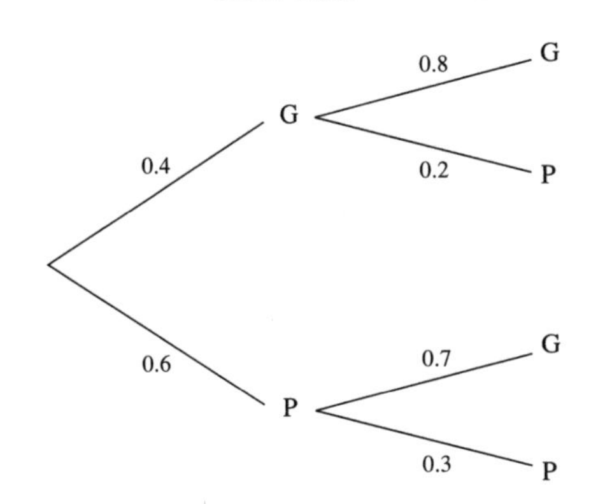

(b) 0.32
(c) 0.74

7. (a) $\frac{16}{125}$; (b) $\frac{16}{41}$; (c) $\frac{16}{53}$

8. (a)

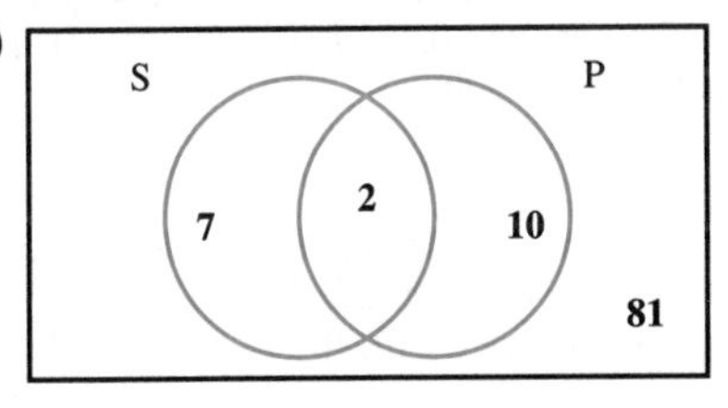

(b) (i) 0.12; (ii) $\frac{2}{9}$; (iii) $\frac{1}{6}$

9. (a) $\frac{36}{55}$; (b) $\frac{5}{12}$; (c) $\frac{15}{28}$

10. (a) $\frac{1}{3}$; (b) $\frac{3}{5}$; (c) $\frac{3}{4}$

Revision Exercise 7

1. (a) $\frac{5}{56}$ (b) $\frac{13}{56}$ (c) $\frac{5}{13}$ (6) 0.054

2. (a)

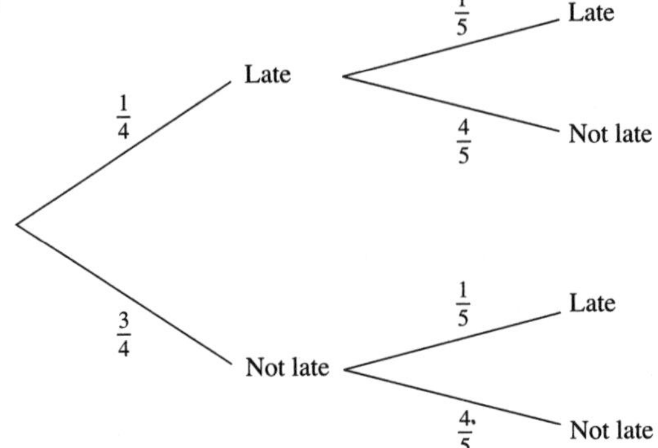

(b) (i) $\frac{1}{20}$ (ii) $\frac{7}{20}$

3. (a) Fractions from left to right, top to bottom: $\frac{1}{5}$; $\frac{1}{10}$, $\frac{1}{10}$, $\frac{1}{10}$
(b) (i) $\frac{5}{12}$ (ii) $\frac{3}{10}$

4. (a)

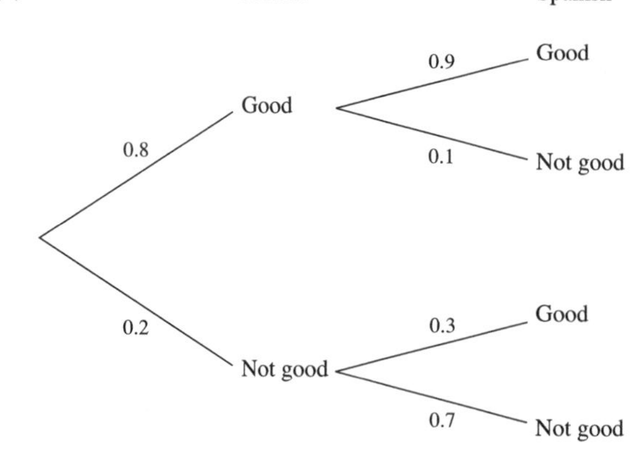

(b) 0.72 (c) 0.78 (d) 360

5. (a) 4 (b) Neither wears earrings nor glasses (c) (i) $\frac{5}{24}$ (ii) $\frac{1}{8}$ (d) $\frac{3}{8}$
6. (a) Impossible, very unlikely, equal chance, likely, certain. (b) It is equally likely to land on heads as on tails. (c) H at midpoint, S at $\frac{1}{6}$ of distance from left-hand end. (d) (i) Blue; Probabiliity of circle on red spinner is 0.4, on blue spinner is 0.2 (ii) Probabilities from left to right, top to bottom: 0.6, 0.4; 0.8, 0.2, 0.8, 0.2 (iii) 0.48
7. (a) From left to right: 124, 1820, 1944; 341, 239, 580; 155, 21, 176; 620, 2080, 2700. (b) (i) $\frac{239}{2700}$ (ii) $\frac{859}{2700}$ (iii) $\frac{7}{8}$ (c) Approx. 11
8. (a) (i) A at 0.5, B at 0.17, C at 0.83 (ii) B and C (b) $\frac{4}{5}$ or 0.8.
9. (a) 0.3 (b) In general, the more times the experiment is carried out the more reliable the relative frequency. (c) 0.15 (d) If the spinner were fair, the relative frequency for red would be close to 0.2. It may not be fair.
10. (a) 0.35, 0.36, 0.37 (b) 0.37: On general, the more times the experiment is carried out, the more reliable the relative frequency
11. (a) 5 (b) B
12. (a) 140 (b) $\frac{9}{28}$ (c) $\frac{3}{7}$ (d) $\frac{1}{15}$
13. (a) $\frac{13}{20}$ (b) $\frac{7}{20}$ (c) 0 (d) 15 (e) 10
14. (a) $\frac{1}{6}$ (b) $\frac{1}{6}$ (c) $\frac{1}{36}$ (d) 6, 6, 6; 5, 5, 6; 5, 6, 5. (e) $\frac{1}{72}$
15. (a) $\frac{1}{3}$ (b) $\frac{1}{3}$ (c) (i) 3, 4, 5 etc (ii) 10 (d) (i) 3 (ii) $\frac{1}{216}$
16. (a) 35 (b) $\frac{27}{35}$ (d) $\frac{14}{17}$ (e) $\frac{11}{27}$
17. (a) 0.336 (b) 0.452 (c) 0.212
18. (a) (i) $\frac{3}{4}$ (ii) $\frac{1}{4}$ (b) $\frac{9}{16}$ (c) $\frac{81}{256}$
19. (a) $\frac{6}{25}$ (b) $\frac{23}{50}$ (c) $\frac{13}{23}$
20. (b) $\frac{115}{208}$ (c) 0.1243
21. (a) $\frac{1}{80}$ (c) (i) $\frac{1}{8}$ (ii) $\frac{31}{40}$
22. (a) 8, 9, 10 (b) 1, 1; 1, 2; 2, 1; 2, 2 (c) $\frac{2}{5}$ (e) $\frac{4}{25}$
23. (a) (i) $\frac{1}{2}$ (ii) 1 (iii) 0 (iv) $\frac{1}{4}$ (b) (i) 22 (ii) liked both (iii) $\frac{1}{10}$ (iv) $\frac{11}{13}$
24. (b) (i) 0.28 (ii) 0.9895
25. (a) $\frac{6}{7}$ (b) $\frac{25}{49}$ (d) $\frac{1}{21}$

8 Coursework

Before you start 8

1. (i) Colour, shape, ..., (ii) Bridge length, (iii) Number of lenses.
2.

	Under 20	20–44	45–64	65 and over
Male				
Female				

Exercise 8A

1. Pocket money is dependent upon age.
2. GCSE grades are a good predictor of A level grades.
3. Book Royalties are dependent upon their length.
4. There is a relationship between age and the colour of cars.
5. There is a relationship between age and ability to estimate length of time.
6. Hand/eye coordination skills can be developed through playing computer games.
7. Life expectancy is greater now than 100 years ago.

Exercise 8B

1. Primary, conduct an experiment.
2. Primary, carry out a survey; Secondary, look at records of births.
3. Primary, conduct a taste test experiment.
4. Secondary, records of fatal road traffic accidents.
5. Secondary, GNP, population, land mass, number of doctors, ...
6. Secondary, past meteorological records.

Exercise 8C

1. Two-way tables (for different eras) with length of track & type of music.
2. Table with headings height, arm span, hand span, wrist circumference.
3. Table with headings age, number recalled.
4. Two-way table with days of the week and number per table. (Collect number of tables booked).
5. Table with headings brand X, brand Y, ...
6. Two-way tables (for blonde and non-blondes) with age & level of higher education/career.

Controlled Assessment – Written Assessment

1. Full marks for statistical rationale to support the chosen calculation and the chosen diagram were suitable to analyse the data plus identifying one other calculation or diagram with reasons. For the memory investigation an explanation for drawing box and whisker plots with reasons for calculating median and interquartile range. A further suitable calculation may be Spearman's coefficient of rank correlation to show time taken against number remembered; a different graph could be scatter graphs of time taken against objects remembered to look for trends as number of objects increases or (comparative) pie charts displaying first object recalled.
2. Full marks awarded for sensible suggestions that would enhance the statistical enquiry with clear rationale for their choice and statistical explanation as to how it would enhance the investigation. For the memory investigation you could have asked for ethnic origin of individuals to explore a connection between ethnicity and memory; or for the data on the pilot survey to explore the reasons why the grid sizes 9, 16 and 25 were chosen, time needed to carry out survey, why the contrasting colours were chosen and so on; or for sampling method used to determine if there could be bias in the results.
3. Full marks for choice of primary data that would naturally expand the students own project with all issues of primary data collection addressed presented concisely.
   For this memory investigation a student could investigate other school year groups or investigate boys' memory or investigate adults. A survey could be carried out and in this situation would need to be a personal interview with discussion as to how this would be carried out.
4. Full marks for choosing two calculations, different from those used in the first part of the investigation, that are appropriate to use with the primary data suggested in question 3 each with clear reasons for their suitability for the data.
   For this memory investigation if median and interquartile range had been calculated in the first part of the investigation then mean and standard deviation could be suggested here with a clear rationale as to how this would aid the conclusions to be drawn.

Exam practice paper: Foundation tier

1. (a) Length; (b) Number of spots; (c) Colouring.
2. X very close to zero; Y ~ 0.7; Z ~ 0.1.
3. (a) £5600; (b) £8000; (c) Angles 252°, 36°, 45°, 27°.
4. (a) 3; (b) M; (c) 7.
5. (a) Already buying fish and chips, all one place; (b) Random sample, put names in hat and pick required number; (c) Leading; (d) Non leading question with tick box choices; (e) Check wording or find typical responses.
6. (a) 107.9; (b) Housing; (c) £2424.40
7. (a)

	5	6	7	8	9
Across	5	4	3	1	0
Down	5	4	2	0	1

(b) 4; (c) 6;

(d) Cryptic has longer words on average and more varied length of answer.

8. Do not use thick lines; Begin scale at zero.
9. (a) Key: 3|1 means 3.1 seconds

Stem	Leaf
8	2 3
7	2 2 2 3 5 7
6	0 1 9
5	2 5
4	4
3	1

(b) 7.2 7.5, 5.5;
(c) B & W leaves 3.1–8.3;
(d) Negative;
(e) Girls were quicker, but times more varied.

10. (b) Negative; (c) January 2000; (d) February – April 2001; (f) Time would eventually become zero.
11. (a) $\frac{1}{4}$; (b) 50; (c) (i) $\frac{2}{5}$ (ii) $\frac{3}{10}$ (iii) $\frac{5}{20}$; (d) No, same probability as guess.
12. (a) Data logging; (b) Plot (5, 130) (10, 134) (15, 142) (20, 144) (25, 146) (30, 148) (35, 145) (40, 140); (c) 10–15 minutes
13. (c) ~£90 – 91 million; (d) Christmas purchases.

Exam practice paper: Higher tier

1. (a) $\frac{72}{100}$, $\frac{75}{100}$, $\frac{55}{100}$; (b) two box and whisker diagrams; (c) girls quicker and middle 50% more spread out.
2. (a) Find typical response/check wording; (b) Will be leaving/do not wear uniform; (c) 22, 22, 19, 19, 18; (d) 33.5, 33.5, 28, 28, 27 first two groups need rounding up, but that would give one too many and we have no reason to round one up and the other down.
3. (a) $\frac{4}{5}$ (b) Tree diagram (c) $\frac{19}{35}$.
4. (a) 0.142; (b) No correlation; (c) Change, no, only marginal difference.
5. (a) Plot (2, 0.81) (4, 1.69) (6, 2.56) (8, 3.24) (10, 4) (12, 4.84) (15, 6.25) (20, 8.41); (b) Line through (0, 0); (c) m = 0.85.
6. 4.84 cm
7. (a) Frequency density 0.6, 1.2, 3.6, 1.15, 0.8, 0.1; (b) (i) 189.2; (ii) 18.45; (c) 112 kmph, less than 10% of cars travelling faster than this.
8. (a) 1.367, 0.856; (b) Centre of new distribution at 2.35, slightly taller and similar shape. (c) First class ~ 1 day quicker, spread about the same.
9. (a) 3; (b) CF 16, 51, 76, 94, 108, 117, 120; (c) 2.
10. (a) 107.9; (b) 102; (c) Increase by 2%.
11. (a) Plot data; (b) 87.6, 88.325, 89.4, 90.625, 91.975, 93.175, 94.4; (c) trend line; (d) ~98.1; (e) ~ –£3.7 million; (ii) ~£95.6 million.

Index

VENEZUELA
GUYANA
SURINAME
COLOMBIA
French Guiana
(France)
ECUADOR
BRAZIL
PERU
BOLIVIA
PARAGUAY
CHILE
URUGUAY
ARGENTINA

POLAND
GERMANY
CZECH REP
SLOVAKIA
MOLDOVA
AUSTRIA
HUNGARY
SLOVENIA
CROATIA
ROMANIA
BOSNIA
SERBIA
ITALY
BULGARIA
FYRO
MACEDONIA
ALBANIA